Random Signal Analysis
in Engineering Systems

Random Signal Analysis
in Engineering Systems

John J. Komo

DEPARTMENT OF ELECTRICAL AND COMPUTER ENGINEERING
CLEMSON UNIVERSITY
CLEMSON, SOUTH CAROLINA

ACADEMIC PRESS, INC.
Harcourt Brace Jovanovich, Publishers
Orlando   San Diego   New York   Austin
Boston   London   Sydney   Tokyo   Toronto

ACADEMIC PRESS, INC.
Orlando, Florida 32887

United Kingdom Edition published by
ACADEMIC PRESS INC. (LONDON) LTD.
24–28 Oval Road, London NW1 7DX

Library of Congress Cataloging in Publication Data

Komo, John J.
    Random signal analysis in engineering systems.

    Includes index.
    1. Signal theory (Telecommunication)   2. Stochastic
processes.   3. Random variables.   I. Title.
TK5102.5.K618   1987   621.38'0433   87-1494
ISBN 0—12—418660—2 (alk. paper)

PRINTED IN THE UNITED STATES OF AMERICA

87 88 89 90   9 8 7 6 5 4 3 2 1

To God

and his children

Johanna, Donna, Jacqueline, Regina, Martin

Let us learn from those we teach

Contents

Preface

Random Signal Analysis in Engineering Systems is designed primarily as a textbook for undergraduate engineering students. The concepts of probability, random variables, averages, simulation, and random signals are introduced here at an introductory level. The notes from which this book has evolved have served for several years as the material taught in a one-semester course to electrical engineering juniors. By omitting some of the material at the ends of Chapters 4, 5, 6, and 7, this book has been essentially covered in one semester. Answers to selected problems are given at the end of the book.

The concept of randomness is important in almost all aspects of modern engineering systems. Many electrical engineering and computer engineering departments, as well as other engineering departments, are introducing the engineering applications of probability and statistics into the undergraduate curriculum. This book is intended to give such an introduction. Many of the examples and problems are related to communication systems and the reliability of systems.

The approach taken in this presentation is not to dwell on the fine points of probability but to emphasize the statistical concepts of random variables. In this regard, transformations on random variables and statistical averages are treated in depth. Simulation and statistical inference are emphasized in separate chapters since these are important concepts in the practical analysis of engineering systems. The material on random processes is intended to be an introduction and is included for completeness. In general, the material has been developed rigorously, but depending on the presentation, the main results can be presented while bypassing some of the developments. For instance, in Chapter 6, the Cramer–Rao bound on the variance of an unbiased estimator can be used without the extensive development of this bound. Several unique topics of this book are the treatments of soft decisions for a binary communication scheme, confidence statements for simulations, goodness-of-fit tests, Cholesky's method for obtaining correlated random variables, and sequential estimation (which is included on most scientific calculators for the estimation of the mean and variance).

The main prerequisite for this book is knowledge of multivariate calculus, which is normally obtained in the sophomore year for engineering students. Some background in electrical circuits and systems and knowledge of transforms would be helpful but is not required since references to circuits and systems and Fourier transforms are at an introductory level. Also, some elementary matrix manipulation is performed, but Appendix D is included to supply this background.

Chapter 1 deals with introductory set theory and probability. The concept of a sigma algebra is given for the assignment of probabilities for completeness. Bayes' rule is illustrated using a binary communication example, and statistical independence is illustrated by examples of communicating over a system that comprises many separate lines, which is equivalent to determining the reliability of a system consisting of many components. Chapter 2 defines random variables and random vectors and gives the probability density function, probability distribution function, and probability function for many different random variables. The Gaussian random variable is emphasized as one of the most important random variables. Conditional distribution and density functions are developed along with the concept of statistical independence for random variables. Chapter 3 describes the process of transforming random variables and random vectors. Included are the integral transform method and the Box–Muller method for obtaining Gaussian random variables. The convolution integral for determining the distribution of the sum of two random variables is developed and illustrated for both continuous and discrete random variables. Chapter 4 develops statistical averages for single random variables as well as multiple random variables. Included is the characteristic function, the Fourier transform of the density function, and its utility in determining the distribution of the sum of random variables. The vector form of the multivariate Gaussian density function is presented and a binary communication scheme involving Gaussian noise samples is considered. The required accuracy of the sample values is obtained by considering the degradation of hard and soft decisions on these sample values. This chapter concludes with the development of the Chebyshev inequality, the Chernoff bound, and the central limit theorem.

Chapter 5 presents several methods of generating pseudouniform random numbers and presents the histogram as an approximation to a density function. The chi-square goodness-of-fit test is given along with a table of percentage points for this test. Confidence statements for simulation results, Monte Carlo integration, and importance sampling are also presented. Cholesky's method is developed for obtaining correlated random variables from statistically independent random variables. Chapter 6 develops the method of maximum likelihood estimation for unknown parameters and presents and illustrates the desirable properties of estimators. The joint maximum likelihood estimators of the mean and variance of a Gaussian distribution function are developed along with the means and variances of these estimators. The sequential forms of the estimators for the mean and variance of a Gaussian distribution function are also presented. This chapter concludes with the development of the maximum *a posteriori* estimation of random parameters. Chapter 7 introduces random processes and their statistical averages. Included are the concepts of stationarity, ergodicity, autocorrelation, and spectral density. Linear systems with random inputs are considered, and the concepts of cross correlation and cross spectral density are introduced.

Appendix A gives a table of Gaussian probabilities in the form of the Q function, which is one minus the distribution function, along with an approximation for the Q function. The development of the density function of the sum of N uniform random variables and how the sum approaches the Gaussian density function is given in Appendix B. Appendix C gives a tabulation of the mean, variance, and characteristic function for various continuous and discrete random variables, and Appendix D gives an introduction to matrix manipulation. Appendix E gives a tabulation of various trigonometric identities, integrals, and Fourier transforms.

I would like to thank Lymuel McRae for a very thorough and helpful review and proofreading of the manuscript, in addition to many discussions of the material, which provided many improvements. In addition, I would like to thank George Schroeder for reviewing the manuscript and offering various improvements and Rich Yost for proofreading the manuscript and offering helpful suggestions. Also, I appreciate the contributions of my colleagues John Spragins, Kent Bryan, Joe Hammond, Madjid Mousabi, and Krisnan Aurora, who have taught from the manuscript and offered helpful suggestions. I am grateful to Farzana Ahmad McRae for reading various parts of the manuscript and to the many students who have found mistakes in the manuscript. I have benefited from statistical discussions with Joel Brawley, Bob Snelsire, and Lew Fitch. Lastly, I would like to thank Wayne Bennett and Imtiaz Haque for their encouragement of this project.

Set Theory and Probability

1.1 Introduction

Even though most of the analyses in engineering deal with deterministic quantities, such as the voltages and currents in basic circuits, some quantities cannot be adequately described in a deterministic manner. These nondeterministic or random quantities are characterized by uncertainty or unpredictability. This uncertainty may come from various sources, but no matter how much is known of past values of the quantity, its future value cannot be predicted precisely. Undesired random quantities or noise appear in many places, including radio and television receivers, but if there were no uncertainty or randomness in the broadcast signal itself, a desired random quantity, there would be no information transmitted. That is, if the broadcast signal were known precisely by the receiver, there would be no need to transmit it. In addition to uncertainty, if a quantity is so complicated that accurate prediction is not possible, it is also considered a random quantity.

Situations where all parameters are precisely known are very rare. Even the components of electrical circuits are known only within a certain tolerance; e.g., discrete resistors are only guaranteed to have resistance values within a tolerance of 1%, 5%, 10%, etc., depending on the accuracy that is desired, which directly affects the cost. A direct application of probability theory in engineering is in the reliability of components and systems. Although there may be claims that some components never wear out, components with zero failure rate have not been developed. Some large complex systems are required to meet minimum reliability specifications, such as guaranteed uptime. Being able to predict the reliability of equipment and to design equipment to meet certain reliability standards is becoming more and more essential. Such techniques are based on probability theory.

1

With all this unpredictability, how can random quantities be described? Before answering this question, consider the following examples of random phenomena. The first example is that of the queuing problem of student registration. The time of arrival and the time required to complete registration are unpredictable. Then the number of students waiting, their length of wait, and the number that finish in a given time interval are incapable of being precisely known ahead of time. Next, consider the useful life of light bulbs. The actual life of a light bulb is unpredictable, as is the number that fail in a given time interval. The last example is simply the tossing of a coin, the outcome of which could theoretically be predicted if the force exerted on the coin, the angle of release, the properties of the landing surface, etc. were known exactly. Because of the extreme complexity, the outcome is assumed unpredictable or random.

Experimentally, each of the above examples exhibits certain average properties. The average number of students registered per unit time, the average life of light bulbs, and the average number of times a given side of the coin occurs tend to stabilize as the number of observations (students, light bulbs, or tosses) becomes large. Thus random quantities cannot be described precisely, but can be described on the average. Also, any mathematical or probability model that is to be meaningful must describe occurrences in the real world and their averages.

Consider the electrical circuits of Fig. 1.1.1. In Fig. 1.1.1a, with the dc source, the current should obviously be 1 A in the direction shown. But what does this mean? Is there a physical quantity called an ampere that moves in the wire as shown? No, in reality, current is a representation of the negative flow of electrons, and for 1 A this would be $1/(1.602 \times 10^{-19})$ or 6.242×10^{18} electrons per second moving in the direction opposite to the indicated current direction. Do all of the electrons move in this direction? No, the electrons move in both directions, but this indicates that on the average 6.242×10^{18} electrons per second move in this direction. With the ac source in Fig. 1.1.1b there is a maximum current of 1 A or a maximum net flow of 6.242×10^{18} electrons per second. Half of the time the average movement is in one direction and half of the time in the other direction with the magnitude determined by the value of the cosine. The dc component

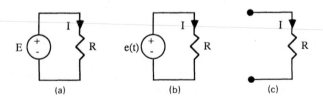

Fig. 1.1.1. Electrical circuit with $R = 1 \ \Omega$: (a) dc, $E = 1$ V; (b) ac, $e(t) = \cos(2\pi t)$; (c) no source.

is zero here. In Fig. 1.1.1c, with no source, there is no current (no ac or dc component) or average electron movement, but the electrons do not stop moving (unless the temperature is absolute zero) and thus there will be some ac voltage across the resistor. The dc voltage is zero but the ac voltage is nonzero. The voltage measured across the 1-Ω resistor (which is equal to the current, in this case, once the measuring device is connected) is a function of the measuring device (bandwidth of the device); for a digital voltmeter (100-kHz bandwidth) it is 0.040 μV and for a 30-MHz oscilloscope it is 0.690 μV. This random voltage or thermal noise is present in all electronic material. Sometimes this noise is small compared to the desired signal and may be neglected, but at other times it is of the same magnitude as the desired signal, such as satellite communication, and cannot be neglected.

Before proceeding to a formal definition of probability and the associated set theory, the following examples are considered to illustrate that although probability statements are sometimes obvious, at other times they are complicated and not obvious. First, consider the tossing of a six-sided fair die.

Example 1.1.1.   If a six-sided fair die is tossed it is assumed that each side has the same probability of occurring. It is also assumed that one of the sides will occur and that this probability is 1 (the probabilities sum to 1). Since there are six sides to the die and each side is assumed to have the same probability of occurring, the probability of obtaining any side is $\frac{1}{6}$. The probability of obtaining either a 1 or a 2 on a single toss of a fair die is easily determined to be $\frac{1}{3}$ (the sum of $\frac{1}{6}$ for a 1 and $\frac{1}{6}$ for a 2).   □

Now, consider the tossing of a six-sided fair die twice.

Example 1.1.2.   For the tossing of a six-sided fair die twice there are 36 possible outcomes (6 outcomes on the first toss times 6 outcomes on the second toss), and each possible outcome is assumed to have the same probability of occurrence of $\frac{1}{36}$ (the probabilities sum to 1). The probability of obtaining at least one 1 on two tosses of the die is not as obvious as the probability as obtained in Example 1.1.1, but can be determined to be $\frac{11}{36}$ by enumerating all favorable possibilities out of the 36 outcomes (11, 12, 13, 14, 15, 16, 21, 31, 41, 51, 61).   □

Next, consider the example of communicating from point A to point B with two telephone lines in two contrasting configurations.

Example 1.1.3.   Consider two alternative configurations for communicating from point A to point B with two telephone lines. In alternative 1 the lines are in series, which requires the availability of both lines for communication; in alternative 2 the lines are in parallel, which requires the availability of either line for communication. This analysis is equivalent to

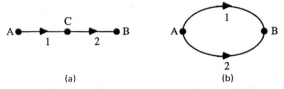

Fig. 1.1.2. Communication over two lines: (a) series; (b) parallel.

determining the reliability of two systems where alternative 1 would be in tandem or series and alternative 2 would be in backup or parallel. These alternatives are depicted in Fig. 1.1.2.

If line 1 is available 90% of the time (or system 1 is 90% reliable), and line 2 is available 80% of the time (or system 2 is 80% reliable), the probability of communicating with alternative 1 (or the reliability of alternative 1) can be observed to be less than 0.8 since both lines will be available less than the worst line (this value will later be shown to be 0.72). Also, the probability of communicating with alternative 2 (or the reliability of alternative 2) is observed to be greater than 0.9 since either line will be available more than the best line (this value will later be shown to be 0.98). Even though the probabilities of communicating with alternatives 1 and 2 have not been developed, it is clear that alternative 2 is a better scheme.   □

Lastly, consider an example that does not seem to follow intuition and is not at all obvious.

Example 1.1.4.   Consider one of three alternatives, A, B, or C, to be chosen at random, where one of these is assumed correct. All of the alternatives are assumed to be chosen with the same probability, and thus the probability of a correct choice is $\frac{1}{3}$. Now, after the first choice, additional information that one of the other alternatives (not the first choice) is incorrect is given, and a second choice is offered. Since there is only one correct alternative, there is at least one incorrect alternative left after the first choice, so the additional information is always given. For instance, if A is the correct alternative and B is the first choice, the information that C is incorrect is given and a second choice is offered. Likewise, if A is the correct alternative and A is the first choice, the information that B (or C) is incorrect is given and a second choice is offered. What would be the best strategy for the second choice: keep the same as choice one (the first choice was as good as any), change from choice one (the alternative that is neither choice one nor the given incorrect alternative), or eliminate the incorrect alternative and choose one of the remaining two (ignore choice one or half of the time keep the same and half of the time change)? For the first strategy, since the additional information is unused and nothing has changed, the probability of a correct choice will be $\frac{1}{3}$; for the third strategy, since the choice is now between two alternatives, the probability of a correct choice will be $\frac{1}{2}$. The second choice is the best because it yields a probability of correct choice of $\frac{2}{3}$, since a correct second choice will be made when an incorrect first choice was made, and an incorrect second choice made when a correct first choice was made (incorrect and correct have been interchanged). $\quad\square$

The probability of an event can be considered to be the limit of the relative frequency of this event in a sequence of independent trials of the random phenomenon which gives rise to the event, as the number of repetitions approaches infinity. In this way probability is a model of a real-world happening. A fair coin may then be defined as one where the relative frequency of heads approaches the relative frequency of tails as the number of tosses of the coin approaches infinity. This is also referred to as an equally likely assumption, since there is no basis for preferring a head or a tail. A single toss of a die is assumed to have 6 equally likely outcomes, while two tosses of a die are assumed to have 36 equally likely outcomes.

The axiomatic probability development that is used here will be shown to yield probabilities that are the same as these limiting relative frequencies, in situations where the relative frequencies make sense. This development is accomplished according to standard rules of mathematics by defining a set of objects to work with, a set of operations to perform on these objects, and a set of axioms these objects and operations must satisfy. All necessary results of probability theory can then be derived rigorously as consequences of these definitions and axioms.

The set relationships necessary for the axiomatic probability development will now be considered.

1.2 Set Theory

A set is a collection of objects called elements. If the set A has a finite number of elements, A can be denoted as $A = \{a_1, a_2, \ldots, a_n\}$ by listing all of the elements a_i, $i = 1, 2, \ldots, n$, or as $A = \{a : R(a) \text{ is satisfied}\}$ where $R(a)$ is a rule for determining if $a \in A$ (: means such that, $\in$ means element of). Normally sets are denoted by capital letters and elements by lowercase letters. Thus, the set of outcomes B for the toss of a die can be represented as $B = \{1, 2, 3, 4, 5, 6\}$ or $B = \{\text{integer } i : 1 \le i \le 6\}$. Also, the possible outcomes of one toss of a coin, C, can be represented as $C = \{H, T\}$, where H represents heads and T represents tails. Other sets of interest for the tossing of a coin are $\{H\}$, the outcome of heads; $\{T\}$, the outcome of tails; $\{\ \} = \varnothing$, no outcome or the empty set or null set; and $\{H, T\} = S$, all outcomes or the universal set or sample space. The sample space for the tossing of two coins would be $S_1 = \{HH, HT, TH, TT\}$ if the coins are distinguishable and $S_2 = \{HH, HT, TT\}$ if the coins are indistinguishable since a head on the first coin and a tail on the second coin cannot be distinguished from a tail on the first coin and a head on the second coin. Other sets of interest can be listed for either S_1 or S_2, as was done for the tossing of a single coin.

Example 1.2.1.   The sample space for the tossing of two dice would be given as

$$S_1 = \{11, 12, \ldots, 16, 21, \ldots, 26, 31, \ldots, 66\}$$

if the dice are distinguishable, where S_1 contains 36 elements, and

$$S_2 = \{11, 12, \ldots, 16, 22, \ldots, 26, 33, \ldots, 66\}$$

if the dice are indistinguishable, where S_2 contains 21 elements.   □

A set is finite or infinite if the number of elements in the set is finite or infinite, respectively. All of the previous sets have been examples of finite sets. If a coin is tossed until the first head appears, then the sample space is

$$S = \{H, TH, TTH, TTTH, TTTTH, \ldots\}$$

an infinite set. Also, the elements of a set may take on a continuum of values rather than a discrete set of values. An example of this is a random voltage that can take on any real number, which yields $S = \{x : -\infty < x < \infty\}$. Other sets of interest in this case are commonly taken as intervals on the real line.

Even though the outcome of many random quantities can be described in terms of sets, a geometric representation of a sample space is sometimes useful. The sample space for the toss of a single die is shown in Fig. 1.2.1a, while the sample space for the toss of two distinguishable dice is shown in Fig. 1.2.1b. The geometric representation gives exactly the same information

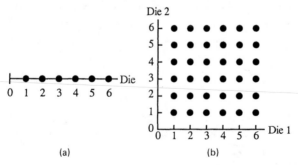

Fig. 1.2.1. Sample space for dice: (a) single die; (b) two distinguishable dice.

as the previously given S's. For two indistinguishable dice the geometric representation would be similar to Fig. 1.2.1b but with only 21 elements.

The set A is a subset of the set B (A is contained in B) if $x \in A$ implies that $x \in B$, and this is denoted as $A \subset B$. Since no distinction will be made here between subsets and proper subsets, $A \subset B$ can include the case $A = B$. In this notation the two sets A and B are equal, $A = B$, if and only if $A \subset B$ and $B \subset A$. Then by the definition of a sample space $A \subset S$ and $B \subset S$.

The union of two sets $A \subset S$ and $B \subset S$ is defined as

$$A \cup B = \{x : x \in A \text{ or } x \in B\}$$

where the "or" is interpreted as either one or the other or both. The union operation is very similar to the logical OR operation, with most of the properties being the same, when the union operation interpreted as a logical OR operation has meaning. A Venn diagram, normally a general two-dimensional sample space, can be used to illustrate set relationships, but the use of a Venn diagram does not constitute a proof of set relationships. A Venn diagram illustrating $A \subset B$ is given in Fig. 1.2.2a and a Venn diagram illustrating $A \cup B$ is given in Fig. 1.2.2b.

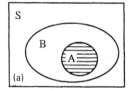 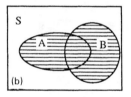

Fig. 1.2.2. Venn diagrams for $A \subset B$ and $A \cup B$: (a) $A \subset B$; (b) $A \cup B$.

For a single die, with $S = \{1, 2, 3, 4, 5, 6\}$, if $A = \{3\}$ and $B = \{1, 3, 5\}$ then $A \subset B$. With $C = \{1, 2, 3, 4\}$, $B \cup C = \{1, 2, 3, 4, 5\}$. These sets are shown in the Venn diagram in Fig. 1.2.3. Also, from Example 1.1.2 obtaining at least one 1 on two tosses of a die is a union given as $\{1$ on first toss$\} \cup \{1$ on second toss$\}$ and communication over the parallel connection of Fig. 1.1.2b is given as $\{1\} \cup \{2\}$.

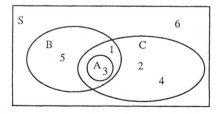

Fig. 1.2.3. Venn diagram for a single die example.

There are many interesting set relationships which can be rigorously proved, but the emphasis here will be on using these relationships rather than proving them. Several proofs will be given to illustrate the procedure though. The proof that $C \subset D$ is accomplished by assuming that $x \in C$ (x is a general element), using known results, and concluding that this implies that $x \in D$. These proofs are as unstructured as the proofs of digital logic relationships by Boolean algebra, where each step is basically a trial-and-error procedure. From Fig. 1.2.2b it is observed that

$$A \subset (A \cup B) \qquad B \subset (A \cup B) \qquad \text{union property}$$

Example 1.2.2. Prove the union property $A \subset (A \cup B)$. The proof of the union property is obtained by assuming that x is an arbitrary element of A and, by proper manipulation, concluding that this implies that x is an element of $A \cup B$. Implies will be represented by the symbol $\Rightarrow$. The union property is then proved as

$$x \in A \Rightarrow x \in A \text{ or } x \in (\text{anything}) \Rightarrow x \in A \text{ or } x \in B \Rightarrow x \in (A \cup B)$$

thus

$$A \subset (A \cup B) \qquad \square$$

A Venn diagram is useful in illustrating the property that is to be proved but is not a proof itself.

Consider one more example to illustrate this procedure for proving set relationships.

Example 1.2.3. Let S be a sample space and A and B be arbitrary sets such that $A \subset S$ and $B \subset S$. Prove that $A \subset B$ if and only if $A \cup B = B$. From Fig. 1.2.2a this appears to be true. For the "if" condition, given that $A \cup B = B$ prove that $A \subset B$. This is accomplished as

$$x \in A \Rightarrow x \in A \text{ or } x \in B \Rightarrow x \in (A \cup B) \Rightarrow x \in B \qquad (\text{since } A \cup B = B)$$

thus

$$A \subset B$$

For the "only if" condition, given that $A \subset B$ prove that $A \cup B = B$. In general $B \subset (A \cup B)$ (union property), so all that is left to prove is that $(A \cup B) \subset B$. This follows as

$$x \in (A \cup B) \Rightarrow x \in A \text{ or } x \in B \Rightarrow x \in B \qquad (\text{since } A \subset B)$$

thus

$$(A \cup B) \subset B$$

Combining $B \subset (A \cup B)$ and $(A \cup B) \subset B$ yields the desired result, $A \cup B = B$. $\quad \square$

The intersection of the two sets $A \subset S$ and $B \subset S$ is defined as

$$A \cap B = AB = \{x : x \in A \text{ and } x \in B\}$$

which is very similar to the logical AND operation, with most of the properties being the same, when the intersection operation interpreted as a logical AND operation has meaning. Also, the complement of the set A, A^c, is defined as

$$A^c = \{x : x \in S \text{ and } x \notin A\}$$

which is similar to the logical NOT operation. A Venn diagram illustrating $A \cap B$ is given in Fig. 1.2.4a and one illustrating A^c in Fig. 1.2.4b. Again, for a single die, with $S = \{1, 2, 3, 4, 5, 6\}$, $B = \{1, 3, 5\}$, and $C = \{1, 2, 3, 4\}$, $B \cap C = \{1, 3\}$ and $C^c = \{5, 6\}$. Also, communication over the series connection of Fig. 1.1.2a is given as $\{1\} \cap \{2\}$.

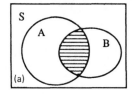 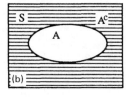

Fig. 1.2.4. Venn diagrams for $A \cap B$ and A^c: (a) $A \cap B$; (b) A^c.

From Fig. 1.2.4a it can be seen that

$$(A \cap B) \subset A \qquad (A \cap B) \subset B \qquad \text{intersection property}$$

and from Fig. 1.2.4b that

$$(A^c)^c = A$$

In addition, from Fig. 1.2.2a it can be seen that

$$A \subset B \Leftrightarrow B^c \subset A^c$$

where $\Leftrightarrow$ means implies and is implied by. Some other useful set relationships are

$$A \cup B = B \cup A \qquad\qquad A \cap B = B \cap A$$
$$\text{commutative property}$$

$$A \cup (B \cup C) = (A \cup B) \cup C \qquad A \cap (B \cap C) = (A \cap B) \cap C$$
$$\text{associative property}$$

$$A \cap (B \cup C) = (A \cap B) \cup (A \cap C) \qquad A \cup (B \cap C) = (A \cup B) \cap (A \cup C)$$
$$\text{distributive property}$$

$$(A \cup B)^c = A^c \cap B^c \qquad\qquad (A \cap B)^c = A^c \cup B^c$$
$$\text{De Morgan's property}$$

All of these set relationships have corresponding digital logic operations. These set relationships can be rigorously proved, but this will not be done here.

The sets $A \cap (B \cup C)$ and $A \cup (B \cap C)$ are shown in Venn diagrams in Fig. 1.2.5. From these Venn diagrams it is seen that $[A \cap (B \cup C)] \subset [A \cup (B \cap C)]$.

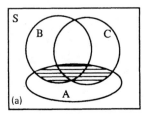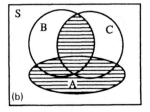

Fig. 1.2.5. Venn diagrams for $A \cap (B \cup C)$ and $A \cup (B \cap C)$: (a) $A \cap (B \cup C)$; (b) $A \cup (B \cap C)$.

Example 1.2.4. Prove $[A \cap (B \cup C)] \subset [A \cup (B \cap C)]$ when $A \subset S$, $B \subset S$, and $C \subset S$. This is proved by using the intersection property and the union property as

$$A \cap (B \cup C) \subset A \subset A \cup (B \cap C)$$

thus

$$[A \cap (B \cup C)] \subset [A \cup (B \cap C)] \qquad \square$$

For convenience let $A_1 \cup A_2 \cup \cdots \cup A_N = \bigcup_{i=1}^{N} A_i$ and $A_1 \cap A_2 \cap \cdots \cap A_N = \bigcap_{i=1}^{N} A_i$.

The sample space S is also referred to as the universal set, the reference set, and the largest set. All other sets, with respect to this sample space, are subsets of S, e.g., $A \subset S$, $B \subset S$, $C \subset S$. The set with no elements, $\emptyset$, the null set or empty set, is related to the universal set by

$$\emptyset = S^c \qquad \emptyset^c = S$$

The null set is a subset of every set, e.g., $\emptyset \subset A$, $\emptyset \subset B$, since

$$A^c \subset S \Rightarrow S^c = \emptyset \subset (A^c)^c = A$$

thus

$$\emptyset \subset A$$

When $A \cap B = \emptyset$, A and B are said to be mutually exclusive or disjoint. Mutually exclusive sets do not have any common elements and in a Venn diagram would be shown as not overlapping. The outcomes for the single toss of a die are all mutually exclusive, as would be the outcomes for the single toss of a coin.

Some useful set relationships involving the universal set and the null set are

$$A \cup \varnothing = A \qquad A \cap \varnothing = \varnothing$$

$$A \cup S = S \qquad A \cap S = A$$

$$A \cup A^c = S \qquad A \cap A^c = \varnothing$$

All of these set relationships are equivalent to logical operations with the correspondences $\cup$ to OR, $\cap$ to AND, $\varnothing$ to 0, and S to 1.

Many other set relationships can be developed when restrictions are placed on some of the sets. For example, when $A \subset S$, $B \subset S$, $C \subset S$, and $A \subset B$ the union relationship $(A \cup C) \subset (B \cup C)$ and the intersection relationship $(A \cap C) \subset (B \cap C)$ are true.

Example 1.2.5. Prove $(A \cap C) \subset (B \cap C)$ when $A \subset S$, $B \subset S$, $C \subset S$, and $A \subset B$. To prove this express B as

$$B = (A \cup B) \qquad \text{(since } A \subset B)$$

Intersecting both sides of the equality with C then yields

$$B \cap C = (A \cup B) \cap C = (A \cap C) \cup (B \cap C) \qquad \text{(distributive property)}$$

and

$$(A \cap C) \subset (A \cap C) \cup (B \cap C) = B \cap C$$

thus

$$(A \cap C) \subset (B \cap C) \qquad \text{for } A \subset B \qquad \square$$

Also, for $A \subset B$ the expression $A \cup (B \cap C) = B \cap (A \cup C)$ holds.

Example 1.2.6. Prove $A \cup (B \cap C) = B \cap (A \cup C)$ for $A \subset B$ when $A \subset S$, $B \subset S$, and $C \subset S$. This is proved as follows:

$$A \cup (B \cap C) = (A \cup B) \cap (A \cup C) \qquad \text{(distributive property)}$$

$$= B \cap (A \cup C) \qquad (A \cup B = B \text{ since } A \subset B) \qquad \square$$

Now that the set theory relationships have been developed, probability will be defined on the appropriate subsets of S.

1.3 Probability Theory

In order to define probability, all events for which probabilities may need to be computed will be included in the mathematical model. Including all these events leads to the definition of a σ-algebra (sigma algebra or Borel field). In talking about probability assignments it is not necessary to discuss a σ-algebra, but it is not that complicated and will be considered here for completeness. The utility of a σ-algebra is to guarantee that S and all events obtainable from S by taking complements, unions, or intersections of events in the σ-algebra are included for probability assignments. As in most mathematical developments, the number of statements in the definition of a σ-algebra is minimized by omitting any other properties that can be derived from these few.

A class $\mathcal{A}$ of subsets of a nonempty set S is called a σ-algebra if

    (a) $S \in \mathcal{A}$
    (b) $A \in \mathcal{A}$ implies $A^c \in \mathcal{A}$
    (c) $A_i \in \mathcal{A}$ $i = 1, 2, \ldots$ implies $\bigcup_{i=1}^{\infty} A_i \in \mathcal{A}$

Members of $\mathcal{A}$ are called events, while members of S are called elementary events or sample points. If there is a finite number of events in (c), $\mathcal{A}$ is simply called an algebra. It may seem strange that S, the universal or largest set, is an element of $\mathcal{A}$, but $\mathcal{A}$ is just a listing of events to which probability will be assigned, a set of subsets of S. Even though intersections are not explicitly mentioned in the definition of a σ-algebra, they can be obtained from complements and unions, which are included in the definition, by De Morgan's property as

$$A \cap B = (A^c \cup B^c)^c$$

Example 1.3.1. Determine $\mathcal{A}_1$ for the universal set $S = \{1, 2, 3, 4\}$ with $\{1\} \in \mathcal{A}_1$, $\{2\} \in \mathcal{A}_1$, $\{3\} \in \mathcal{A}_1$, and $\{4\} \in \mathcal{A}_1$. The algebra $\mathcal{A}_1$ consists of all possible subsets of S or

$$\mathcal{A}_1 = \{S, \varnothing, \{1\}, \{2\}, \{3\}, \{4\}, \{1, 2\}, \{1, 3\}, \{1, 4\}, \{2, 3\}, \{2, 4\}, \{3, 4\},$$

$$\{1, 2, 3\}, \{1, 2, 4\}, \{1, 3, 4\}, \{2, 3, 4\}\}$$

where $\{1, 2, 3\}$ is interpreted as $\{1\} \cup \{2\} \cup \{3\}$. Thus when $\{1\}$, $\{2\}$, $\{3\}$, and $\{4\}$ are distinguishable, $\mathcal{A}_1$ is obtained. (The smallest σ-algebra containing the required sets is the desired result.) It can be noted that there are 16 events (2^4 combinations of 4 mutually exclusive events) in $\mathcal{A}_1$.   □

Example 1.3.2. Determine $\mathcal{A}_2$ for the same universal set $S = \{1, 2, 3, 4\}$ but with $\{1\} \in \mathcal{A}_2$, $\{2, 3\} \in \mathcal{A}_2$, and $\{4\} \in \mathcal{A}_2$ ($\{2\}$ and $\{3\}$ are indistinguishable). The algebra $\mathcal{A}_2$ is given as

$$\mathcal{A}_2 = \{S, \varnothing, \{1\}, \{2, 3\}, \{4\}, \{1, 2, 3\}, \{1, 4\}, \{2, 3, 4\}\}$$

When $\{2\}$ and $\{3\}$ are indistinguishable the number of events that will be assigned probability is reduced. There are 8 (2^3 combinations of 3 mutually exclusive) events in $\mathcal{A}_2$.   □

Some physical meaning can be given to these algebras by taking S as the sample space for the tossing of two coins where in $\mathscr{A}_1$ the coins are distinguishable and in $\mathscr{A}_2$ they are indistinguishable. Then $\{HH\} = \{1\}$, $\{HT\} = \{2\}$, $\{TH\} = \{3\}$, and $\{TT\} = \{4\}$, and if the coins are indistinguishable $\{HT\}$ and $\{TH\}$ are indistinguishable, which is the case for $\mathscr{A}_2$. These algebras could also be generated by the tossing of a four-sided object (pyramid) with each side a different color in $\mathscr{A}_1$ and two sides the same color in $\mathscr{A}_2$. The reason for these σ-algebras, the probability assignments, will be given shortly.

It was not necessary to specify that all three events were elements of $\mathscr{A}_2$ to determine $\mathscr{A}_2$, but two events being elements of $\mathscr{A}_2$ would suffice to determine A_2. Consider the example with $S = \{1, 2, 3, 4\}$ with $\{1, 2, 3\} \in \mathscr{A}_3$ and $\{2, 3, 4\} \in \mathscr{A}_3$.

Example 1.3.3. Determine $\mathscr{A}_3$ for the universal set $S = \{1, 2, 3, 4\}$ with $\{1, 2, 3\} \in \mathscr{A}_3$ and $\{2, 3, 4\} \in \mathscr{A}_3$. The algebra $\mathscr{A}_3$ is given as

$$\mathscr{A}_3 = \{S, \varnothing, \{1,2,3\}, \{2,3,4\}, \{1,2,3\}^c = \{4\}, \{2,3,4\}^c = \{1\}, \{4\} \cup \{1\} = \{1,4\},$$
$$\{1,4\}^c = \{2,3\}\}$$

which is equal to $\mathscr{A}_2$. No other unions, complements, or intersections of events in $\mathscr{A}_3$ will yield any new events. $\qquad\square$

It can be shown that if an algebra contains N mutually exclusive (or disjoint) events there are 2^N events in the algebra, which was seen to be the case for $\mathscr{A}_1$ (16 events) and $\mathscr{A}_2$ (8 events).

For sample spaces defined as finite or infinite intervals of real numbers σ-algebras are normally defined by unions and intersections of various intervals. An open interval (a, b) is the set $\{x : a < x < b\}$, a half-open interval $(a, b] = \{x : a < x \le b\}$ or $[a, b) = \{x : a \le x < b\}$, and a closed interval $[a, b] = \{x : a \le x \le b\}$. A single point is given as $[a, a] = \{a\}$. The σ-algebra that contains the intervals of the form $(-\infty, x]$, x a real number, contains all open, closed, and half-open intervals both finite and infinite. (The smallest σ-algebra containing the intervals is called the σ-algebra of Borel sets.)

The final step in setting up a probability system is to define the assignment of probability to events in the σ-algebra, which is referred to as a probability space, and to set up a set of axioms that these probabilities obey. A probability space consists of

    (a) a set, S, called the sample space
    (b) a class, $\mathscr{A}$, of subsets (of S)
    (c) a set function, P, defined for each set (or event) in $\mathscr{A}$

and is denoted by the triple $(S, \mathcal{A}, P)$. The value of the set function P, of any member A of $\mathcal{A}$, is called the probability of the event A and written $P(A)$.

The choice of axioms (or assumed truths) satisfied by a probability space is not unique, but a minimum number will be chosen, with all other properties being deducible from these. The following axioms are satisfied by a probability space:

axiom 1: $S \in \mathcal{A}$ and $P(S) = 1$
axiom 2: $P(A) \geq 0$ for all $A \in \mathcal{A}$
axiom 3: $\mathcal{A}$ is a σ-algebra
axiom 4: if $A_i \in \mathcal{A}$ $i = 1, 2, \ldots$ and $A_i \cap A_k = \varnothing$ $i \neq k = 1, 2, \ldots$, then $P(\bigcup_{i=1}^{\infty} A_i) = \sum_{i=1}^{\infty} P(A_i)$

These axioms are motivated by intuitive concepts of probability theory. Consider the experiment of taking N samples from $S = \{1, 2, \ldots, 6\}$ (toss a die N times and observe the number each time) and let the number of samples corresponding to i be N_i, $i = 1, 2, \ldots, 6$. For the event $A \subset S$ it is clear that $0 \leq N_A \leq N$ and

$$0 \leq \frac{N_A}{N} \leq 1$$

$P(A)$ then models the quantity N_A / N, called the relative frequency of occurrence of the event A, and is nonnegative as in axiom 2. It is also less than or equal to 1, which is a direct consequence of the axioms and will be shown shortly. Also,

$$\sum_{i=1}^{6} N_i = N \quad \text{and} \quad \sum_{i=1}^{6} \frac{N_i}{N} = 1$$

which is modeled in axiom 1 as the probability of the certain event being 1. If $A \subset S$ and $B \subset S$ are mutually exclusive events (cannot occur simultaneously) and $C = A \cup B$, then $N_C = N_A + N_B$ and

$$\frac{N_C}{N} = \frac{N_A}{N} + \frac{N_B}{N}$$

which for two events is modeled in axiom 4. Axiom 4 extends the probability of the union of mutually exclusive events to be the sum of the individual probabilities for infinite sets of events. Thus the probability space defined here appears to model real-world occurrences, as well it should.

For the toss of a single die $S = \{1, 2, 3, 4, 5, 6\}$ and with $\{i\} \in \mathcal{A}$ (all sides distinguishable) and $P(i) = \frac{1}{6}$, $i = 1, 2, \ldots, 6$, where the probability assignment is the equally likely assignment since no side is favored over any other side, $P(1 \cup 2) = P(1) + P(2) = \frac{1}{3}$ and $P(\text{odd number}) = P(1) + P(3) + P(5) = \frac{1}{2}$.

Example 1.3.4. Determine the probability assignment for $\mathcal{A}_2$ that was developed in Example 1.3.1. $\mathcal{A}_2$ was given as

$$\mathcal{A}_2 = \{S, \varnothing, \{1\}, \{2, 3\}, \{4\}, \{1, 2, 3\}, \{1, 4\}, \{2, 3, 4\}\}$$

$$= \{S, \varnothing, \{HH\}, \{HT, TH\}, \{TT\}, \{HH, HT, TH\}, \{HH, TT\}, \{HT, TH, TT\}\}$$

which yields the probability assignment as

$$P = \{1, 0, \tfrac{1}{4}, \tfrac{1}{2}, \tfrac{1}{4}, \tfrac{3}{4}, \tfrac{1}{2}, \tfrac{3}{4}\}$$

where each number is equally likely, and the probability of each event in the algebra is obtained as $\tfrac{1}{4}$ times the number of elementary events contained in it. □

This is not the only probability assignment that can be made to $\mathcal{A}_2$. In fact, a more general assignment can be obtained by letting the probability of a head be p and the probability of a tail be $1 - p$, with the probabilities of the composite events obtained by multiplying and summing these terms, e.g., $P(\{1, 4\}) = P(\{HH, TT\}) = p^2 + (1 - p)^2$. For $p = 0.4$ the probability assignment for $\mathcal{A}_2$ would be

$$P = \{1, 0, 0.16, 0.48, 0.36, 0.64, 0.52, 0.84\}$$

Additional useful properties of probability theory, or direct consequences of the axioms, can now be developed. Some of these could have been interchanged with the axioms, but in any case they are straightforward and do model the relative frequency of occurrences.

The first property states that

$$P(A^c) = 1 - P(A) \qquad \text{for } A \in \mathcal{A} \qquad \text{property 1}$$

which satisfies intuition for the probability of the complement of A. This is proved as

$$A \in \mathcal{A} \Rightarrow A \subset S \Rightarrow A \cup A^c = S \qquad \text{with} \quad A \cap A^c = \varnothing$$

and

$$P(A \cup A^c) = P(A) + P(A^c) = P(S) \qquad \text{(from axiom 4)}$$

which yields

$$P(A) + P(A^c) = 1 \qquad \text{(from axiom 1)}$$

thus

$$P(A^c) = 1 - P(A)$$

A direct consequence of property 1 yields $P(\varnothing)$. Since $S \in \mathcal{A}$, $S^c = \varnothing \in \mathcal{A}$ and $P(S^c) = 1 - P(S) = 1 - 1 = P(\varnothing)$ or $P(\varnothing) = 0$. The converse of this is not necessarily true; that is, if $P(A) = 0$, this does not necessarily imply that A equals $\emptyset$. Consider $S = \{\theta : 0 \le \theta < 2\pi\}$, where θ is the angle or phase of a sine wave which is assumed random; the probability of stopping in the interval $[a, b]$ is appropriately modeled, as will be seen later, as $P(\{\theta : a \le \theta \le b\}) = (b-a)/2\pi, 0 \le a \le b < 2\pi$. This model assumes that the probability of being in an interval of a given length is directly proportional to that length, and $P(\{\theta : 0 \le \theta \le 2\pi\}) = 1$. Now $P(\{\theta : \theta = \pi\}) = 0$ but $\{\theta : \theta = \pi\} \ne \emptyset$.

The second property states that

$$P(A) \le P(B) \qquad \text{for} \quad A \subset B \text{ when } A \in \mathcal{A} \text{ and } B \in \mathcal{A} \qquad \text{property 2}$$

which indicates that the probabilities of events that are included in another set cannot exceed the probabilities of the other set (larger set). Since the only probability expression that is available at this time is the probability of the union of two mutually exclusive sets (axiom 4), divide B (the larger set) into the two mutually exclusive sets as shown in Fig. 1.3.1.

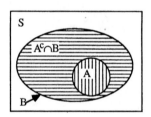

Fig. 1.3.1. $B = A \cup (A^c \cap B)$.

Now property 2 is proved as

$$B = A \cup (A^c \cap B) \qquad \text{with} \quad A \cap (A^c \cap B) = \emptyset \qquad (\text{since } A \subset B)$$

Then,

$$P(B) = P(A) + P(A^c \cap B) \qquad (\text{from axiom 4})$$

and

$$P(A^c \cap B) \ge 0 \qquad (\text{from axiom 2})$$

which yields

$$P(B) \ge P(A)$$

A direct consequence of property 2 gives $P(A) \le 1$. Since $A \subset S$, $P(A) \le P(S) = 1$ or $P(A) \le 1$.

The third property determines $P(A \cup B)$ as

$$P(A \cup B) = P(A) + P(B) - P(A \cap B) \qquad A \in \mathscr{A}, B \in \mathscr{A}, \text{ and } A \cap B \neq \varnothing$$

property 3

which is the more general case of axiom 4 for the probability of the union of two sets. Again, the only probability expression available at this time is the probability of the union of two mutually exclusive sets. Thus $A \cup B$ is divided into the mutually exclusive sets as shown in Fig. 1.3.2a.

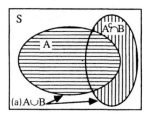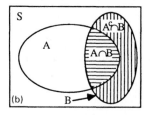

Fig. 1.3.2. Division of $A \cup B$ into mutually exclusive sets: (a) $A \cup B = A \cup (A^c \cap B)$; (b) $B = (A^c \cap B) \cup (A \cap B)$.

Property 3 is proved by expressing $A \cup B$ as given in Fig. 1.3.2a as

$$A \cup B = A \cup (A^c \cap B) \qquad \text{with} \quad A \cap (A^c \cap B) = \varnothing$$

This gives

$$P(A \cup B) = P(A) + P(A^c \cap B) \qquad \text{(from axiom 4)}$$

Next express B as given in Figure 1.3.2b as

$$B = (A \cap B) \cup (A^c \cap B) \qquad \text{with} \quad (A \cap B) \cap (A^c \cap B) = \varnothing$$

to yield

$$P(B) = P(A \cap B) + P(A^c \cap B) \qquad \text{(from axiom 4)}$$

or

$$P(A^c \cap B) = P(B) - P(A \cap B)$$

Putting this into the $P(A \cup B)$ expression produces property 3 as

$$P(A \cup B) = P(A) + P(B) - P(A \cap B) \qquad (1.3.1)$$

A direct consequence of property 3, since $P(A \cap B) \geq 0$ from axiom 2, is the upper bound

$$P(A \cup B) \leq P(A) + P(B) \qquad (1.3.2)$$

Example 1.3.5. Determine the probability of obtaining at least one 1 on two tosses of a six-sided die. This result was stated in Example 1.1.2. The sample space is given as $S = \{11, 12, 13, \ldots, 21, 22, \ldots, 66\}$ (36 elements), and the probability of obtaining at least one 1 on two tosses is readily obtainable from Eq. (1.3.1) as

$$P(1_1 \cup 1_2) = P(1_1) + P(1_2) - P(1_1 \cap 1_2) = \tfrac{6}{36} + \tfrac{6}{36} - \tfrac{1}{36} = \tfrac{11}{36}$$

where the subscript indicates the toss.   □

The probability of the union, property 3, can be extended for three events $A \in \mathscr{A}$, $B \in \mathscr{A}$, and $C \in \mathscr{A}$ as

$$P(A \cup B \cup C) = P([A \cup B] \cup C) = P(A \cup B) + P(C) - P([A \cup B] \cap C)$$
$$= P(A) + P(B) - P(A \cap B) + P(C) - P([A \cap C] \cup [B \cap C])$$

which reduces to

$$P(A \cup B \cup C) = P(A) + P(B) + P(C) - P(A \cap B)$$
$$- P(A \cap C) - P(B \cap C) + P(A \cap B \cap C) \quad (1.3.3)$$

Example 1.3.6. Determine the probability of obtaining at least one 1 on three tosses of a fair die. If a die is tossed three times, $S = \{111, 112, \ldots, 121, \ldots, 211, \ldots, 666\}$ ($6^3 = 216$ elements) and the probability of obtaining at least one 1 on three tosses can be obtained using Eq. (1.3.3) as

$$P(1_1 \cup 1_2 \cup 1_3) = P(1_1) + P(1_2) + P(1_3) - P(1_1 \cap 1_2) - P(1_1 \cap 1_3)$$
$$- P(1_2 \cap 1_3) + P(1_1 \cap 1_2 \cap 1_3)$$
$$= \tfrac{1}{6} + \tfrac{1}{6} + \tfrac{1}{6} - \tfrac{1}{36} - \tfrac{1}{36} - \tfrac{1}{36} + \tfrac{1}{216} = \tfrac{91}{216} \quad □$$

For four events (adding $D \in \mathscr{A}$) the probability of the union becomes

$$P(A \cup B \cup C \cup D) = P(A) + P(B) + P(C) + P(D) - P(A \cap B)$$
$$- P(A \cap C) - P(A \cap D) - P(B \cap C)$$
$$- P(B \cap D) - P(C \cap D) + P(A \cap B \cap C)$$
$$+ P(A \cap B \cap D) + P(A \cap C \cap D)$$
$$+ P(B \cap C \cap D) - P(A \cap B \cap C \cap D) \quad (1.3.4)$$

The general expression for the probability of the union involves adding all probabilities of single events, subtracting all probabilities of intersections of double events, adding all probabilities of intersections of triple events, etc. The probability of the union for more than three events becomes quite cumbersome, but a useful and compact upper bound, called the union bound, can readily be developed. The union bound states that for $A_i \in \mathcal{A}$, $i = 1, 2, \ldots, N$,

$$P\left(\bigcup_{i=1}^{N} A_i\right) \leq \sum_{i=1}^{N} P(A_i) \qquad (1.3.5)$$

Even for $N = 3$ the bound is not immediately obvious, as can be seen from Eq. (1.3.3), since not all of the terms neglected are negative. But $(A \cap B \cap C) \subset (B \cap C)$ and $P(A \cap B \cap C) \leq P(B \cap C)$ or $[P(B \cap C) - P(A \cap B \cap C)] \geq 0$ or effectively the terms neglected are all negative and the bound is true for $N = 3$ or

$$P(A \cup B \cup C) \leq P(A) + P(B) + P(C) \qquad (1.3.6)$$

Using this bound for the probability of obtaining at least one 1 on three tosses of a die, Example 1.3.6, gives $P(1_1 \cup 1_2 \cup 1_3) \leq \frac{1}{2}$, which is close to the correct value of $\frac{91}{216}$. The general case will be proved using mathematical induction. The steps used in induction are

(i) show the statement is true for a starting value

$$N = 1 \qquad P(A_1) = P(A_1) \qquad (= \text{satisfies} \leq)$$

or

$$N = 2 \qquad P(A_1 \cup A_2) \leq P(A_1) + P(A_2) \qquad [\text{Eq. (1.3.2)}]$$

(ii) assume the statement is true for N

$$P\left(\bigcup_{i=1}^{N} A_i\right) \leq \sum_{i=1}^{N} P(A_i)$$

(iii) show the statement is true for $N + 1$

$$P\left(\bigcup_{i=1}^{N+1} A_i\right) = P\left(\left[\bigcup_{i=1}^{N} A_i\right] \cup A_{N+1}\right) \qquad \text{(from associative property)}$$

$$= P\left(\bigcup_{i=1}^{N} A_i\right) + P(A_{N+1}) - P\left(\left[\bigcup_{i=1}^{N} A_i\right] \cap A_{N+1}\right)$$

$$\text{(from property 3)}$$

$$\leq P\left(\bigcup_{i=1}^{N} A_i\right) + P(A_{N+1}) \qquad \text{(from axiom 2)}$$

$$\leq \sum_{i=1}^{N} P(A_i) + P(A_{N+1}) \qquad \text{(from ii)}$$

thus

$$P\left(\bigcup_{i=1}^{N+1} A_i\right) \le \sum_{i=1}^{N+1} P(A_i)$$

and the proof is complete.

1.4   Conditional Probability and Statistical Independence

In several of the examples of Section 1.3 different coin tosses, die tosses, etc. were implicitly assumed to be statistically independent, e.g., $P(\{HH\}) = (\frac{1}{2})(\frac{1}{2}) = \frac{1}{4}$. These examples were straightforward, so an explicit statement of this assumption was not necessary (and would have been meaningless without the definitions given in this section). The occurrence or nonoccurrence of a particular event, in some situations, may affect the probabilities of other events, whereas in other situations there may be no such influence. To illustrate this idea, consider a box that contains 5 red and 3 white balls from which 2 balls will be drawn. If there is no reason to favor one color over the other (same size, shape, weight, etc., and no looking in the box), the equally likely assumption, the probability of drawing a red ball on the first drawing is $\frac{5}{8}$ and of a white ball is $\frac{3}{8}$. If this ball is replaced before the second drawing (everything is the same as for the first drawing) the probability of drawing a red ball on the second drawing is $\frac{5}{8}$ and of a white ball is $\frac{3}{8}$. The first drawing has not affected the second drawing. This is an example of events that are statistically independent (this will be defined shortly). Now if the ball on the first drawing is not replaced before the second drawing there are only 7 balls available for the second drawing. If the first ball was red, the probability of drawing a red ball on the second drawing is $\frac{4}{7}$ (4 red and 3 white balls were left) and of a white ball is $\frac{3}{7}$, while if the first ball was white, the probability of drawing a red ball on the second drawing is $\frac{5}{7}$ (5 red and 2 white balls were left) and of a white ball is $\frac{2}{7}$. This example without replacement is a situation where the event first drawing has affected the second drawing (first drawing and second drawing are not statistically independent). If the first ball was red and if the first ball was white are conditions, and the probabilities associated with them are called conditional probabilities.

For $A \in \mathscr{A}$ and $B \in \mathscr{A}$, the conditional probability of the event A given that the event B has occurred is defined as

$$P(A|B) = \frac{P(A \cap B)}{P(B)} \quad \text{for} \quad P(B) > 0 \tag{1.4.1}$$

which means the probability of the set A given the set B (B has occurred or has been observed). For $P(A|B)$, knowing that B has occurred limits the range of possible outcomes of the random phenomenon to those contained in B and the possible outcomes of A to those contained in the intersection of A and B. Conditional probability can be viewed as probability on a restricted sample space. The Venn diagram of Fig. 1.4.1 indicates the restricted outcomes due to conditioning. Essentially the set B is a new sample space (the new set of possible outcomes). From Eq. (1.4.1) it can be seen that $P(B|B) = 1$. For the box with 5 red and 3 white balls the conditional probabilities of the second drawing given the first drawing without replacement are $P(R_2|R_1) = \frac{4}{7}$, $P(W_2|R_1) = \frac{3}{7}$, $P(R_2|W_1) = \frac{5}{7}$, and $P(W_2|W_1) = \frac{2}{7}$, where R indicates red, W indicates white, and the subscript indicates the drawing.

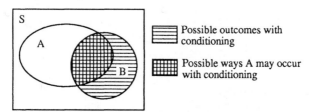

Fig. 1.4.1.   Restricted outcomes due to conditioning.

Equation (1.4.1) can also be written, including the conditional probability of B given A, as

$$P(A \cap B) = P(A|B)P(B) = P(B|A)P(A) \qquad \text{for} \quad P(B) > 0 \quad P(A) > 0$$

$$(1.4.2)$$

and for three events $A \in \mathscr{A}$, $B \in \mathscr{A}$, and $C \in \mathscr{A}$ can be extended to

$$P(A \cap B \cap C) = \left[\frac{P(A \cap B \cap C)}{P(B \cap C)}\right]\left[\frac{P(B \cap C)}{P(C)}\right]P(C)$$

$$= P(A|(B \cap C))P(B|C)P(C) \qquad (1.4.3)$$

which is the chain rule for expanding probabilities of intersections.

To illustrate that in general $P(A|B)$ is not related to $P(A)$ consider two examples.

Example 1.4.1.   Relate $P(A|B)$ to $P(A)$ for $A \subset B$ and for $A \cap B = \varnothing$. First, for $A \subset B$

$$P(A|B) = \frac{P(A \cap B)}{P(B)} = \frac{P(A)}{P(B)} \qquad \text{(since } A \cap B = A \text{ for } A \subset B\text{)}$$

$$\geq P(A) \qquad \text{(since } P(B) \leq 1\text{)}$$

and second, for $A \cap B = \emptyset$

$$P(A|B) = \frac{P(A \cap B)}{P(B)} = \frac{P(\emptyset)}{P(B)} = \frac{0}{P(B)} = 0 \leq P(A) \qquad \square$$

Thus no general statement regarding the value of $P(A|B)$ relative to the value of $P(A)$ can be made.

Example 1.4.2. Relate $P(\{1\}|\{odd\})$ and $P(\{1\}|\{even\})$ to $P(\{1\})$ for the single tossing of a fair die. For the toss of a single die $S = \{1, 2, 3, 4, 5, 6\}$ and $P(\{i\}) = \frac{1}{6}$, $i = 1, \ldots, 6$. Now $P(\{1\}|\{odd\}) = \frac{1}{3}$, which can be obtained from Eq. (1.4.1) as

$$P(\{1\}|\{odd\}) = \frac{P(\{1\} \cap \{odd\})}{P(\{odd\})} = \frac{P(\{1\})}{P(\{odd\})} = \frac{\frac{1}{6}}{\frac{1}{2}} = \frac{1}{3}$$

and $P(\{1\}|\{even\}) = 0$. Thus

$$P(\{1\}|\{even\}) < P(\{1\}) < P(\{1\}|\{odd\}) \qquad \square$$

Example 1.4.2 is another illustration that no general statement regarding the values of conditional and unconditional probabilities can be made.

Conditional probabilities satisfy the four axioms that are satisfied by a probability space, and as such the triple $(S, \mathcal{A}, P(A|B))$ is itself a probability space (P replaced by $P(A|B)$). It will now be shown that the four axioms are satisfied.

Since $B \subset S$, $P(S \cap B) = P(B)$ and using Eq. (1.4.1),

$$P(S|B) = \frac{P(S \cap B)}{P(B)} = \frac{P(B)}{P(B)} = 1$$

and axiom 1 is satisfied.

Axiom 2 follows from Eq. (1.4.1) since $P(A \cap B) \geq 0$ and $P(B) > 0$, which yields

$$P(A|B) \geq 0$$

The σ-algebra for the conditional probabilities $\mathcal{A}$ is the same as for the unconditional probabilities and thus axiom 3 is satisfied.

For $A_i \cap A_k = \emptyset$, $i \neq k = 1, 2, \ldots$, $(A_i \cap B) \cap (A_k \cap B) = (A_i \cap A_k) \cap B = \emptyset$, $i \neq k = 1, 2, \ldots$, and

$$P\left[\left(\bigcup_{i=1}^{\infty} A_i \right) \bigg| B \right] = \frac{P[\bigcup_{i=1}^{\infty} (A_i \cap B)]}{P(B)} = \frac{\sum_{i=1}^{\infty} P(A_i \cap B)}{P(B)} = \sum_{i=1}^{\infty} P(A_i|B)$$

which shows that axiom 4 is satisfied.

Also, $P(A^c|B) = 1 - P(A|B)$, if $(A \cap B) \subset (C \cap B)$ then $P(A|B) \leq P(C|B)$, $P(A|B) \leq 1$, $P[(A \cup C)|B] = P(A|B) + P(C|B) - P[(A \cap C)|B]$, etc.

If a region is divided into nonoverlapping (mutually exclusive) parts and the parts make up the total region (cover it), the parts are said to partition the region. Since $A \cup A^c = S$ (covers the sample space) and $A \cap A^c = \emptyset$ (mutually exclusive), A and A^c partition the sample space. In general, a collection of sets $A_1, A_2, \ldots$ is said to partition the sample space S if and only if

$$S = \bigcup_{i=1}^{\infty} A_i \quad \text{and} \quad A_i \cap A_k = \emptyset \quad i \neq k = 1, 2, \ldots$$

Thus

$$\sum_{i=1}^{\infty} P(A_i) = P\left(\bigcup_{i=1}^{\infty} A_i\right) = P(S) = 1 \quad \text{(axiom 4)}$$

Now let $B \subset S$ and form $A_i \cap B$, $i = 1, 2, \ldots$, as shown in Fig. 1.4.2, where $\{A_i\}$ partitions S. Then

$$\bigcup_{i=1}^{\infty} (A_i \cap B) = B \cap \left(\bigcup_{i=1}^{\infty} A_i\right) = B \cap S = B \quad \text{(distributive property)}$$

and

$$(A_i \cap B) \cap (A_k \cap B) = B \cap (A_i \cap A_k) = B \cap \emptyset = \emptyset \quad i \neq k = 1, 2, \ldots$$

(associative property)

Thus $\{A_i \cap B\}$ partitions B and

$$P(B) = P\left[\bigcup_{i=1}^{\infty} (A_i \cap B)\right] = \sum_{i=1}^{\infty} P(A_i \cap B) = \sum_{i=1}^{\infty} P(B|A_i)P(A_i) \quad (1.4.4)$$

which is referred to as the total probability. This expression says that the total probability of an event can be obtained by summing the set of mutually exclusive and exhaustive ways of the event occurring.

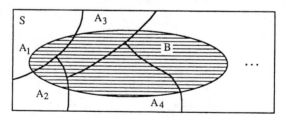

Fig. 1.4.2. Venn diagram for a partition of S and of B.

Example 1.4.3. Determine the total probability of obtaining a Red ball on the second drawing (without replacement on the first drawing) from a box with 5 red and 3 white equally likely balls. The unconditional probabilities of the first drawing are given as $P(R_1) = \frac{5}{8}$ and $P(W_1) = \frac{3}{8}$ and the conditional probabilities of the second drawing given the first drawing are $P(R_2|R_1) = \frac{4}{7}$, $P(W_2|R_1) = \frac{3}{7}$, $P(R_2|W_1) = \frac{5}{7}$, and $P(W_2|W_1) = \frac{2}{7}$. The total probability of obtaining a red ball on the second drawing is determined using Eq. (1.4.4) as

$$P(R_2) = P(R_2|R_1)P(R_1) + P(R_2|W_1)P(W_1) = (\tfrac{4}{7})(\tfrac{5}{8}) + (\tfrac{5}{7})(\tfrac{3}{8}) = \tfrac{5}{8}$$

In a similar manner, the total probability of obtaining a white ball on the second drawing is given as

$$P(W_2) = P(W_2|R_1)P(R_1) + P(W_2|W_1)P(W_1) = (\tfrac{3}{7})(\tfrac{5}{8}) + (\tfrac{2}{7})(\tfrac{3}{8}) = (\tfrac{3}{8})$$

or

$$P(W_2) = 1 - P(R_2) = \tfrac{3}{8} \quad \square$$

It can be noted in this example that $P(R_2) = P(R_1)$, since without knowing the outcome of the first drawing the possible outcomes for the second drawing are the same as for the first drawing.

Example 1.4.4. Determine the probability of being correct on choice two for Example 1.1.4. This was the case of choosing one of three alternatives at random where, after a first choice, additional information that one of the other alternatives is incorrect is obtained, and a second choice is given. Let C_1 be the event that choice one is correct, with C_1^c the event choice one is incorrect, and C_2 be the event that choice two is correct, with C_2^c the event choice two is incorrect. Then the total probability of choice 2 being correct is obtained as

$$P(C_2) = P(C_2|C_1)P(C_1) + P(C_2|C_1^c)P(C_1^c)$$
$$= P(C_2|C_1)(\tfrac{1}{3}) + P(C_2|C_1^c)(\tfrac{2}{3})$$

To maximize $P(C_2)$ it would appear that the coefficient $P(C_2|C_1^c)$ should be as large as possible. This is indeed what happens in the second strategy of changing choices (the alternative that is neither choice one nor the given incorrect alternative) to yield $P(C_2|C_1) = 0$ and $P(C_2|C_1^c) = 1$, which results in $P(C_2) = \frac{2}{3}$. $\square$

The probability of one of the events in the partition of B, using Eq. (1.4.2), is given as

$$P(A_k \cap B) = P(B|A_k)P(A_k)$$

and using Eq. (1.4.1)

$$P(A_k|B) = \frac{P(A_k \cap B)}{P(B)} = \frac{P(B|A_k)P(A_k)}{P(B)}$$

which, using Eq. (1.4.4), yields

$$P(A_k|B) = \frac{P(B|A_k)P(A_k)}{\sum_{i=1}^{\infty} P(B|A_i)P(A_i)} \qquad (1.4.5)$$

This expression is called Bayes' theorem or rule. Thus if $\{A_i\}$ correspond to events before the performance of an experiment and B corresponds to the outcome of the experiment or observation, Bayes' rule expresses the conditional probability of a particular event given the outcome, in terms of the unconditional probabilities of the $\{A_i\}$ and the conditional probabilities of the particular outcome B given each of the events $\{A_i\}$.

Using Bayes' rule enables the calculation of the probability of the event A_k given that an observation or measurement B has been taken. This probability, $P(A_k|B)$, is called the *a posteriori* probability (probability after obtaining B) and is expressible in terms of the $P(A_i)$'s, which are called the *a priori* probabilities (probabilities before obtaining B), and the conditional probabilities $P(B|A_i)$, which are normally obtainable from the system.

Example 1.4.5.   Consider a binary communication system consisting of a transmitter that emits one of two possible signals, an A_0 or A_1 (0 or 1), over a given channel to a receiver that processes one of two possible signals, a B_0 or B_1 (0 or 1). The transmitter sample space is given as $S_T = \{A_0, A_1\}$ and the receiver sample space as $S_R = \{B_0, B_1\}$. Let $P(A_0) = \frac{2}{5}$ and $P(A_1) = \frac{3}{5}$ (50% more 1's are transmitted than 0's). Without any additional information (not using the channel), the best performance is obtained by deciding that A_1 is transmitted all of the time (not very interesting though). Doing this, the probability of being correct, $P(C)$, would be $\frac{3}{5}$ while the probability of error would be $P(e) = \frac{2}{5}$. Now model this digital channel as shown in Fig. 1.4.3. The conditional probabilities of the channel output given the channel input, $P(B_k|A_i)$, commonly called the channel transition probabilities, are depicted in the channel model as $P(B_0|A_0) = \frac{7}{8}$, $P(B_1|A_0) = \frac{1}{8}$, $P(B_0|A_1) = \frac{1}{6}$, and $P(B_1|A_1) = \frac{5}{6}$. The channel transition probabilities are normally known prior to conducting the experiment; they may be obtained by transmitting

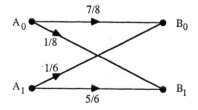

Fig. 1.4.3. Binary channel model.

A_0 a large number of times and counting the number of times B_0 occurs and B_1 occurs to approximate $P(B_0|A_0)$ and $P(B_1|A_0)$, and by transmitting A_1 a large number of times to approximate $P(B_0|A_1)$ and $P(B_1|A_1)$. In any case, the *a priori* probabilities $\{P(A_i)\}$ and the channel transition probabilities $\{P(B_k|A_i)\}$ are assumed known.

The objective in this communication system is, after observing each received digit, to make a decision as to which digit was transmitted. This decision should be made using the information of the *a priori* probabilities and the channel transition probabilities. For each received digit the most likely transmitted digit should be picked, to give the largest probability of being correct. This decision is accomplished by picking the largest *a posteriori* probability, $P(A_i|B_k)$, over all i for each k (referred to as the maximum *a posteriori* decision rule). Using Bayes' rule, $P(A_i|B_k)$ is calculated as

$$P(A_i|B_k) = \frac{P(B_k|A_i)P(A_i)}{P(B_k)} \qquad i = 0, 1 \quad k = 0, 1$$

The received digit probabilities are given, from Eq. (1.4.4), as

$$P(B_0) = P(B_0|A_0)P(A_0) + P(B_0|A_1)P(A_1) = (\tfrac{7}{8})(\tfrac{2}{5}) + (\tfrac{1}{6})(\tfrac{3}{5}) = \tfrac{9}{20}$$

and

$$P(B_1) = P(B_1|A_0)P(A_0) + P(B_1|A_1)P(A_1) = (\tfrac{1}{8})(\tfrac{2}{5}) + (\tfrac{5}{6})(\tfrac{3}{5}) = \tfrac{11}{20}$$

or in this case $P(B_1)$ could have been obtained as

$$P(B_1) = 1 - P(B_0) = \tfrac{11}{20}$$

Given B_0, the conditional input probabilities are obtained as

$$P(A_0|B_0) = \frac{P(B_0|A_0)P(A_0)}{P(B_0)} = \frac{(\tfrac{7}{8})(\tfrac{2}{5})}{\tfrac{9}{20}} = \tfrac{7}{9}$$

and

$$P(A_1|B_0) = \frac{P(B_0|A_1)P(A_1)}{P(B_0)} = \frac{(\tfrac{1}{6})(\tfrac{3}{5})}{\tfrac{9}{20}} = \tfrac{2}{9}$$

or in this case

$$P(A_1|B_0) = 1 - P(A_0|B_0) = \tfrac{2}{9}$$

The best choice of inputs, given that B_0 is received, is A_0 since it is the most probable and will maximize the probability of being correct (minimize the probability of error). Using this choice of inputs, the conditional probability of correct given B_0 is

$$P(C|B_0) = P(A_0|B_0) = \tfrac{7}{9}$$

and the conditional probability of error given B_0 is

$$P(e \mid B_0) = P(A_1 \mid B_0) = \tfrac{2}{9}$$

Now given B_1

$$P(A_0 \mid B_1) = \frac{P(B_1 \mid A_0)P(A_0)}{P(B_1)} = \frac{(\tfrac{1}{8})(\tfrac{2}{5})}{\tfrac{11}{20}} = \tfrac{1}{11}$$

and

$$P(A_1 \mid B_1) = \frac{P(B_1 \mid A_1)P(A_1)}{P(B_1)} = \frac{(\tfrac{5}{6})(\tfrac{3}{5})}{\tfrac{11}{20}} = \tfrac{10}{11}$$

or in this case

$$P(A_1 \mid B_1) = 1 - P(A_0 \mid B_1) = \tfrac{10}{11}$$

The best choice of inputs, given that B_1 is received, is A_1 since it is the most probable, and the resulting conditional probability of correct is

$$P(C \mid B_1) = P(A_1 \mid B_1) = \tfrac{10}{11}$$

and the conditional probability of error given B_1 is

$$P(e \mid B_1) = P(A_0 \mid B_1) = \tfrac{1}{11}$$

The resulting probability of correct, using Eq. (1.4.4) (averaging over all outcomes), is then given as

$$P(C) = P(C \mid B_0)P(B_0) + P(C \mid B_1)P(B_1) = (\tfrac{7}{9})(\tfrac{9}{20}) + (\tfrac{10}{11})(\tfrac{11}{20}) = \tfrac{17}{20}$$

and the corresponding probability of error is

$$P(e) = 1 - P(C) = \tfrac{3}{20}$$

For two inputs $P(e)$ can be calculated directly as

$$P(e) = P(e \mid B_0)P(B_0) + P(e \mid B_1)P(B_1) = (\tfrac{2}{9})(\tfrac{9}{20}) + (\tfrac{1}{11})(\tfrac{11}{20}) = \tfrac{3}{20}$$

but for cases with more than two inputs it is easier to calculate $P(C)$ directly and then obtain $P(e) = 1 - P(C)$. The reason for this is that there is only one correct input for a given output while there may be many incorrect inputs. An alternative way of calculating $P(C)$ using the probabilities conditioned on $\{A_i\}$ is given as

$$P(C) = P(C \mid A_0)P(A_0) + P(C \mid A_1)P(A_1)$$
$$= P(B_0 \mid A_0)P(A_0) + P(B_1 \mid A_1)P(A_1)$$
$$= (\tfrac{7}{8})(\tfrac{2}{5}) + (\tfrac{5}{6})(\tfrac{3}{5}) = \tfrac{17}{20}$$

In conclusion, for this example, making use of the channel has reduced the probability of error from 0.4 to 0.15.   □

Many digital communication systems can be modeled similarly to that in Example 1.4.5. Time-varying signals corresponding to the zeros and ones are transmitted over a channel where they are corrupted by noise, which causes the transmitted signals to be received as the other signal part of the time. The receiver, after observing the received values, then attempts to determine whether zeros or ones were transmitted.

Consider another example where Bayes' rule is applicable.

Example 1.4.6. Three boxes contain transistors, where box 1 contains 2 good and 8 bad transistors, box 2 contains 7 good and 3 bad transistors, and box 3 contains 4 good and 6 bad transistors. If a transistor is drawn from a box, where $P(1) = 0.35$ (probability of choosing box 1 is 0.35), $P(2) = 0.25$, and $P(3) = 0.4$, determine the most likely box the transistor came from if a good transistor is obtained. For the equally likely assumption of transistors in each box, then $P(G|1) = 0.2$ (G indicates good and B indicates bad), $P(B|1) = 0.8$, $P(G|2) = 0.7$, $P(B|2) = 0.3$, $P(G|3) = 0.4$, and $P(B|3) = 0.6$. $P(G)$ is given, from Eq. (1.4.4), as

$$P(G) = P(G|1)P(1) + P(G|2)P(2) + P(G|3)P(3)$$

$$= (0.2)(0.35) + (0.7)(0.25) + (0.4)(0.4) = 0.405$$

and $P(B) = 1 - P(G) = 0.595$. Using Bayes' rule, $P(1|G)$ is obtained as

$$P(1|G) = \frac{P(G|1)P(1)}{P(G)} = \frac{(0.2)(0.35)}{(0.405)} = 0.173$$

Also, $P(2|G)$ is given as

$$P(2|G) = \frac{P(G|2)P(2)}{P(G)} = \frac{(0.7)(0.25)}{0.405} = 0.432$$

and

$$P(3|G) = \frac{P(G|3)P(3)}{P(G)} = \frac{(0.4)(0.4)}{0.405} = 0.395$$

Comparing $P(1|G)$, $P(2|G)$, and $P(3|G)$, the good transistor was most likely to have come from box 2 (with probability 0.432).   □

In introducing conditional probability, an example of statistical independence was given. The definition of statistical independence will now be given. Two events $A \in \mathcal{A}$ and $B \in \mathcal{A}$ are said to be statistically independent if and only if

$$P(A \cap B) = P(A)P(B) \tag{1.4.6a}$$

For $P(A) > 0$ and $P(B) > 0$ Eq. (1.4.6a) implies that

$$P(A|B) = \frac{P(A \cap B)}{P(B)} = \frac{P(A)P(B)}{P(B)}$$

or

$$P(A|B) = P(A) \tag{1.4.6b}$$

and

$$P(B|A) = \frac{P(A \cap B)}{P(A)} = \frac{P(A)P(B)}{P(A)}$$

or

$$P(B|A) = P(B) \tag{1.4.6c}$$

when A and B are statistically independent. Equations (1.4.6a), (1.4.6b), and (1.4.6c) are all equivalent expressions of the statistical independence of the events A and B. Thus A and B are statistically independent when the probability of A does not change knowing B, and likewise the probability of B does not change knowing A. It is reasonable to believe that successive tosses of a coin or a die are not dependent on the previous tosses. The tosses of a coin or a die are normally assumed to be statistically independent and hence the probability on several tosses is the product of the probabilities of the individual tosses.

Example 1.4.7. Consider the series communication configuration of Example 1.1.3 given in Fig. 1.1.2a. If line 1 and line 2 are statistically independent, the probability of communicating from A to B, $P(\text{comm})$, is given by

$$P(\text{comm}) = P(1 \cap 2) = P_1 P_2$$

where P_i indicates the probability of communicating over line i. With $P_1 = 0.9$ and $P_2 = 0.8$, $P(\text{comm}) = 0.72$. Also, for the parallel communication configuration of Example 1.1.3 given in Fig. 1.1.2b

$$P(\text{comm}) = P(1 \cup 2) = P_1 + P_2 - P(1 \cap 2) = P_1 + P_2 - P_1 P_2$$

$$= 0.9 + 0.8 - (0.9)(0.8) = 0.98 \qquad \square$$

The probability of obtaining at least one 1 on three tosses of a die, as in Example 1.3.6, is aided by statistical independence to yield

$$P(1_1 \cup 1_2 \cup 1_3) = P(1_1) + P(1_2) + P(1_3) - P(1_1)P(1_2) - P(1_1)P(1_3)$$

$$- P(1_2)P(1_3) + P(1_1)P(1_2)P(1_3) = 3(\tfrac{1}{6}) - 3(\tfrac{1}{6})^2 + (\tfrac{1}{6})^3 = \tfrac{91}{216}$$

If A and B are statistically independent then the pairs A and B^c, A^c and B, and A^c and B^c are all statistically independent. If the probability of A is not affected by knowing that B has occurred, it should seem reasonable that the probability of A should not be affected by knowing that B has not occurred. To prove the first pair, that A and B^c are statistically independent, express $P(B^c|A)$ as

$$P(B^c|A) = 1 - P(B|A)$$

Then, since $P(B|A) = P(B)$ by assumption,

$$P(B^c|A) = 1 - P(B) = P(B^c)$$

and thus A and B^c are statistically independent if A and B are statistically independent.

Using the statistical independence of the complements and De Morgan's property, $P(\text{comm})$ for the parallel communication of Example 1.4.7 can be obtained as

$$P(\text{comm}) = P(1 \cup 2) = P([1^c \cap 2^c]^c) = 1 - P(1^c)P(2^c)$$
$$= 1 - (1 - 0.9)(1 - 0.8) = 0.98$$

Likewise, $P(1_1 \cup 1_2 \cup 1_3)$ for three tosses of a die, as in Example 1.3.6, can be obtained in a succinct manner as

$$P(1_1 \cup 1_2 \cup 1_3) = P([1_1^c \cap 1_2^c \cap 1_3^c]^c) = 1 - P(1_1^c)P(1_2^c)P(1_3^c)$$
$$= 1 - (1 - \tfrac{1}{6})^3 = \tfrac{91}{216}$$

A common misconception is that mutually exclusive and statistically independent are the same. To show that this is not true, consider $A \in \mathscr{A}$ and $B \in \mathscr{A}$ mutually exclusive, $A \cap B = \varnothing$, which implies that

$$P(A \cap B) = 0$$

and for A and B statistically independent

$$P(A \cap B) = P(A)P(B)$$

Combining yields

$$P(A)P(B) = 0$$

and either $P(A) = 0$ or $P(B) = 0$ or both equal 0. Thus, if A and B are both mutually exclusive and statistically independent, then at least one of the events has probability zero. Normally, mutually exclusive events are not statistically independent, and the only time they are statistically independent is in the special case just considered. Mutual exclusiveness is a set relationship (nonoverlapping sets) and statistical independence is a probability relationship [given by Eq. (1.4.6)].

The definition of statistical independence for more than two events can be extended, but not as easily as might be thought. The simple extension of Eq. (1.4.6a) for N events would be

$$P(A_1 \cap A_2 \cap \cdots \cap A_N) = P(A_1)P(A_2) \cdots P(A_N)$$

which is satisfied if the events $A_1, A_2, \ldots, A_N$ are statistically independent, but satisfying this single equation is not sufficient to guarantee statistical independence. The complete definition for the events $A_i \in \mathcal{A}$, $i = 1, 2, \ldots, N$, to be statistically independent is if and only if

$$P(A_i \cap A_k) = P(A_i)P(A_k)$$

$$P(A_i \cap A_k \cap A_m) = P(A_i)P(A_k)P(A_m)$$

$$1 \leq i < k < m < \cdots \leq N$$

$$\vdots \qquad\qquad (1.4.7)$$

$$P(A_1 \cap A_2 \cap \cdots \cap A_N) = P(A_1)P(A_2) \cdots P(A_N)$$

In fact, there are $2^N - N - 1$ equations in this definition. If only the first equality of Eq. (1.4.7) holds, the events $\{A_i\}$ are called pairwise statistically independent. It is possible to find probability assignments for events in a probability space such that most of the expressions in Eq. (1.4.7) are satisfied but not all are.

Now, for the three events $A \in \mathcal{A}$, $B \in \mathcal{A}$, and $C \in \mathcal{A}$ being statistically independent, Eq. (1.4.7) reduces to

(a) $P(A \cap B) = P(A)P(B)$
(b) $P(A \cap C) = P(A)P(C)$
(c) $P(B \cap C) = P(B)P(C)$ $\qquad\qquad (1.4.8)$
(d) $P(A \cap B \cap C) = P(A)P(B)P(C)$

That no three of these conditions necessarily implies the fourth will be illustrated in the following example.

Example 1.4.8. Consider the probability assignment shown in the Venn diagram of Fig. 1.4.4. The number in each subset is used to indicate the

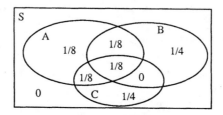

Fig. 1.4.4. Venn diagram illustrating statistical dependence.

probability of that subset. From Fig. 1.4.4 and summing the probabilities in the appropriate subsets

$$P(A \cap B) = \tfrac{1}{4} = (\tfrac{1}{2})(\tfrac{1}{2}) = P(A)P(B) \qquad \text{(a) is satisfied}$$

$$P(A \cap C) = \tfrac{1}{4} = (\tfrac{1}{2})(\tfrac{1}{2}) = P(A)P(C) \qquad \text{(b) is satisfied}$$

$$P(B \cap C) = \tfrac{1}{8} \ne (\tfrac{1}{2})(\tfrac{1}{2}) = P(B)P(C) \qquad \text{(c) is not satisfied}$$

$$P(A \cap B \cap C) = \tfrac{1}{8} = (\tfrac{1}{2})(\tfrac{1}{2})(\tfrac{1}{2}) = P(A)P(B)P(C) \qquad \text{(d) is satisfied}$$

By appropriate choices of the probabilities assigned to the subsets, (a), (b), and (c) can be shown to be satisfied while (d) is not satisfied.   □

If $A_i \in \mathscr{A}$, $i = 1, 2, \ldots, N$, are statistically independent, then any one of them is statistically independent of any event formed by unions, complements, and intersections of the others. This means that if the probability of A_i is not affected by knowing that the other events have occurred, the probability of A_i is also not affected by knowing that set operations of the other events have occurred. An example of this that has already been shown is that if A and B are statistically independent then A and B^c are also statistically independent. For the three statistically independent events A_1, A_2, and A_3

$$P[A_1 \cap (A_2 \cup A_3)] = P(A_1)P(A_2 \cup A_3)$$

is another example. This can be proved as

$$P[A_1 \cap (A_2 \cup A_3)] = P[(A_1 \cap A_2) \cup (A_1 \cap A_3)]$$
$$= P(A_1 \cap A_2) + P(A_1 \cap A_3) - P(A_1 \cap A_2 \cap A_1 \cap A_3)$$
$$= P(A_1)P(A_2) + P(A_1)P(A_3) - P(A_1)(P(A_2)P(A_3))$$
$$= P(A_1)[P(A_2) + P(A_3) - P(A_2)P(A_3)]$$
$$= P(A_1)[P(A_2) + P(A_3) - P(A_2 \cap A_3)]$$
$$= P(A_1)P(A_2 \cup A_3)$$

and thus A_1 and $A_2 \cup A_3$ are statistically independent.

Consider now the somewhat general problem of communicating from point A to point B where many separate lines have to be utilized. The analysis considered here is equivalent to determining the reliability of a system from A to B. For the series connection given in Fig. 1.4.5a, communication requires all of the lines to be available. If the lines are statistically independent (the usual assumption), the probability of communication from A to B, $P(\text{comm})$, is the probability of the intersections given as

$$P(\text{comm}) = P(1 \cap 2 \cap \cdots \cap N) = P(1)P(2) \cdots P(N) = P_1 P_2 \cdots P_N$$

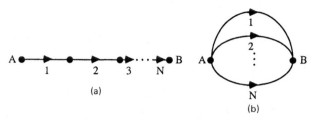

Fig. 1.4.5. Communication schemes: (a) series; (b) parallel.

where P_i is the probability that line i is available. For the parallel connection given in Fig. 1.4.5b, communication requires any of the lines to be available, and $P(\text{comm})$ is the probability of the unions given as

$$P(\text{comm}) = P(1 \cup 2 \cup \cdots \cup N) = 1 - P(1^c \cap 2^c \cap \cdots \cap N^c)$$

$$= 1 - P(1^c)P(2^c) \cdots P(N^c)$$

$$= 1 - (1 - P_1)(1 - P_2) \cdots (1 - P_N)$$

With $N = 3$ and $P_1 = 0.9$, $P_2 = 0.8$, and $P_3 = 0.7$, $P(\text{comm})$ for the series connection is $(0.9)(0.8)(0.7) = 0.504$ and for the parallel connection is $1 - (0.1)(0.2)(0.3) = 0.994$. These values are typical since the probability of communicating is normally far superior over a parallel connection than over the corresponding series connection.

Example 1.4.9.   Determine the probability of communicating from A to B for the system in Fig. 1.4.6, where lines 1, 2, 3, 4, 5, and 6 are statistically independent with $P_1 = 0.75$, $P_2 = 0.6$, $P_3 = 0.5$, $P_4 = 0.8$, $P_5 = 0.4$, and $P_6 = 0.25$. The probability of communicating from A to B will be calculated by combining series and parallel lines into equivalent lines as appropriate. Combining 1 and 2 as $C = (1 \cup 2)$ yields

$$P_C = 1 - (1 - P_1)(1 - P_2) = 1 - (0.25)(0.4) = 0.9$$

Then combining C and 4 as $D = (C \cap 4)$ results in

$$P_D = P_C P_4 = (0.9)(0.8) = 0.72$$

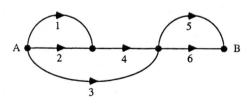

Fig. 1.4.6. Series–parallel communication system.

Next $E = (D \cup 3)$ gives

$$P_E = 1 - (1 - P_D)(1 - P_3) = 1 - (0.28)(0.5) = 0.86$$

Now let $F = (5 \cup 6)$, which yields

$$P_F = 1 - (1 - P_5)(1 - P_6) = 1 - (0.6)(0.75) = 0.55$$

Finally, comm $= (E \cap F)$ to obtain

$$P(\text{comm}) = P_E P_F = (0.86)(0.55) = 0.473 \qquad \square$$

An alternative solution to Example 1.4.9 would be to express $P(\text{comm})$ in terms of the direct paths through Fig. 1.4.6 as

$$P(\text{comm}) = P([1 \cap 4 \cap 5] \cup [1 \cap 4 \cap 6] \cup [2 \cap 4 \cap 5]$$

$$\cup [2 \cap 4 \cap 6] \cup [3 \cap 5] \cup [3 \cap 6])$$

which is somewhat tedious in this case. If this approach is used it should be noted that many of the direct paths are not statistically independent; e.g., $[3 \cap 5]$ and $[3 \cap 6]$ are not statistically independent since they both contain the path 3.

Example 1.4.10. Determine the probability of communicating from A to B for the system in Fig. 1.4.7, where lines 1, 2, 3, 4, and 5 are statistically

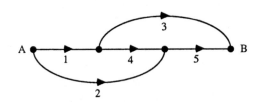

Fig. 1.4.7. Non-series-parallel communication system.

independent with $P_1 = 0.75$, $P_2 = 0.6$, $P_3 = 0.5$, $P_4 = 0.8$, and $P_5 = 0.4$. Since none of the lines are in series or parallel, the system cannot be reduced as in the previous example. But $P(\text{comm})$ can be expressed in terms of the direct paths as

$$P(\text{comm}) = P([1 \cap 3] \cup [1 \cap 4 \cap 5] \cup [2 \cap 5])$$

$$= P(1 \cap 3) + P(1 \cap 4 \cap 5) + P(2 \cap 5) - P(1 \cap 3 \cap 4 \cap 5)$$

$$- P(1 \cap 2 \cap 3 \cap 5) - P(1 \cap 2 \cap 4 \cap 5) + P(1 \cap 2 \cap 3 \cap 4 \cap 5)$$

where terms like $1 \cap 1 = 1$ have been used. This then becomes

$$P(\text{comm}) = P_1 P_3 + P_1 P_4 P_5 + P_2 P_5 - P_1 P_3 P_4 P_5 - P_1 P_2 P_3 P_5 - P_1 P_2 P_4 P_5$$
$$+ P_1 P_2 P_3 P_4 P_5 = 0.375 + 0.24 + 0.24 - 0.12$$
$$- 0.09 - 0.144 + 0.72 = 0.573 \qquad \square$$

An alternative approach to Example 1.4.10 is to use conditioning, as illustrated in the next example.

Example 1.4.11.   For Example 1.4.10 $P(\text{comm})$ can be expressed as

$$P(\text{comm}) = P(\text{comm}|1)P(1) + P(\text{comm}|1^c)P(1^c)$$
$$= P(\text{comm}|1)P_1 + P(\text{comm}|1^c)(1 - P_1)$$

Given 1, 2 and 4 can be combined as $C = 2 \cup 4$ to yield

$$P_C = 1 - (1 - P_2)(1 - P_4) = 1 - (0.4)(0.2) = 0.92$$

Next, C and 5 are combined as $D = (C \cap 5)$ to give

$$P_D = P_C P_5 = (0.92)(0.4) = 0.368$$

Then $P(\text{comm}|1)$ is obtained as

$$P(\text{comm}|1) = P(D \cup 3) = 1 - (1 - P_D)(1 - P_3) = 1 - (0.632)(0.5) = 0.684$$

Given 1^c, $P(\text{comm}|1^c)$ is obtained as

$$P(\text{comm}|1^c) = P(2 \cap 5) = P_2 P_5 = (0.6)(0.4) = 0.24$$

Finally, $P(\text{comm})$ is given as

$$P(\text{comm}) = P(\text{comm}|1)P_1 + P(\text{comm}|1^c)(1 - P_1)$$
$$= (0.684)(0.75) + (0.24)(0.25) = 0.513 + 0.06 = 0.573 \qquad \square$$

One final concept that will be considered in this chapter is that of a combined experiment. Even though it was not explicitly stated, the tossing of a die twice constituted a combined experiment, where a combined experiment can be viewed as a single experiment consisting of several subexperiments. At times, it is convenient to consider experiments as combined experiments. For the tossing of a die twice the combined sample space S is given in terms of the sample spaces $S_i = \{1, 2, 3, 4, 5, 6\}$, $i = 1, 2$, of each toss as

$$S = S_1 \times S_2 = \{11, 12, 13, \ldots, 21, 22, \ldots, 66\}$$

This is exactly the way the sample space was represented in Section 1.3 when it was used there. In the general case of N subexperiments with the sample spaces S_i, $i = 1, 2, \ldots, N$, the combined sample space is given as

$$S = S_1 \times S_2 \times \cdots \times S_N$$

where the number of elements in S equals the product of the numbers of elements in the individual S_i. The ith component of each N-tuple is a member of S_i.

If $B_i \in \mathcal{A}_i$, $i = 1, 2, \ldots, N$, and $A \subset S$, where

$$A = B_1 \times B_2 \times \cdots \times B_N$$

a combined σ-algebra $\mathcal{A}$ is defined as

(a) $S \in \mathcal{A}$
(b) $A \in \mathcal{A}$ implies $A^c \in \mathcal{A}$
(c) $A_i \in \mathcal{A}$, $i = 1, 2, \ldots$, implies $\bigcup_{i=1}^{\infty} A_i \in \mathcal{A}$

The convenience of subexperiments is that in most situations they can be considered statistically independent. For statistical independence

$$P(A) = P(B_1 \times B_2 \times \cdots \times B_N) = P(B_1)P(B_2) \cdots P(B_N)$$

and probability assignments on $\mathcal{A}$ are completely determined from probability assignments on $\mathcal{A}_i$, $i = 1, 2, \ldots, N$. This is what has been done for the cases considered here.

PROBLEMS

1.2.1. Sketch an appropriate sample space to represent the possible outcomes of the sum of the faces when two dice are tossed.

1.2.2. Sketch an appropriate sample space to represent the possible outcomes of the toss of two indistinguishable dice.

1.2.3. Given 2 red and 8 white balls in box A, 4 red and 6 white balls in box B, and 5 red and 5 white balls in box C, sketch an appropriate sample space to represent the possible outcomes of drawing a ball from a box.

1.2.4. Sketch an appropriate sample space to represent the possible outcomes of the flip of three coins (penny, nickel, dime).

1.2.5. With only the restriction that $(A \cap B) \subset C$, fill in the blanks (one letter per blank) $A \cap (B \cup C) = \underline{\hspace{1cm}} \cap \underline{\hspace{1cm}}$ and show in a Venn diagram.

1.2.6. Prove Problem 1.2.5.

1.2.7. With only the restriction that $B \subset C$ fill in the blanks (one letter per blank) $(A \cup B) \cap C = \underline{\hspace{1cm}} \cup (\underline{\hspace{1cm}} \cap \underline{\hspace{1cm}})$ and show in a Venn diagram.

1.2.8. Prove Problem 1.2.7.

1.2.9. Determine the least restrictive set relationship on A, B, and C for $(A \cup C) \subset (A \cup B)$.

1.2.10. Determine the least restrictive set relationship on A, B, and C for $(A \cap B) \subset (A \cap C)$.

1.2.11. For $S = (i : 1 \le i \le 10)$, $A = \{1, 2, 3, 4, 5\}$, $B = \{4, 5, 6, 7, 8\}$, and $C = \{3, 4, 7, 9, 10\}$ determine $(A \cap C) \cup B$ and $(A \cup C)^c \cap B$.

1.2.12. How many subsets of $S = \{1, 2, 3\}$ are there? List them.

1.3.1. For $S = \{1, 2, 3, 4\}$, $A = \{1\} \in \mathscr{A}$, and $B = \{1, 3, 4\} \in \mathscr{A}$, where $\mathscr{A}$ is an algebra, develop $\mathscr{A}$.

1.3.2. For $S = \{1, 2, 3, 4, 5\}$, $A = \{1, 2, 3\} \in \mathscr{A}$, and $B = \{3, 4, 5\} \in \mathscr{A}$, where $\mathscr{A}$ is an algebra, develop $\mathscr{A}$.

1.3.3. For $S = \{1, 2, 3, 4, 5, 6\}$, $A = \{1, 3, 5\} \in \mathscr{A}$, and $B = \{2, 3, 4, 5, 6\} \in \mathscr{A}$, where $\mathscr{A}$ is an algebra, develop $\mathscr{A}$.

1.3.4. With $P(i) = \frac{1}{4}$ in Problem 1.3.1 determine the probability assignment for $\mathscr{A}$.

1.3.5. With $P(i) = \frac{1}{5}$ in Problem 1.3.2 determine the probability assignment for $\mathscr{A}$.

1.3.6. With $P(i) = \frac{1}{6}$ in Problem 1.3.3 determine the probability assignment for $\mathscr{A}$.

1.3.7. For $A \subset (B \cup C)$ fill in the blank and prove $P(A \cup B)$_____$P(B \cup C)$.

$$(\le, =, \ge)$$

1.3.8. For $(A \cap B) \subset C$ fill in the blank and prove $P(A \cap B)$_____$P(A \cap C)$.

$$(\le, =, \ge)$$

1.3.9. Fill in the blank and prove $P[A \cap (B \cup C)]$_____$P(A \cap B) +$

$P(A \cap C)$. $(\le, =, \ge)$

1.3.10. Fill in the blank and prove $P[(A \cup B) \cap C]$_____$P[(A \cap B) \cup C]$.

$$(\le, =, \ge)$$

1.3.11. For three tossings of a coin determine P(at least one H in three tosses).

1.4.1. A four-sided object with $S = \{1, 2, 3, 4\}$ and $P(i) = \frac{1}{4}$, $i = 1, 2, 3, 4$, is tossed three times, where J_i denotes the outcome J on the ith toss. Determine P(at least one 1 in two tosses) $= P(1_1 \cup 1_2)$, P(at least one 1 in three tosses) $= P(1_1 \cup 1_2 \cup 1_3)$, and P(no 1's in three tosses).

1.4.2. For three tossings of a die where $A_i = \{$outcome ≤ 2 on the ith toss$\}$, $i = 1$, 2, 3, determine $P(A_1 \cup A_2)$, $P(A_1 \cup A_2 \cup A_3)$, and P(outcomes > 2 on all three tosses).

1.4.3. For three tossings of a die where J_i denotes the outcome J on the ith toss determine P(at least two numbers match out of three tosses).

1.4.4. An experiment consists of tossing a die until two successive tosses are the same. Determine the probability P_i of stopping with the ith toss.

1.4.5. For the toss of two dice the probability of winning a game given the sum of the two dice, i, is as given in Table P1.45. Determine P(winning) $= P(w)$.

i	2	3	4	5	6	7	8	9	10	11	12
$P(w\|i)$	0	0	$\frac{1}{3}$	$\frac{2}{5}$	$\frac{5}{11}$	1	$\frac{5}{11}$	$\frac{2}{5}$	$\frac{1}{3}$	1	0

Table P1.4.5

1.4.6. For 3 white, 4 green, and 5 red balls in box A and 3 white, 2 green, and 1 red ball in box B with $P(A) = \frac{1}{3}$ and $P(B) = \frac{2}{3}$, determine $P(B|W)$, determine whether B and W are statistically independent, and determine $P(G)$.

1.4.7. For 8 white and 2 green balls in box A, 5 white and 5 green balls in box B, and 6 white and 4 green balls in box C with $P(A) = \frac{1}{4}$, $P(B) = \frac{1}{2}$, and $P(C) = \frac{1}{4}$, determine $P(C|W)$, determine whether C and W are statistically independent, and determine $P(G)$.

1.4.8. For the digital communication system given in Fig. P1.4.8, where $P(A_0) = 0.4$ and $P(A_1) = 0.6$, determine the best choice for A given B_0, the best choice for A given B_1, and the probability of error for these choices.

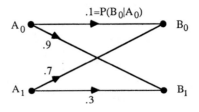

Fig. P1.4.8.

1.4.9. For the digital communication system given in Fig. P1.4.9, where $P(A_0) = 0.6$ and $P(A_1) = 0.4$, determine the best choice for A given B_0, the best choice for A given B_1, the best choice for A given B_2, and the probability of error for these choices.

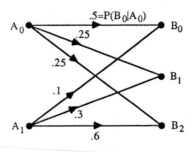

Fig. P1.4.9.

1.4.10. For the digital communication system given in Fig. P1.4.10, where $P(A_0) = 0.5$, $P(A_1) = 0.4$, and $P(A_2) = 0.1$, determine the best choice for A given B_0, the best choice for A given B_1, and the probability of error for these choices.

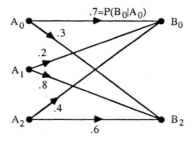

Fig. P1.4.10.

1.4.11. For the digital communication system given in Fig. P1.4.11, where $P(m_0) = 0.4$ and $P(m_1) = 0.6$, determine which labeling, $m_0 \to A_0$ and $m_1 \to A_1$ or $m_0 \to A_1$ and $m_1 \to A_0$, yields the minimum probability of error and evaluate this probability of error.

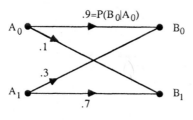

Fig. P1.4.11.

1.4.12. Determine $P(\text{communicating from A to B}) = P(\text{comm})$ for Fig. P1.4.12, where $P(\text{communicating over line } i) = P_i$ and lines 1, 2, and 3 are statistically independent with $P_1 = 0.8$, $P_2 = 0.6$, and $P_3 = 0.5$.

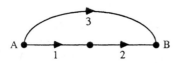

Fig. P1.4.12.

1.4.13. Determine $P(\text{comm})$ as in Problem 1.4.12 for Fig. P1.4.13.

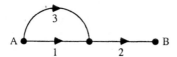

Fig. P1.4.13.

1.4.14. Determine $P(\text{comm})$ as in Problem 1.4.12 for Fig. 1.4.14, where lines 1, 2, 3, and 4 are statistically independent with $P_1 = 0.75$, $P_2 = 0.8$, $P_3 = 0.4$, and $P_4 = 0.5$.

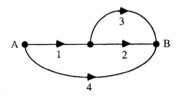

Fig. P1.4.14.

1.4.15. Determine $P(\text{comm})$ as in Problem 1.4.12 for Fig. P1.4.15, where lines 1, 2, 3, 4, and 5 are statistically independent with $P_1 = 0.75$, $P_2 = 0.8$, $P_3 = 0.6$, $P_4 = 0.4$, and $P_5 = 0.5$.

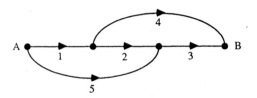

Fig. P1.4.15.

1.4.16. For A and B statistically independent show that A^c and B are also statistically independent.

1.4.17. For A and B statistically independent show that A^c and B^c are also statistically independent.

1.4.18. If a system that consists of three statistically independent components with identical reliability ($P_1 = P_2 = P_3$, where P_i, $i = 1, 2, 3$, is the reliability of each component), has $P(\text{oper}) = 0.8$ (reliability of the system), determine the required P_1 for the components in series and the required P_1 for the components in parallel.

1.4.19. If a system that consists of three statistically independent components with identical reliability ($P_1 = P_2 = P_3$, where P_i, $i = 1, 2, 3$, is the reliability of each component), has $P(\text{oper}) = 0.9$ (reliability of the system), determine the required P_1 for the components in series and the required P_1 for the components in parallel.

1.4.20. If a system that consists of three statistically independent components with identical reliability ($P_1 = P_2 = P_3$, where P_i, $i = 1, 2, 3$ is the reliability of each component), has $P(\text{oper}) = 0.8$ (reliability of the system), determine the required P_1 for component 3 in series with the parallel combination of 1 and 2.

1.4.21. If a system that consists of three statistically independent components with identical reliability ($P_1 = P_2 = P_3$, where P_i, $i = 1, 2, 3$, is the reliability of each component), has $P(\text{oper}) = 0.8$ (reliability of the system), determine the required P_1 for component 3 in parallel with the series combination of 1 and 2.

1.4.22. Two systems with four statistically independent components with reliabilities P_1, P_2, P_3, and P_4 are configured in the following ways: system A, the series combination of 1 and 2 in parallel with the series combination of 3 and 4, and system B, the parallel combination of 1 and 3 in series with the parallel combination of 2 and 4. Determine which system has the higher reliability and prove this.

1.4.23. Three lines, with $P_1 = 0.7$, $P_2 = 0.8$, and $P_3 = 0.9$ (1, 2, and 3 are statistically independent), are available for communication. Determine the assignment for A, B, and C to 1, 2, and 3 to maximize the probability of communication and determine this probability, where A and B are in parallel and this combination is in series with C.

1.4.24. Three lines, with $P_1 = 0.7$, $P_2 = 0.8$, and $P_3 = 0.9$ (1, 2, and 3 are statistically independent), are available for communication. Determine the assignment for A, B, and C to 1, 2, and 3 to maximize the probability of communication and determine this probability, where A and B are in series and this combination is in parallel with C.

1.4.25. Determine $P(A|B)$ for $P(A) = 0.5$, $P(B) = 0.7$, and $P(A \cup B) = 0.8$.

1.4.26. Determine $P(A^c \cap B)$ for $P(A) = 0.5$, $P(B) = 0.7$, and $P(A \cup B) = 0.9$.

1.4.27. Determine $P(B)$ for $P(A) = 0.5$, $P(A|B) = 0.6$, and $P(A \cup B) = 0.8$.

1.4.28. For $P(A|B) \geq P(A)$ fill in the blank $P(B|A)$_____$P(B)$ and prove.

$$(\leq, =, \geq)$$

1.4.29. For $P(A|B) \geq P(A)$ fill in the blank $P(A^c|B)$_____$P(A^c)$ and prove.

$$(\leq, =, \geq)$$

1.4.30. Fill in the blank $P(A) + P(B) - P(A)P(B)$_____1, state when true

$$(\leq, =, \geq)$$

(for all A and B or only for A and B statistically independent), and prove.

Random Variables and Vectors

2

2.1 Random Variables

A random variable can be thought of as just a numerically valued random occurrence, or a random variable is obtained as a result of some random occurrence that has a numerical value, which is determined from the outcome of the random occurrence. Most of the examples of random quantities of Chapter 1 already were assigned numerical values and thus were already random variables, but some of the random quantities were not, e.g., the tossing of a coin where $S = \{H, T\}$. The values of random quantities that do not take on numerical values can be mapped (transformed) into numerical values and thus random variables. The majority of random quantities encountered in engineering systems have numerical values and random variables have wide applicability in engineering. A more precise definition of a random variable is now given.

Let S be an arbitrary sample space and $\mathcal{A}$ be a σ-algebra of events over S. Then a real random variable $X(s)$ (denoted by a capital letter) is defined as a real-valued function on S such that, for every real number x, $\{s: X(s) \leq x\} \in \mathcal{A}$. Thus, a random variable $X(s)$ or just X is a function that maps all elements of S into points on the real line. In most applications the functional dependence on s will be suppressed, since the random variable (e.g., voltage or current) is the output of interest and not the underlying random phenomena generating the variable.

For the tossing of a single coin $S = \{H, T\} = \{s_1, s_2\}$, with the mapping shown in Fig. 2.1.1, the two values of the random variable $X(s)$ are $x(s_1) = 1$ and $x(s_2) = 0$ (the value that the random variable can take on is indicated by a lowercase letter). The probability assignment here would be $P[X(s) = 0] = \frac{1}{2}$ and $P[X(s) = 1] = \frac{1}{2}$. The mapping in Fig. 2.1.1 is by no means

42

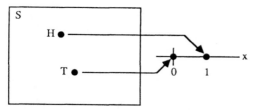

Fig. 2.1.1. A mapping of $S = \{H, T\}$ into the real line.

unique, and $x(s_1) = 13$ and $x(s_2) = -93$ would yield a binary random variable also.

Example 2.1.1. Consider the tossing of a single die. The mapping for the tossing of a single die, where $S = \{1, 2, 3, 4, 5, 6\}$, when the values of the random variable are taken as the set values themselves, is simply $x(s_i) = x(i) = i, i = 1, 2, \ldots, 6$ with the probability assignment $P[X(s) = i] = \frac{1}{6}, i = 1, 2, \ldots, 6$. $\square$

Now for the tossing of a coin twice, $S = \{HH, HT, TH, TT\} = \{s_1, s_2, s_3, s_4\}$, and with the mapping shown in Fig. 2.1.2, the two values of the random variable $X(s)$ are $x(s_1) = x(s_2) = x(s_3) = 1$ and $x(s_4) = 0$ with the probability assignment $P[X(s) = 0] = \frac{1}{4}$ and $P[X(s) = 1] = \frac{3}{4}$. This illustrates that many elements in S may map into a single value of X. It is required, however, that every $s \in S$ correspond to only one value of X. In this case, the value $x = 1$ can be interpreted as at least one head and the value $x = 0$ interpreted as no heads.

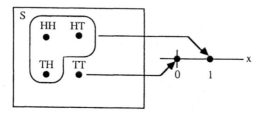

Fig. 2.1.2. A mapping of $S = \{HH, HT, TH, TT\}$ into the real line.

The range of $X(s)$, some subset of the real line, is itself a sample space and denoted as

$$S_X = \{x: x = X(s), s \in S\} \subset (-\infty < x < \infty)$$

where as before "(" indicates an open interval and "[" indicates a closed interval. The probability space is transformed to a new probability space with sample space S_X.

Example 2.1.2. Consider a different mapping for the tossing of two coins. With $S = \{HH, HT, TH, TT\} = \{s_1, s_2, s_3, s_4\}$ the mapping is given as

$$x(s_1) = x(\{HH\}) = 3 \qquad x(s_3) = x(\{TH\}) = 1$$

$$x(s_2) = x(\{HT\}) = 2 \qquad x(s_4) = x(\{TT\}) = 0$$

with the probability assignment $P[X(s) = i] = \frac{1}{4}$, $i = 0, 1, 2, 3$. An important set of sample space values is the set for which $X(s) \leq x$ as given in the definition of a random variable. For this random variable

$$\{s: X(s) \leq 2\} = \{HT, TH, TT\} \qquad \text{with} \quad P[X(s) \leq 2] = \frac{3}{4}$$

$$\{s: X(s) \leq 1\} = \{TH, TT\} \qquad \text{with} \quad P[X(s) \leq 1] = \frac{1}{2} \qquad \square$$

Normally, for notational convenience, the (s) in $X(s)$ will be suppressed and the probabilities in Example 2.1.2 will be written as $P(X \leq 2) = \frac{3}{4}$ and $P(X \leq 1) = \frac{1}{2}$.

Random variables may be classified into two main categories, discrete and continuous random variables. It is possible to have a combination of a discrete and a continuous random. This situation is referred to as a mixed random variable. A discrete random variable is one which takes on only discrete values (finite number or countable infinity of possible values), while a continuous random variable is one which can take on a continuum of values or any values in one or more intervals on the real line. Most of the random quantities encountered in Chapter 1 were discrete random variables. Tossing a die and tossing a coin (with a mapping into the real line) are examples of discrete random variables.

Example 2.1.3. Another example of a discrete random variable is the tossing of a coin until a head H comes up where X is the number of tosses made. This gives a sample space with an infinite number of elements. The sample space is given as

$$S = \{H, TH, TTH, \ldots\} = \{s_1, s_2, s_3, \ldots\}$$

and the sample space contained in the real line as

$$S_X = \{1, 2, 3, \ldots\}$$

For independent tosses of the coin with the equally likely assumption, the probability of specifying each toss is $\frac{1}{2}$ and $P(H) = \frac{1}{2}$, $P(TH) = \frac{1}{4}$, etc. Thus, the probability assignment for the random variable X is

$$P(X = i) = (\tfrac{1}{2})^i \qquad i = 1, 2, 3, \ldots$$

For this random variable

$$P(X \leq 2) = \frac{3}{4} \qquad \text{and} \qquad P(X \leq 4) = \frac{15}{16} \qquad \square$$

An example of a continuous random variable is the phase Θ of a sine wave at the receiver in a communication system with unpredictable or random delay.

Example 2.1.4.   Consider Θ as a phase random variable. Since the phase can take on values many times larger than the value 2π, but can always be folded back into the range 0 to 2π, a common assumption for the phase is that it is equally likely to take on any value in the interval 0 to 2π. Thus, the sample space is

$$S_\Theta = \{\theta: 0 \le \theta < 2\pi\} = [0, 2\pi)$$

and the probability assignment of intervals of S_Θ given as

$$P(a \le \Theta \le b) = \frac{b-a}{2\pi} \qquad 0 \le a < b < 2\pi$$

With this random phase model, then,

$$P\left(\Theta \le \frac{\pi}{2}\right) = P\left(0 \le \Theta \le \frac{\pi}{2}\right) = P\left(\pi \le \Theta \le \frac{3\pi}{2}\right) = \frac{1}{4}$$

or equal-length intervals have equal probability.   ☐

For continuous random variables, it seems reasonable that the σ-algebra (the listing of sets that will be assigned probability) should be defined in terms of intervals of real numbers, plus complements, unions, and intersections of such intervals. Now $P(X \le x)$ (X is the random variable and x is any real number) can be used to simplify the computation of the probabilities of intervals. $P(X \le x)$ is a probability distribution function, sometimes called cumulative distribution function or just distribution function, which is defined for both continuous and discrete random variables. Thus, the probability distribution function will give a common base for continuous and discrete random variables.

Let $(S, \mathcal{A}, P)$ be a probability space and $X(s)$ a random variable defined on S. The probability distribution function of X, $F_X(x)$, is defined as

$$F_X(x) = P[\{s: X(s) \in (-\infty, x] \text{ and } s \in S\}] = P(X \le x) \qquad (2.1.1)$$

The probability distribution function is a probability and satisfies all of the axioms and properties of probability.

Examples of probability distribution functions for a discrete and a continuous random variable are given in Fig. 2.1.3. It can be noted that the distribution function for the continuous random variable in Fig. 2.1.3a is a continuous function, while the distribution function for the discrete random variable has discontinuities. Even with these differences the general shapes of the distribution functions are similar in that they start at 0 and build up

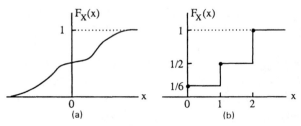

Fig. 2.1.3. Probability distribution functions: (a) continuous random variable with $S_X = \{x: -\infty < x < \infty\}$; (b) discrete random variable with $S_X = \{0, 1, 2\}$.

to 1, from left to right, never decreasing. Before noting other properties of these distribution functions, the general properties will be given.

The probability distribution function or distribution function has the following properties:

(1) $0 \le F_X(x) \le 1$
(2) $F_X(-\infty) = 0$ and $F_X(\infty) = 1$
(3) $F_X(x)$ is a monotonically nondecreasing function, i.e., $F_X(a) \le F_X(b)$ if and only if $a \le b$
(4) $P(a < X \le b) = F_X(b) - F_X(a)$, $a < b$
(5) $F_X(x)$ is continuous on the right, i.e., $F_X(a) = F_X(a+0)$, where $F_X(a+0) = \lim_{\varepsilon \to 0} F_X(a+\varepsilon)$, $\varepsilon > 0$.

Most of these properties should be somewhat obvious. Property 1 follows from the fact that $F_X(x)$ is a probability. Now,

$$F_X(-\infty) = P(X \in (-\infty, -\infty]) = P(\varnothing) = 0$$

and

$$F_X(\infty) = P(X \in (-\infty, \infty]) = P(S_X) = 1$$

which yields property 2. Let $B = (-\infty, b]$ and $A = (-\infty, a]$ with $a < b$; then $B = A \cup (a, b]$ and $A \cap (a, b] = \varnothing$. Using the probability of the union of two mutually exclusive sets gives

$$P(X \in (-\infty, b]) = P(X \in (-\infty, a]) + P(X \in (a, b])$$

or

$$F_X(b) = F_X(a) + P(a < X \le b)$$

and

$$P(a < X \le b) = F_X(b) - F_X(a) \qquad a < b$$

which is property 4. Property 3 follows immediately from property 4 since $P(a < X \le b) \ge 0$ and illustrates that as x increases, the interval length on the real axis, whose probability is being computed, increases, so the probability of this interval cannot decrease. Now, property 5 follows from the definition of $F_X(x)$ in Eq. (2.1.1) [the equality in $P(X \leq x)$], which means that the value at the discontinuity is the value obtained by approaching the discontinuity from the right (the value after the jump). The equality in Eq. (2.1.1) is included by convention [if $F_X(x)$ were defined as $P(X < x)$, property 5 would state that $F_X(x)$ is continuous on the left]. Property 5 does imply that $F_X(a) = F_X(a-0) + P(X = a)$, and the only way for $F_X(a) = F_X(a-0)$ is for $P(X = a) = 0$ (no discrete value at $x = a$). If $P(X = a) > 0$, then, there is a jump discontinuity in $F_X(x)$ at $x = a$, as illustrated in Fig. 2.1.4. The height of this jump is $P(X = a)$ (the discrete probability at $x = a$). Considering Fig. 2.1.3b again, $F_X(0) = \frac{1}{6}$ while $F_X(-0.0000001) = 0$, so that $P(X = 0) = \frac{1}{6}$, which illustrates the continuity on the right and the height of the jump discontinuity. Also, $F_X(1) = \frac{1}{2}$ with $F_X(0.9999999) = \frac{1}{6}$ to yield $P(X = 1) = \frac{1}{2} - \frac{1}{6} = \frac{1}{3}$ and $F_X(2) = 1$ with $F_X(1.9999999) = \frac{1}{2}$ to yield $P(X = 2) = \frac{1}{2}$.

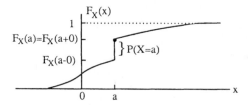

Fig. 2.1.4. Jump discontinuity at $x = a$.

The discontinuities in $F_X(x)$ can be represented by step functions of the form

$$P(X = x_i)u(x - x_i)$$

where

$$u(x - a) = 1 \qquad x \geq a$$
$$= 0 \qquad x < a \qquad (2.1.2)$$

The value 1 being assigned to the equality makes the unit step continuous on the right and consistent with the definition of the probability distribution function. The distribution function of Fig. 2.1.3b can be written as

$$F_X(x) = \frac{1}{6}u(x) + \frac{1}{3}u(x-1) + \frac{1}{2}u(x-2)$$

for all x.

Example 2.1.5.   For $S_X = \{1, 2, 3, 4, 5, 6\}$, the tossing of a single die, with $P(X = i) = \frac{1}{6}$, $i = 1, 2, \ldots, 6$, the distribution function is given as

$$F_X(x) = \sum_{i=1}^{6} P(X = i)u(x - i) = \frac{1}{6} \sum_{i=1}^{6} u(x - i)$$

and shown in Fig. 2.1.5.   □

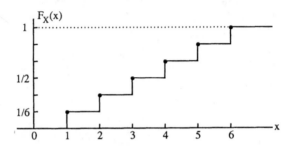

Fig. 2.1.5. Distribution function for the tossing of a die.

Example 2.1.6.   The distribution function for the random phase angle of a sine wave, $S_\Theta = [0, 2\pi)$, is shown in Fig. 2.1.6. Over S_Θ, $F_\Theta(\theta)$ is a linear function of θ or directly proportional to the interval length. From this figure the distribution function can be expressed as

$$F_\Theta(\theta) = \frac{\theta}{2\pi} u(\theta) - \frac{\theta - 2\pi}{2\pi} u(\theta - 2\pi)$$

or

$$F_\Theta(\theta) = 0 \qquad \theta < 0$$

$$= \frac{\theta}{2\pi} \qquad 0 \leq \theta < 2\pi$$

$$= 1 \qquad \theta \geq 2\pi \qquad \square$$

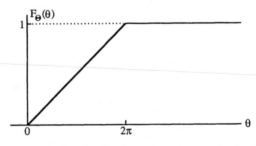

Fig. 2.1.6. Distribution function for the random phase angle of a sine wave.

The original probability assignment $P(a \le \Theta \le b)$ on the interval $[a, b]$ for the random phase angle can be obtained from $F_\Theta(\theta)$ as

$$P(a \le \Theta \le b) = F_\Theta(b) - F_\Theta(a) = \frac{b-a}{2\pi} \quad 0 \le a \le b < 2\pi$$

From this expression it can be seen that $P(\Theta = a) = 0$, which is true for any continuous random variable; i.e., the probability of a single point is zero for any continuous random variable.

Although the probability distribution function adequately describes both continuous and discrete random variables and allows the probabilities to be computed for intervals and complements, unions, and intersections of these intervals, so does the probability density function (also the probability function or probability mass function). In many instances the probability density function is more convenient and simplifies the computations.

The probability density function or density function (or pdf), $f_X(x)$, of a random variable X is defined as the derivative (may not exist at some places) of the distribution function, $F_X(x)$, of X. Thus,

$$f_X(x) = \frac{dF_X(x)}{dx} \tag{2.1.3a}$$

or in the limiting form as

$$f_X(x) = \lim_{\Delta x \to 0} \frac{F_X(x + \Delta x) - F_X(x)}{\Delta x} \tag{2.1.3b}$$

The second form of $f_X(x)$ lends itself to an approximation of the density function called a histogram, which will be considered in Chapter 5. The density function is not a probability, but the integral of the density function is a probability. It will be shown that the probability density function has the following properties:

(1) $f_X(x) \ge 0, \quad -\infty < x < \infty$
(2) $\int_{-\infty}^{\infty} f_X(x) \, dx = 1$
(3) $F_X(x) = \int_{-\infty}^{x} f_X(t) \, dt$
(4) $P(a < X \le b) = \int_a^b f_X(x) \, dx$

From property 3 of the distribution function $F_X(x + \Delta x) - F_X(x) \ge 0$ for $\Delta x \ge 0$ and from Eq. (2.1.3b)

$$f_X(x) = \lim_{\Delta x \to 0} \frac{F_X(x + \Delta x) - F_X(x)}{\Delta x} \ge 0$$

which gives property 1. This can also be seen from the fact that the distribution function is a monotonically nondecreasing function and the derivative of a monotonically nondecreasing function is always nonnegative.

Since $f_X(x)$ is a density function it does not necessarily have to be ≤ 1. Property 3 is just the basic definition of the relationship of a derivative to an integral; i.e., since $f_X(x)$ is the derivative of $F_X(x)$, $F_X(x)$ is the integral of $f_X(x)$. [Strictly speaking, for property 3 to hold $F_X(x)$ must be absolutely continuous (the derivative exists almost everywhere). All random variables that are considered here are absolutely continuous, discrete, or a combination of these.] It should be noted that if x was not in the limits of the integral in property 3 there would be no variation with x. Property 2 follows directly from property 3 since

$$\int_{-\infty}^{\infty} f_X(x) \, dx = F_X(\infty) = 1$$

or property 2 reflects the fact that the real line is the sample space for X and the probability of the sample space equals 1. Observing that

$$P(a < X \leq b) = F_X(b) - F_X(a)$$

$$= \int_{-\infty}^{b} f_X(x) \, dx - \int_{-\infty}^{a} f_X(x) \, dx = \int_{a}^{b} f_X(x) \, dx$$

which is property 4.

The representation in $f_X(x)$ for discontinuities in $F_X(x)$ is given as

$$\frac{d}{dx}[P(X = x_i)u(x = x_i)] - P(X = x_i)\delta(x - x_i)$$

where $\delta(x - x_i)$ is the unit impulse function at $x = x_i$ and $P(X = x_i)$ is the weight of the impulse function. [Strictly speaking $\delta(x)$ is not a function but a useful formalism, even though it will be referred to here as a function.]

The unit impulse function is defined as

$$\int_{-\infty}^{\infty} g(t)\delta(t - a) \, dt = g(a) \tag{2.1.4}$$

Several other properties of the unit impulse function are

$$\delta(t - a) = 0 \qquad t \neq a$$

$$= \infty \qquad t = a \tag{2.1.5}$$

$$\int_{-\infty}^{\infty} \delta(t - a) \, dt = 1$$

which indicates that the impulse is a zero width, infinite height function with unity area, and

$$\delta(x - a) = \frac{du(x - a)}{dx}; \qquad u(x - a) = \int_{-\infty}^{x} \delta(t - a) \, dt \tag{2.1.6}$$

which are the derivative and integral relationships of impulse and step functions.

Example 2.1.7. For $S_X = \{1, 2, 3, 4, 5, 6\}$ with $P(X = i) = \frac{1}{6}$, $i = 1, 2, \ldots, 6$, the probability density function is given as

$$f_X(x) = \frac{1}{6} \sum_{i=1}^{6} \delta(x - i)$$

and shown in Fig. 2.1.7. The $\frac{1}{6}$ is not the height of the impulses but the weight or area of the impulses. □

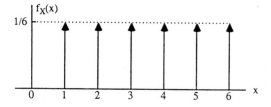

Fig. 2.1.7. Probability density function for the tossing of a die.

The density function of Example 2.1.7 is an example of a discrete random variable that has a constant weight for all of the finite values.

Example 2.1.8. The density function for the random phase angle of a sine wave is

$$f_\Theta(\theta) = \frac{1}{2\pi} [u(\theta) - u(\theta - 2\pi)]$$

or

$$f_\Theta(\theta) = \frac{1}{2\pi} \qquad 0 \le \theta < 2\pi$$

$$= 0 \qquad \text{otherwise}$$

and shown in Fig. 2.1.8. □

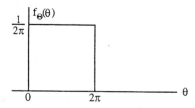

Fig. 2.1.8. Probability density function for the random phase angle of a sine wave.

The random phase angle is an example of a continuous random variable that is uniformly distributed (or constant) over a finite range.

The general form of a probability density function of a **uniform** random variable (uniform probability density function) is given as

$$f_X(x) = \frac{1}{b-a}[u(x-a) - u(x-b)]$$

or

$$f_X(x) = \frac{1}{b-a} \qquad a \le x < b \tag{2.1.7}$$

$$= 0 \qquad \text{otherwise}$$

where a and b are real constants. The constant $1/(b-a)$ is what makes the integral of $f_X(x)$ equal to 1. Now, the distribution function of X is evaluated as

$$F_X(x) = \int_a^x \frac{1}{b-a}\, dt = \frac{x-a}{b-a} \qquad a \le x < b$$

and

$$F_X(x) = 0 \qquad x < a$$

$$= \frac{x-a}{b-a} \qquad a \le x < b \tag{2.1.8}$$

$$= 1 \qquad x \ge b$$

The most common descriptor of random variables is their density function rather than their distribution function.

For discrete random variables the impulse functions can be avoided by using probability (or probability mass) functions, rather than density functions, to describe the probability that a discrete random variable takes on a particular value. The symbol $P(X = x)$ will be used to denote the probability function, which is basically the same as the notation used in Chapter 1. If there is a discrete value at a, $P(X = a)$ can be obtained from the density function with impulses as

$$\int_{a-0}^{a+0} f_X(x)\, dx = \int_{a-0}^{a+0} P(X = a)\delta(x-a)\, dx = P(X = a)(1) = P(X = a)$$

Example 2.1.9.   For the toss of a single die where $S_X = \{1, 2, 3, 4, 5, 6\}$, the probability function becomes

$$P(X = x) = \tfrac{1}{6} \qquad x = 1, 2, \ldots, 6$$

$$= 0 \qquad \text{otherwise}$$

This probability function would look like Fig. 2.1.7 with the impulses replaced by discrete values of $\frac{1}{6}$.   □

Some basic properties of the probability function are

(1) $0 \le P(X = x) \le 1$
(2) $\sum_{x \in S} P(X = x) = 1$
(3) $F_X(x) = \sum_{t \le x} P(X = t)$
(4) $P(a < X \le b) = \sum_{x \in (a, b]} P(X = x)$

Using property 4, for $S_X = \{1, 2, 3, 4, 5, 6\}$,

$$P(1.5 < X \le 4.1) = P(X = 2) + P(X = 3) + P(X = 4) = \tfrac{1}{6} + \tfrac{1}{6} + \tfrac{1}{6} = \tfrac{1}{2}$$

For continuous random variables the probability of being in an interval is obtained by integrating the density function over this interval, while for discrete random variables the probability of being in an interval is obtained by summing up the probability functions over this interval (integration replaced by summation). The probability at point x is given as $P(X = x)$ for discrete random variables, while the corresponding probability for a continuous random variable is $f_X(x)\, dx$ (differential probability that X lies in the interval $(x, x + dx]$). This again illustrates that the probability of a continuous random variable equaling any point is zero.

To conclude this section the relationship between the density function and the distribution function will be illustrated by considering the following two examples.

Example 2.1.10.   Determine the distribution function for the mixed random variable X where $f_X(x) = \tfrac{4}{3} e^{-4x} u(x) + \tfrac{5}{12} \delta(x) + \tfrac{1}{4} \delta(x - \tfrac{1}{2})$. This distribution function is determined as

$$F_X(x) = \int_{-\infty}^{x} f_X(t)\, dt$$

$$= u(x) \int_0^x \frac{4}{3} e^{-4t}\, dt + \int_{-\infty}^{x} \frac{5}{12} \delta(t)\, dt + \int_{-\infty}^{x} \frac{1}{4} \delta\left(t - \frac{1}{2}\right) dt$$

$$= (\tfrac{1}{3} - \tfrac{1}{3} e^{-4x}) u(x) + \tfrac{5}{12} u(x) + \tfrac{1}{4} u(x - \tfrac{1}{2})$$

$$= (\tfrac{3}{4} - \tfrac{1}{3} e^{-4x}) u(x) + \tfrac{1}{4} u(x - \tfrac{1}{2})   □$$

Example 2.1.11.   Determine the density function for the mixed random variable Y where $F_Y(y) = (\tfrac{2}{3} - \tfrac{1}{2} e^{-2y}) u(y) + \tfrac{1}{3} u(y - 1)$. This density function is determined as

$$f_Y(y) = \frac{dF_Y(y)}{dy} = \left[\left(\frac{2}{3} - \frac{1}{2} e^{-2y} \right) \bigg|_{y=0} \right] \delta(y) + e^{-2y} u(y) + \frac{1}{3} \delta(y - 1)$$

$$= \tfrac{1}{6} \delta(y) + e^{-2y} u(y) + \tfrac{1}{3} \delta(y - 1)$$

where the derivative of a product has been used and the first function evaluated at $y = 0$ since $\delta(y)$ is 0 except at $y = 0$. $\square$

2.2   Gaussian Random Variable

A random variable X with the density function

$$f_X(x) = \frac{1}{\sqrt{2\pi\sigma^2}} e^{-(x-\mu)^2/2\sigma^2} \qquad -\infty < x < \infty \qquad (2.2.1)$$

is denoted as a **Gaussian** or normal random variable, where μ (mean) and σ (standard deviation; σ^2 is called the variance) are suitably chosen parameters (the terminology will become clear in Chapter 4) such that $-\infty < \mu < \infty$ and $\sigma > 0$ are real constants. This density function is shown in Fig. 2.2.1

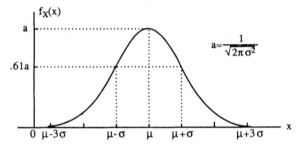

Fig. 2.2.1. Gaussian density function.

and is a bell-shaped curve. The parameter μ indicates the midpoint of $f_X(x)$ while the parameter σ indicates the spread about μ. From this figure, it can be seen that the peak value of $f_X(x)$, $a = 1/(2\pi\sigma^2)^{1/2}$, occurs at $x = \mu$ and that $f_X(x)$ drops to 0.61 of its peak value at $x = \mu \pm \sigma$ (drops to 0.14 of its peak value at $x = \mu \pm 2\sigma$). The corresponding Gaussian distribution function is shown in Fig. 2.2.2. From this figure, it can be seen that 0.16 of the

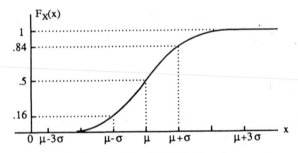

Fig. 2.2.2. Gaussian distribution function.

probability has been accumulated at $x = \mu - \sigma$, 0.5 at $x = \mu$, and 0.84 at $x = \mu + \sigma$ (0.02 at $x = \mu - 2\sigma$ and 0.98 at $x = \mu + 2\sigma$).

The Gaussian probability density function is one of the most important density functions known and models more different random occurrences than any other density function. Its importance stems mainly from the central limit theorem. The central limit theorem states that the sum of random variables (or the average of the sum) of almost any type is described by Gaussian statements as the number of terms in the summation becomes large. If the random variables in the summation are continuous, the density function of the sum tends to a Gaussian density function. The Gaussian probability density function is encountered in all areas of engineering. Noise in electronic material, which results from the individual motions of a large number of electrons, is closely described by Gaussian density functions. Also, much of the noise in communication in outer space, including satellite communication, is closely described by Gaussian density functions.

The Gaussian probability distribution function is expressed as

$$F_x(x) = \int_{-\infty}^{x} \frac{1}{\sqrt{2\pi\sigma^2}} e^{-(t-\mu)^2/(2\sigma^2)} \, dt \qquad (2.2.2)$$

which cannot be evaluated in closed form. Evaluating probabilities of intervals is more difficult for Gaussian random variables than for many other types because of this fact. But, because of its importance, $F_X(x)$ for the Gaussian random variable has been extensively tabulated. These tables have been developed by numerical integration and good approximation expressions. Before considering this tabulation, property 2 for density functions, that the integral of $f_X(x)$ over its entire range equals 1, will be justified for the Gaussian density function. This approach is not straightforward, but it does accomplish the task. Let

$$I = \int_{-\infty}^{\infty} \frac{1}{\sqrt{2\pi}} e^{-x^2/2} \, dx$$

then

$$I^2 = I \times I = \int_{-\infty}^{\infty} \int_{-\infty}^{\infty} \frac{1}{2\pi} e^{-x^2/2} e^{-y^2/2} \, dx \, dy$$

Changing from rectangular to polar coordinates, where

$$x = r \cos \theta \qquad \text{and} \qquad y = r \sin \theta$$

with the inverse transformation

$$r = \sqrt{x^2 + y^2} \qquad \text{and} \qquad \theta = \tan^{-1} \frac{y}{x}$$

and

$$dx\, dy = r\, dr\, d\theta$$

yields

$$I^2 = \int_0^{2\pi} \int_0^{\infty} \frac{1}{2\pi} e^{-r^2/2} r\, dr\, d\theta = \int_0^{2\pi} \frac{-1}{2\pi} e^{-r^2/2} \Big|_{r=0}^{r=\infty} d\theta$$

$$= \int_0^{2\pi} \frac{1}{2\pi} d\theta = 1$$

With $x = (t - \mu)/\sigma$

$$\int_{-\infty}^{\infty} \frac{1}{\sqrt{2\pi\sigma^2}} e^{-(t-\mu)^2/2\sigma^2}\, dt = 1$$

This change of coordinates will be encountered again in Chapter 3.

Since μ can take on an infinite number of values, as can σ, which would give an infinite number of Gaussian density functions, it is only reasonable to tabulate $F_X(x)$ in some normalized (or standardized) form and obtain all of the other distribution functions in terms of this. This normalized form has $\mu = 0$ (zero mean) and $\sigma^2 = 1$ (unit variance). Thus,

$$F_X(x) = \int_{-\infty}^{x} \frac{1}{\sqrt{2\pi}} e^{-t^2/2}\, dt \qquad (2.2.3)$$

has been extensively tabulated. In many engineering applications

$$Q(x) = 1 - F_X(x) = \int_{x}^{\infty} \frac{1}{\sqrt{2\pi}} e^{-t^2/2}\, dt \qquad (2.2.4)$$

is a more convenient form. In many cases the probability of error in a communication system (which should be small) is given directly as $Q(x)$. It can be noted from Eq. (2.2.4) that $Q(x) < \frac{1}{2}$ for $x > 0$ or that $Q(x)$ is small for positive values of x. $Q(x)$ is used exclusively for a probability statement on a normalized Gaussian density function, where $F_X(x)$ is used for many different density functions, as has been seen. $Q(x)$ is often referred to as the upper tail of the Gaussian density function and is shown in Fig. 2.2.3. An approximation for the Q function is given in Appendix A and the Q function is tabulated in Table A.1. This approximation is easily implemented on a programmable calculator. The Q function can also be approximated by a Taylor series expansion or by numerical integration. Table A.1 lists only Q values for positive values of the argument, but the Q values for negative values of the argument can be expressed in terms of these values.

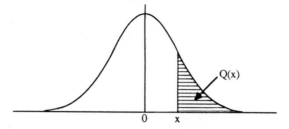

Fig. 2.2.3. Q function for Gaussian probabilities.

To use the Q function table when the Gaussian random variable is not normalized (mean not 0 and variance not 1) consider X, a Gaussian random variable, with mean μ and variance σ^2. Then,

$$P(X > a) = \int_a^\infty \frac{1}{\sqrt{2\pi\sigma^2}} e^{-(x-\mu)^2/2\sigma^2} \, dx$$

and with the change of variable $t = (x - \mu)/\sigma$

$$P(X > a) = \int_{(a-\mu)/\sigma}^\infty \frac{1}{\sqrt{2\pi}} e^{-t^2/2} \, dt$$

or

$$P(X > a) = Q\left(\frac{a - \mu}{\sigma}\right) \tag{2.2.5}$$

Note that the divisor is σ and not σ^2. Next,

$$P(X \le b) = 1 - P(X > b)$$

or

$$P(X \le b) = 1 - Q\left(\frac{b - \mu}{\sigma}\right) \tag{2.2.6}$$

A combination of Eqs. (2.2.5) and (2.2.6) yields

$$P(a < X \le b) = P(X > a) - P(X > b)$$

or

$$P(a < X \le b) = Q\left(\frac{a - \mu}{\sigma}\right) - Q\left(\frac{b - \mu}{\sigma}\right) \tag{2.2.7}$$

Also,

$$Q(-c) = \int_{-c}^\infty \frac{1}{\sqrt{2\pi}} e^{-t^2/2} \, dt = 1 - \int_{-\infty}^{-c} \frac{1}{\sqrt{2\pi}} e^{-t^2/2} \, dt$$

and with $x = -t$ (or symmetry)

$$Q(-c) = 1 - \int_c^\infty \frac{1}{\sqrt{2\pi}} e^{-x^2/2} \, dx$$

or

$$Q(-c) = 1 - Q(c) \tag{2.2.8}$$

from which the Q function of negative arguments can be obtained from the Q function of positive arguments.

The values of the cumulative Gaussian distribution function, given in Fig. 2.2.2, can now be justified by using the Q function. The probability that the Gaussian random variable X, with mean μ and variance σ^2, has a value less than or equal to $\mu - \sigma$ is obtained from Eqs. (2.2.6) and (2.2.8) as

$$P(X \le \mu - \sigma) = 1 - P(X > \mu - \sigma) = 1 - P\left(\frac{X - \mu}{\sigma} > \frac{\mu - \sigma - \mu}{\sigma}\right)$$

$$= 1 - Q\left(\frac{\mu - \sigma - \mu}{\sigma}\right)$$

$$= 1 - Q(-1) = Q(1) = 0.1587$$

In addition,

$$P(X \le \mu) = 1 - P(X > \mu)$$

$$= 1 - P\left(\frac{X - \mu}{\sigma} > \frac{\mu - \mu}{\sigma}\right) = 1 - Q\left(\frac{\mu - \mu}{\sigma}\right)$$

$$= 1 - Q(0) = 0.5$$

and

$$P(X \le \mu + \sigma) = 1 - P(X > \mu + \sigma) = 1 - P\left(\frac{X - \mu}{\sigma} > \frac{\mu + \sigma - \mu}{\sigma}\right)$$

$$= 1 - Q\left(\frac{\mu + \sigma - \mu}{\sigma}\right) = 1 - Q(1) = 0.8413$$

as given in Fig. 2.2.2. Not included in this figure is

$$P(X \le \mu - 2\sigma) = 1 - P(X > \mu - 2\sigma) = 1 - P\left(\frac{X - \mu}{\sigma} > \frac{\mu - 2\sigma - \mu}{\sigma}\right)$$

$$= 1 - Q\left(\frac{\mu - 2\sigma - \mu}{\sigma}\right) = 1 - Q(-2) = Q(2) = 0.0228$$

and

$$P(X \le \mu + 2\sigma) = 0.9772$$

Example 2.2.1.   Determine the probability of obtaining the grades A, B, C, D, and F when the grading is done on the true (Gaussian) curve. The cutoffs for the grades A, B, C, and D are $\mu + 2\sigma$, $\mu + \sigma$, $\mu - \sigma$, and $\mu - 2\sigma$, respectively. The probability of an A (and a F) is obtained as

$$P(A) = P(X > \mu + 2\sigma) = P\left(\frac{X - \mu}{\sigma} > \frac{\mu + 2\sigma - \mu}{\sigma}\right) = Q\left(\frac{\mu + 2\sigma - \mu}{\sigma}\right)$$

$$= Q(2) = 0.0228 = P(F)$$

and the probability of a B (and a D) calculated as

$$P(A \cup B) = P(X > \mu + \sigma) = P\left(\frac{X - \mu}{\sigma} > \frac{\mu + \sigma - \mu}{\sigma}\right) = Q\left(\frac{\mu + \sigma - \mu}{\sigma}\right)$$

$$= Q(1) = 0.1587$$

which yields

$$P(B) = P(A \cup B) - P(A) = 0.1587 - 0.0228 = 0.1359$$

The probability of a C is then obtained as

$$P(C) = 1 - 2P(A) - 2P(B) = 1 - 2(0.0228) - 2(0.1359) = 0.6826 \qquad \square$$

Consider another example using the Q function table.

Example 2.2.2.   Let X be a Gaussian random variable with $\mu = 3$ and $\sigma^2 = 4$. The probability that X has a value greater than 6 is obtained as

$$P(X > 6) = P\left(\frac{X - 3}{2} > \frac{6 - 3}{2}\right) = Q\left(\frac{6 - 3}{2}\right) = Q(1.5) = 0.0668$$

while the probability that X has a value less than or equal to 0.5 is

$$P(X \leq 0.5) = 1 - P\left(\frac{X - 3}{2} > \frac{0.5 - 3}{2}\right) = 1 - Q(-1.25) = Q(1.25) = 0.1056 \qquad \square$$

As a final example the mean and variance of a Gaussian random variable can be determined when the probability of being in two intervals is given.

Example 2.2.3.   Determine the mean μ and the variance σ^2 where X is a Gaussian random variable when $P(X < 2) = P(X > 14) = Q(1.5)$. $P(X > 14)$ can be expressed as

$$P(X > 14) = P\left(\frac{X - \mu}{\sigma} > \frac{14 - \mu}{\sigma}\right) = Q\left(\frac{14 - \mu}{\sigma}\right) = Q(1.5)$$

which yields

$$\frac{14 - \mu}{\sigma} = 1.5$$

Then $P(X<2)$ can be expressed as

$$P(X<2)=1-P(X>2)=1-P\left(\frac{X-\mu}{\sigma}>\frac{2-\mu}{\sigma}\right)=1-Q\left(\frac{2-\mu}{\sigma}\right)$$

$$=Q\left(-\frac{2-\mu}{\sigma}\right)=Q(1.5)$$

which yields

$$-\frac{2-\mu}{\sigma}=1.5$$

Solving these two equations in μ and σ results in a mean of $\mu=8$ and $\sigma=4$ or a variance of $\sigma^2=16$. □

If the value of $Q(a)$ is given, the value of a can be obtained by a linear interpolation of Table A.1 or the inverse Q function approximation given in Appendix A. For $Q(a)=0.1$, the values used for linear interpolation (closest to this value) are $Q(1.28)=0.10027$ and $Q(1.29)=0.09853$, and a is obtained as $a=1.28+[(0.10027-0.1)/(0.10027-0.09853)](1.29-1.28)=1.282$, which is the same using the inverse approximation. Also, for $Q(b)=0.05$, $b=1.645$ for both the linear interpolation and the approximation.

2.3   Other Random Variables

There are many probability density functions that model real-world occurrences. Several will be given here, and others will be considered later.

A uniform random variable X is described in Eq. (2.1.7) for the density function and in Eq. (2.1.8) for the distribution function. In addition to being a good model for a random phase angle, it models the resistance values of standard resistors.

Example 2.3.1.   For a 1-Ω resistor with 10% tolerance the density function would be

$$f_R(r)=5 \qquad 0.9<r<1.1$$
$$=0 \qquad \text{otherwise}$$

and the distribution function

$$F_R(r)=0 \qquad\qquad r<0.9$$
$$=5(r-0.9) \qquad 0.9<r<1.1$$
$$=1 \qquad\qquad r\geq 1.1$$

The probability that this 1-Ω resistor falls within a 5% tolerance can then be calculated as

$$P(0.95 < R < 1.05) = F_X(1.05) - F_X(0.95) = 5(1.05 - 0.9) - 5(0.95 - 0.9)$$

$$= 0.75 - 0.25 = 0.5 \quad \square$$

An **exponential** random variable X is described by

$$f_X(x) = a e^{-ax} \qquad x \geq 0 \quad a > 0 \tag{2.3.1a}$$

$$= 0 \qquad x < 0$$

and correspondingly

$$F_X(x) = 1 - e^{-ax} \qquad x \geq 0 \tag{2.3.1b}$$

$$= 0 \qquad x < 0$$

with $f_X(x)$ and $F_X(x)$ plotted in Fig. 2.3.1. The exponential random variable is used to model the reliability of electronic components (and systems) and service time in queuing systems.

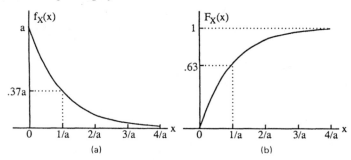

Fig. 2.3.1. Exponential random variable description: (a) exponential density function; (b) exponential distribution function.

Example 2.3.2. The failure time X of an electronic system is modeled by Eqs. (2.3.1a) and (2.3.1b). The probability that the failure time exceeds $1/a$ units of time (the system will work longer than $1/a$ units of time) is given as

$$P\left(X > \frac{1}{a}\right) = 1 - F_X\left(\frac{1}{a}\right) = e^{-a/a} = e^{-1} = 0.368 \quad \square$$

A **Rayleigh** random variable X is described by

$$f_X(x) = \frac{x}{b} e^{-x^2/2b} \qquad x \geq 0 \quad b > 0 \tag{2.3.2a}$$

$$= 0 \qquad x < 0$$

and correspondingly

$$F_X(x) = 1 - e^{-x^2/2b} \qquad x \geq 0 \quad b > 0 \qquad (2.3.2b)$$

$$= 0 \qquad\qquad x < 0$$

with $f_X(x)$ and $F_X(x)$ plotted in Fig. 2.3.2. As will be shown later, a Rayleigh random variable can be obtained from the square root of the sum of the squares of two independent Gaussian random variables.

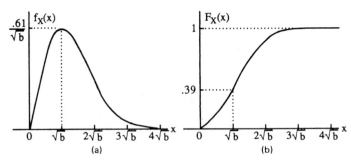

Fig. 2.3.2. Rayleigh random variable description: (a) Rayleigh density function; (b) Rayleigh distribution function.

A **Cauchy** random variable is described by

$$f_X(x) = \frac{a}{\pi} \frac{1}{x^2 + a^2} \qquad -\infty < x < \infty \qquad (2.3.3a)$$

and correspondingly

$$F_X(x) = \frac{1}{2} + \frac{1}{\pi} \tan^{-1} \frac{x}{a} \qquad -\infty < x < \infty \qquad (2.3.3b)$$

The Cauchy density function has a shape similar to the Gaussian density function and its importance arises from the fact that the ratio of two independent Gaussian random variables is a Cauchy random variable.

A **gamma** random variable is described by

$$f_X(x) = \frac{a^{b+1} x^b}{\Gamma(b+1)} e^{-ax} \qquad x \geq 0 \quad a > 0 \quad b \geq 0 \qquad (2.3.4a)$$

$$= 0 \qquad\qquad x < 0$$

where $\Gamma(b+1)$ is the gamma function defined as

$$\Gamma(b+1) = \int_0^\infty x^b e^{-x} \, dx$$

The gamma function satisfies

$$\Gamma(b+1) = b\Gamma(b)$$

and for n a nonnegative integer

$$\Gamma(n+1) = n!$$

where $0! = 1$. With $b = n$ (a nonnegative integer) the distribution function is given as

$$F_X(x) = 1 - e^{-ax} \sum_{i=0}^{n} \frac{(ax)^i}{i!} \qquad x \geq 0 \qquad (2.3.4b)$$

$$= 0 \qquad\qquad x < 0$$

The exponential random variable is a special case of the gamma random variable with $b = n = 0$. The gamma random variable can be thought of as a general exponential random variable.

Several discrete random variables will now be given. The discrete random variable X with only the two possible values 0 and 1, where $P(X = 1) = p$ and $P(X = 0) = 1 - p$ with p values in the interval from 0 to 1, is called a **Bernoulli** random variable. The density function is given as

$$f_X(x) = (1 - p)\delta(x) + p\delta(x - 1)$$

or the probability function as

$$P(X = i) = p^i(1 - p)^{1-i} \qquad i = 0, 1 \qquad (2.3.5)$$

One application of a Bernoulli random variable is the tossing of a coin where 0 indicates tails, 1 indicates heads, and the probability of a head is p. Other applications are random bits in a computer and error (and correct) in a communication system.

The density function for a **binomial** random variable is given as

$$f_Y(y) = \sum_{i=0}^{N} C_i^N p^i(1 - p)^{N-i}\delta(y - i)$$

or the probability function as

$$P(Y = i) = C_i^N p^i(1 - p)^{N-i} \qquad i = 0, 1, \ldots, N \quad N = 1, 2, \ldots \quad (2.3.6a)$$

where

$$C_i^N = \frac{N!}{i![N - i]!}$$

the binomial coefficient, is the number of ways of obtaining i ones out of N binary observations (number of combinations of N things taken i at a time). The sum of N independent Bernoulli random variables is a binomial random variable with the same p as in the Bernoulli probability function. The binomial distribution function is given as

$$F_Y(y) = \sum_{i=0}^{N} C_i^N p^i (1-p)^{N-i} u(y-i) \qquad (2.3.6b)$$

For $N = 5$ there are $2^5 = 32$ words of 5-bit numbers that are given as

$$00000 \quad 00001 \quad 00010 \quad 00011 \quad \cdots \quad 11110 \quad 11111$$

Let X be the bits and Y be the word, where the bits are independent with $P(X = 1) = p$ and $P(X = 0) = 1 - p$. The probability of the word 11111 is

$$P(11111) = (p)(p)(p)(p)(p) = p^5$$

and the number of words with 5 ones is $C_5^5 = 5!/(5!0!) = 1$, which yields the probability of a word with 5 ones as

$$P(Y = 5) = p^5$$

For the word 00111 the probability is

$$P(00111) = (1-p)(1-p)(p)(p)(p) = (1-p)^2 p^3$$

and the number of words with 3 ones (01011, 01101, ...) is $C_3^5 = 5!/(3!2!) = 10$, which yields the probability of a word with 3 ones as

$$P(Y = 3) = 10p^3(1-p)^2$$

In determining these probabilities there are 1 word with 0 ones, 5 words with 1 one, 10 words with 2 ones, 10 words with 3 ones, 5 words with 4 ones, and 1 word with 5 ones, which sum to 32, as they should. For N bits this relationship becomes

$$\sum_{i=0}^{N} C_i^N = 2^N$$

which is a special case of the binomial theorem given as

$$\sum_{i=0}^{N} C_i^N a^i b^{N-i} = (a+b)^N \qquad (2.3.7)$$

If Eq. (2.3.6a) is summed over 0 to N the binomial theorem can be used to show that the binomial probability function sums to 1. The density function and distribution function for a binomial random variable are plotted in Fig. 2.3.3 for $N = 5$ and $p = 0.4$.

Example 2.3.3.   Consider transmitting information in blocks or words of 6 bits with the probability of bit error $p = 0.1$ and the capability of correcting single errors. The block is in error only if two or more bit errors

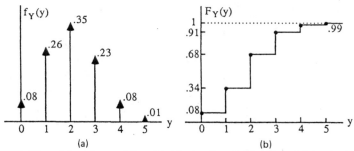

Fig. 2.3.3. Binomial random variable with $N = 5$ and $p = 0.4$: (a) binomial density function; (b) binomial distribution function.

are made. A block in error can appropriately be modeled as a binomial random variable with $N = 6$ and $p = 0.1$. The probability of no bit errors in the block is calculated as

$$P(0 \text{ bit errors in block}) = C_0^6 p^0 (1-p)^6 = (0.9)^6 = 0.531$$

and the probability of a single bit error in the block as

$$P(1 \text{ bit error in block}) = C_1^6 p^1 (1-p)^5 = 6(0.1)(0.9)^5 = 0.354$$

Now, the probability of a block error is

$$P(\text{block error}) = P(2 \text{ or more bit errors in block})$$

$$= 1 - P(0 \text{ bit errors}) - P(1 \text{ bit error})$$

$$= 1 - 0.531 - 0.354 = 0.115 \qquad \square$$

There are many situations that will be modeled as binomial random variables.

The probability function for a **discrete uniform** random variable is given as

$$P(X = i) = \frac{1}{N} \qquad i = 1, 2, \ldots, N \qquad (2.3.8)$$

$$= 0 \qquad \text{otherwise}$$

This is the model assigned to the tossing of a die with $N = 6$. A discrete uniform random variable is applicable whenever a finite number of different outcomes are possible and are considered to be equally likely. Equation (2.3.8) may include negative values of i.

The probability function for a **geometric** random variable is given as

$$P(X = i) = (1-p)^{i-1} p \qquad i = 1, 2, \ldots \qquad (2.3.9a)$$

$$= 0 \qquad \text{otherwise}$$

This is the model assigned to the random variable that was the number of times a coin was tossed until a head first appeared with $p = \frac{1}{2}$. In general, the geometric probability function describes the number of independent observations of a sequence of identically distributed Bernoulli random variables until a 1 first appears. It should be noted that even though there is an infinite number of outcomes in a geometric probability function, the infinite sum of Eq. (2.3.9a) is still 1. The distribution function of the geometric random variable is

$$F_X(i) = 1 - (1-p)^i \qquad i = 1, 2, \ldots \qquad (2.3.9b)$$

$$= 0 \qquad \qquad \text{otherwise}$$

The probability function for the **Poisson** random variable is given as

$$P(X = i) = a^i e^{-a}/i! \qquad i = 0, 1, 2, \ldots \quad a > 0 \qquad (2.3.10a)$$

$$= 0 \qquad \qquad \text{otherwise}$$

The Poisson random variable is commonly referred to as a counting random variable. The number of arrivals in a prescribed interval of time in a queuing system and the number of photons counted in a photomultiplier tube are assumed to be Poisson random variables. The distribution function for the Poisson random variable is

$$F_X(i) = e^{-a} \sum_{k=0}^{i} \frac{a^k}{k!} \qquad i \geq 0 \qquad (2.3.10b)$$

$$= 0 \qquad \qquad i < 0$$

Example 2.3.4. The number of photons counted in a photomultiplier tube is Poisson distributed where $P(0 \text{ photons}) = 0.3$. The parameter of the Poisson probability function can be determined from Eq. (2.3.10a) as

$$P(X = 0) = e^{-a} = 0.3$$

or $a = 1.204$. The probability that 2 or fewer photons are counted is given from Eq. (2.3.10b) as

$$P(X \leq 2) = e^{-1.204}\left[1 + 1.204 + \frac{(1.204)^2}{2}\right] = 0.879 \qquad \square$$

To finish this section, a mixed random variable (one that can take on discrete as well as continuous values), which yields a mixed density function, will now be considered. When a Gaussian random variable X is the input to the diode circuit shown in Fig. 2.3.4, the output Y is a mixed random

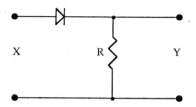

Fig. 2.3.4. Example of a mixed random variable.

variable. The output is given as

$$Y = X \qquad x \geq 0$$
$$= 0 \qquad x < 0$$

since the diode passes unchanged the positive values and blocks the negative values. For the Gaussian random variable with

$$f_X(x) = \frac{1}{\sqrt{2\pi}} e^{-x^2/2} \qquad -\infty < x < \infty$$

the probability of the discrete value of Y is

$$P(Y = 0) = P(X < 0) = \tfrac{1}{2}$$

and

$$f_Y(y) = \frac{1}{2} \delta(y) + \frac{1}{\sqrt{2\pi}} e^{-y^2/2} u(y)$$

The density function of the output along with its distribution function is shown in Fig. 2.3.5.

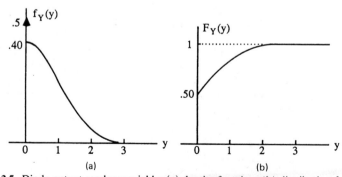

Fig. 2.3.5. Diode output random variable: (a) density function; (b) distribution function.

2.4   Random Vectors

In many situations, in order to model random phenomena, it is necessary to consider several random variables simultaneously. The most important consideration is the two random variable (bivariate) case. An important example of the bivariate case is the random elements of a two-dimensional image. Random vectors are just vectors of random variables. The concepts of random vectors are not difficult to deal with, although actual evaluation of some of the relevant quantities is more difficult. This is typical since it is usually more difficult to work with integrals, sums, etc. of two or more variables than it is to work with the same manipulation of single variables. The bivariate vector case will be considered first and the results will be extended to the general vector case.

Consider the mapping of the sample space S, of the tossing of two coins, into the xy plane (joint sample space, $S_X \times S_Y$) as shown in Fig. 2.4.1. Here,

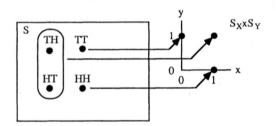

Fig. 2.4.1. Mapping of $S = \{HH, HT, TH, TT\}$ into the xy plane.

$X(s) = 1$ indicates the occurrence of at least one head, $X(s) = 0$ indicates no heads, $Y(s) = 1$ indicates at least one tail, and $Y(s) = 0$ indicates no tails. The probability of the joint occurrence of the random variables X and Y is given as

$$P[(X, Y) = (0, 1)] = P[s \in \{TT\}] = \tfrac{1}{4}$$

$$P[(X, Y) = (1, 0)] = P[s \in \{HH\}] = \tfrac{1}{4}$$

$$P[(X, Y) = (1, 1)] = P[s \in \{HT, TH\}] = \tfrac{1}{2}$$

The joint probability distribution function of the random variables X and Y is defined as

$$F_{XY}(x, y) = P[\{s : X(s) \in (-\infty, x] \text{ and } Y(s) \in (-\infty, y] \text{ and } s \in S\}]$$

$$= P([X \leq x] \cap \{Y \leq y\}) \tag{2.4.1}$$

which is a direct extension of the distribution of a single variable. This is commonly written as

$$F_{XY}(x, y) = P(X \le x, Y \le y)$$

The joint distribution $F_{XY}(a, b)$ is the probability that X and Y lie in the infinite region of the (x, y) plane shown shaded in Fig. 2.4.2.

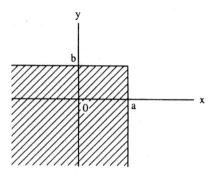

Fig. 2.4.2. Region of $F_{XY}(a, b)$.

Example 2.4.1.   For the sample space of Fig. 2.4.1 the number of points with nonzero probability, in the region for $F_{XY}(x, y)$, can only be zero, one $[(0, 1)$ or $(1, 0)]$, or three; i.e., obtaining two of the points but not the third is impossible. If $(0, 1)$ is in the region, as $(1, 0)$ is included so will $(1, 1)$ be. The joint distribution is then given as

$$
\begin{aligned}
F_{XY}(x, y) &= 1 & & x \ge 1, y \ge 1 \\
&= \tfrac{1}{4} & & x \ge 1, 0 \le y < 1 \\
&= \tfrac{1}{4} & & 0 \le x < 1, y \ge 1 \\
&= 0 & & x < 1, y < 1 \quad \text{or} \quad x < 0 \quad \text{or} \quad y < 0 \quad \text{(otherwise)}
\end{aligned}
$$

or as

$$F_{XY}(x, y) = \tfrac{1}{4}u(x-1)u(y) + \tfrac{1}{4}u(x)u(y-1) + \tfrac{1}{2}u(x-1)u(y-1) \qquad \square$$

Basic properties of the joint distribution function, similar to the single-variable case, are

(1) $0 \le F_{XY}(x, y) \le 1$

(2) $F_{XY}(-\infty, y) = F_{XY}(x, -\infty) = F_{XY}(-\infty, -\infty) = 0$ and $F_{XY}(\infty, \infty) = 1$

(3) $F_{XY}(x, y)$ is a monotonically nondecreasing function of both x and y

(4) $F_{XY}(x, \infty) = F_X(x)$ and $F_{XY}(\infty, y) = F_Y(y)$ (marginal distribution functions)

(5) $P(a_1 < X \le a_2, b_1 < Y \le b_2) = F_{XY}(a_2, b_2) - F_{XY}(a_1, b_2) - F_{XY}(a_2, b_1) + F_{XY}(a_1, b_1)$, $a_1 < a_2$, $b_1 < b_2$

Property 1, as in the single-variable case, indicates that $F_{XY}(x, y)$ is a probability, while property 2 can be obtained as

$$F_{XY}(-\infty, y) = P(\{X \le -\infty\} \cap \{Y \le y\}) = P(\varnothing \cap \{Y \le y\}) = P(\varnothing) = 0$$

Property 3 comes from the fact that if any additional region is included in $F_{XY}(x, y)$ the probability cannot decrease, while formally property 4 is obtained as

$$F_{XY}(x, \infty) = P(\{X \le x\} \cap \{Y \le \infty\}) = P(\{X \le x\} \cap S_Y)$$
$$= P(\{X \le x\}) = F_X(x)$$

Property 4 yields what are called marginal probability distribution functions. The marginal distribution function for X is determined, in a manner similar to the total probability of Eq. (1.4.4) for sets, by obtaining the probability of X with all values of y. Since the distribution function is already an accumulated probability, all values of y are obtained by replacing y by ∞ in the joint distribution function. Likewise, the marginal distribution function for Y is obtained by replacing x by ∞ in the joint distribution function. After the marginal distribution function is obtained, it is the same as any single-variable distribution function. The word marginal just indicates that the single-variable distribution function was obtained from a joint distribution function.

Example 2.4.2.   For Example 2.4.1, with the sample space of Fig. 2.4.1, the marginal distribution functions are

$$F_X(x) = 1 \qquad x \ge 1$$
$$= \tfrac{1}{4} \qquad 0 \le x < 1$$
$$= 0 \qquad x < 0$$

and

$$F_Y(y) = 1 \qquad y \ge 1$$
$$= \tfrac{1}{4} \qquad 0 \le y < 1$$
$$= 0 \qquad y < 0 \qquad \square$$

Property 5 is not an obvious extension of the single-variable case but can be visualized by considering Fig. 2.4.3. The probability of being in the shaded region is equal to $P(a_1 < X \le a_2, b_1 < Y \le b_2)$. This probability is

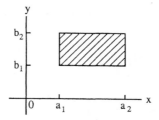

Fig. 2.4.3. Region of $P(a_1 < X \le a_2, b_1 < Y \le b_2)$.

obtained by taking the probability of the region to the left and below the point (a_2, b_2) and subtracting the probabilities of both of the regions to the left and below (a_1, b_2) and (a_2, b_1). In doing this, the probability of the region to the left and below (a_1, b_1) has been subtracted twice, and thus the correct probability is obtained by adding the probability of this region to the other three terms.

The joint probability density function of X and Y is defined as

$$f_{XY}(x, y) = \frac{\partial^2 F_{XY}(x, y)}{\partial x \, \partial y} \tag{2.4.2}$$

which is a direct extension of the single-variable case. Its basic properties are

(1) $f_{XY}(x, y) \ge 0$, $-\infty < x < \infty$, $-\infty < y < \infty$
(2) $\int_{-\infty}^{\infty} \int_{-\infty}^{\infty} f_{XY}(x, y) \, dx \, dy = 1$
(3) $F_{XY}(x, y) = \int_{-\infty}^{y} \int_{-\infty}^{x} f_{XY}(t, v) \, dt \, dv$
(4) $f_X(x) = \int_{-\infty}^{\infty} f_{XY}(x, y) \, dy$ and $f_Y(y) = \int_{-\infty}^{\infty} f_{XY}(x, y) \, dx$ (marginal density functions)
(5) $P(a_1 < X \le a_2, b_1 < Y \le b_2) = \int_{b_1}^{b_2} \int_{a_1}^{a_2} f_{XY}(x, y) \, dx \, dy$

Example 2.4.3. For Example 2.4.1 the joint density function is obtained, using Eq. (2.4.2), as

$$f_{XY}(x, y) = \tfrac{1}{4}\delta(x-1)\delta(y) + \tfrac{1}{4}\delta(x)\delta(y-1) + \tfrac{1}{2}\delta(x-1)\delta(y-1) \qquad \square$$

The joint density function may be greater than 1, but since it is the derivative of a monotonically nondecreasing function, it must be greater than or equal to 0. Property 2 is the probability over all the two-dimensional region, which must be 1, and property 3 is just the integral relationship implied in Eq. (2.4.2). [Strictly speaking, for property 3 to hold $F_{XY}(x, y)$ must be absolutely continuous in both variables. Again, all random variables that are considered here are absolutely continuous, discrete, or a combination of these.] Property 5 is in general a simpler way of obtaining the joint probability over a finite region than the joint distribution function property 5. This property is obtainable directly by observing the integration region of Fig. 2.4.3.

In property 4, the marginal density function for X is determined, in a manner similar to the total probability of Eq. (1.4.4) again, by obtaining the density function of X with all values of y. In this case, the joint density function is integrated over all values of y. After the marginal density function is obtained, it is the same as any single-variable density function, with marginal just indicating that it was obtained from a joint density function. Using property 4 of joint distribution functions

$$\frac{dF_X(x)}{dx} = \frac{dF_{XY}(x, \infty)}{dx}$$

with property 3 of joint density functions (and derivative of an integral)

$$\frac{dF_X(x)}{dx} = \frac{d}{dx} \int_{-\infty}^{x} \int_{-\infty}^{\infty} f_{XY}(t, y)\, dy\, dt = \int_{-\infty}^{\infty} f_{XY}(x, y)\, dy$$

and using property 4 of joint density functions

$$\frac{dF_X(x)}{dx} = f_X(x) \tag{2.4.3a}$$

Similarly for Y

$$f_Y(y) = \frac{dF_Y(y)}{dy} \tag{2.4.3b}$$

which is consistent with previous results.

The corresponding properties of a joint probability function are

(1) $0 \le P(X = x, Y = y) \le 1$
(2) $\sum_{x \in S_X} \sum_{y \in S_Y} P(X = x, Y = y) = 1$
(3) $F_{XY}(x, y) = \sum_{t \le x} \sum_{v \le y} P(X = t, Y = v)$
(4) $P(X = x) = \sum_{y \in S_Y} P(X = x, Y = y)$ and $P(Y = y) = \sum_{x \in S_X} P(X = x, Y = y)$ (marginal probability functions)
(5) $P(a_1 < X \le a_2, b_1 < Y \le b_2) = \sum_{a_1 < x \le a_2} \sum_{b_1 < y \le b_2} P(X = x, Y = y)$

Property 4 for probability functions is equivalent to the total probability expression of Eq. (1.4.4).

Example 2.4.4.   For Example 2.4.1 the joint probability function is

$$
\begin{aligned}
P(X = x, Y = y) &= \tfrac{1}{4} & (x, y) &= (0, 1) \\
&= \tfrac{1}{4} & (x, y) &= (1, 0) \\
&= \tfrac{1}{2} & (x, y) &= (1, 1) \\
&= 0 & &\text{otherwise}
\end{aligned}
$$

and the marginal probability functions are

$$P(X = x) = \tfrac{1}{4} \qquad x = 0$$
$$= \tfrac{3}{4} \qquad x = 1$$
$$= 0 \qquad \text{otherwise}$$

and

$$P(Y = y) = \tfrac{1}{4} \qquad y = 0$$
$$= \tfrac{3}{4} \qquad y = 1$$
$$= 0 \qquad \text{otherwise} \qquad \square$$

Now consider an example of the continuous random variables X and Y.

Example 2.4.5.   Let the continuous random variables X and Y have the joint density function

$$f_{XY}(x, y) = x\, e^{-x^2/2}\, e^{-y} u(x) u(y)$$

The corresponding joint distribution function is then

$$F_{XY}(x, y) = (1 - e^{-x^2/2})(1 - e^{-y}) u(x) u(y)$$

Now $P(X \le 1, Y \le 2)$ is easily evaluated in terms of the joint distribution function as

$$P(X \le 1, Y \le 2) = F_{XY}(1, 2) = (1 - e^{-0.5})(1 - e^{-2}) = 0.3402$$

Also, $P(X > 2, Y > 1)$ is evaluated in terms of the joint distribution function as

$$P(X > 2, Y > 1) = P(2 < X < \infty, 1 < Y < \infty)$$
$$= F_{XY}(\infty, \infty) - F_{XY}(2, \infty) - F_{XY}(\infty, 1) + F_{XY}(2, 1)$$
$$= 1 - 0.8647 - 0.6321 + 0.5466 = 0.0498$$

but is more easily evaluated in terms of the joint density function as

$$P(X > 2, Y > 1) = \int_1^\infty \int_2^\infty x\, e^{-x^2/2}\, e^{-y}\, dx\, dy = e^{-2} e^{-1} = 0.0498$$

The marginal density functions are obtained directly as

$$f_X(x) = \int_0^\infty x\, e^{-x^2/2} u(x)\, e^{-y}\, dy = x\, e^{-x^2/2} u(x)$$

and

$$f_Y(y) = \int_0^\infty x\, e^{-x^2/2}\, e^{-y} u(y)\, dx = e^{-y} u(y)$$

while the marginal distribution functions are obtained directly from the joint distribution function as

$$F_X(x) = F_{XY}(x, \infty) = (1 - e^{-x^2/2})u(x)$$

and

$$F_Y(y) = F_{XY}(\infty, y) = (1 - e^{-y})u(y) \qquad \square$$

As illustrated in Example 2.4.5 and in general

$$F_X(x) = F_{XY}(x, \infty) = \int_{-\infty}^{\infty} \int_{-\infty}^{x} f_{XY}(t, y)\, dt\, dy = \int_{-\infty}^{x} f_X(t)\, dt$$

and

$$f_X(x) = \frac{dF_X(x)}{dx}$$

or marginal distribution functions and marginal density functions are related in the same way as single-variable distribution and density functions.

Statistical independence of random variables will now be considered. This property is depicted in terms of the joint distribution, joint density, and joint probability functions.

Recall that the two events A and B are statistically independent, from Eq. (1.4.6a), if and only if

$$P(A \cap B) = P(A)P(B)$$

If $A = \{X \le x\} = (-\infty, x]$ and $B = \{Y \le y\} = (-\infty, y]$, the random variables X and Y are defined to be statistically independent if and only if

$$P(X \le x, Y \le y) = P(X \le x)P(Y \le y)$$

or

$$F_{XY}(x, y) = F_X(x)F_Y(y) \qquad (2.4.4a)$$

Thus, the two variables X and Y are statistically independent if and only if their joint distribution function factors into the two marginal distribution functions. Also, for X and Y statistically independent,

$$f_{XY}(x, y) = \frac{\partial^2 F_{XY}(x, y)}{\partial x\, \partial y} = \frac{dF_X(x)}{dx}\frac{dF_Y(y)}{dy} = f_X(x)f_Y(y)$$

and likewise, for $f_{XY}(x, y) = f_X(x)f_Y(y)$,

$$F_{XY}(x, y) = \int_{-\infty}^{y} \int_{-\infty}^{x} f_{XY}(t, v)\, dt\, dv = \int_{-\infty}^{x} f_X(t)\, dt \int_{-\infty}^{y} f_Y(v)\, dv$$

$$= F_X(x)F_Y(y)$$

Then,

$$f_{XY}(x, y) = f_X(x)f_Y(y) \qquad (2.4.4b)$$

is an equivalent statement that X and Y are statistically independent. Finally, in terms of probability functions,

$$P(X = x, Y = y) = P(X = x)P(Y = y)$$

$$\text{for all } x \in S_x \text{ and } y \in S_y \quad (2.4.4c)$$

Checking any of these equations, (2.4.4a), (2.4.4b), or (2.4.4c), is sufficient for establishing statistical independence of two random variables.

Example 2.4.6. In Example 2.4.5

$$f_{XY}(x, y) = x e^{-x^2/2} e^{-y} u(x)u(y) = f_X(x)f_Y(y)$$

and the random variables X and Y are statistically independent. $\square$

The random variables X and Y are said to be jointly Gaussian if

$$f_{XY}(x, y) = \frac{1}{2\pi\sqrt{1-\rho^2}} \exp\left[\frac{-(x^2 - 2\rho xy + y^2)}{2(1-\rho^2)}\right]$$

$$-\infty < x < \infty \quad -\infty < y < \infty \quad (2.4.5)$$

where ρ is a parameter such that $|\rho| \leq 1$. Equation (2.4.5) is a special case of the bivariate Gaussian density function where $\mu_x = \mu_y = 0$ (means 0) and $\sigma_x^2 = \sigma_y^2 = 1$ (variances 1). The marginal density function $f_X(x)$ is obtained from

$$f_X(x) = \int_{-\infty}^{\infty} \left[\frac{1}{2\pi\sqrt{(1-\rho^2)}}\right] \exp\left[\frac{-(x^2 - 2\rho xy + y^2)}{2(1-\rho^2)}\right] dy$$

by completing the square on $x^2 - 2\rho xy + y^2$ in y as

$$x^2 - 2\rho xy + y^2 = (y^2 - 2\rho xy + \rho^2 x^2) + x^2 - \rho^2 x^2 = (y - \rho x)^2 + x^2(1 - \rho^2)$$

Then,

$$f_X(x) = \frac{1}{\sqrt{2\pi}} e^{-x^2/2} \int_{-\infty}^{\infty} \frac{1}{\sqrt{2\pi(1-\rho^2)}} \exp\left[\frac{-(y - \rho x)^2}{2(1-\rho^2)}\right] dy$$

and since the integral is over the entire range of a density function

$$\int_{-\infty}^{\infty} \frac{1}{\sqrt{2\pi(1-\rho^2)}} \exp\left[\frac{-(y - \rho x)^2}{2(1-\rho^2)}\right] dy = 1$$

which yields

$$f_X(x) = \frac{1}{\sqrt{2\pi}} e^{-x^2/2} \qquad -\infty < x < \infty \qquad (2.4.6a)$$

which is a Gaussian density function with $\mu_x = 0$ and $\sigma_x^2 = 1$. Likewise,

$$f_Y(y) = \frac{1}{\sqrt{2\pi}} e^{-y^2/2} \qquad -\infty < y < \infty \qquad (2.4.6b)$$

For this bivariate Gaussian density function, since $f_{XY}(x, y) \neq f_X(x)f_Y(y)$, X and Y are not statistically independent. For $\rho = 0$, it can be shown that Eq. (2.4.5) is the product of Eqs. (2.4.6a) and (2.4.6b), and thus X and Y are statistically independent. The parameter ρ is a measure of statistical independence for bivariate Gaussian random variables.

If X and Y are not statistically independent, $f_{XY}(x, y)$ cannot be obtained by knowing $f_X(x)$ and $f_Y(y)$. An example is now given to show that this is true.

Example 2.4.7.   Consider the joint density function

$$f_{XY}(x, y) = \frac{1}{2\pi} e^{-(x^2+y^2)/2}(1 + xy\, e^{-(x^2+y^2-2)})$$

which is not a bivariate Gaussian density function. It can be shown that $f_X(x)$ and $f_Y(y)$ are given by Eqs. (2.4.6a) and (2.4.6b), respectively, but $f_{XY}(x, y) \neq f_X(x)f_Y(y)$. Thus $f_{XY}(x, y)$ cannot be obtained by knowing $f_X(x)$ and $f_Y(y)$. $\square$

Next, an example is given illustrating the calculation of a probability statement on two random variables where there is a constraint between the two random variables.

Example 2.4.8.   Two 1-Ω resistors, R_1 and R_2, with 10% tolerance are statistically independent and uniformly distributed. It is desired to determine the probability that the sum of R_1 and R_2 (R_1 and R_2 in series) is less than or equal to 2.1 Ω. For the uniform assumption and 10% tolerance, the

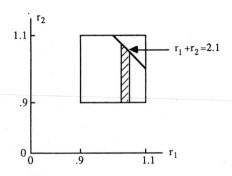

Fig. 2.4.4. Region for $R_1 + R_2 \leq 2.1$.

density functions are given as

$$f_{R_i}(r_i) = 5 \qquad 0.9 < r_i < 1.1 \quad i = 1, 2$$
$$= 0 \qquad \text{otherwise}$$

and the probability of interest is $P(R_1 + R_2 \le 2.1)$. The region of this probability statement is shown in Fig. 2.4.4. This probability can be evaluated as

$$P(R_1 + R_2 \le 2.1) = 1 - P(R_1 + R_2 > 2.1) = 1 - \iint\limits_{r_1 + r_2 > 2.1} f_{R_1}(r_1) f_{R_2}(r_2)\, dr_1\, dr_2$$

$$= 1 - \int_1^{1.1} \int_{2.1 - r_1}^{1.1} 25\, dr_2\, dr_1 = 1 - \int_1^{1.1} 25(r_1 - 1)\, dr_1$$

$$= 1 - \frac{25(0.01)}{2} = \tfrac{7}{8} \qquad \square$$

Now consider an application of joint variables in terms of the reliability of two electronic components.

Example 2.4.9. The failure times X and Y of statistically independent electronic components are modeled by joint exponential random variables where

$$f_{XY}(x, y) = 0.2\, e^{-(0.4x + 0.5y)} u(x) u(y)$$

and correspondingly

$$F_{XY}(x, y) = (1 - e^{-0.4x})(1 - e^{-0.5y}) u(x) u(y)$$

If X and Y are measured in years, the probability that X fails in less than 2 years, $P(X \le 2)$, is obtained as

$$P(X \le 2) = F_{XY}(2, \infty) = (1 - e^{-0.8})(1 - 0) = 0.551$$

and the probability that Y fails in less than 2 years, $P(Y \le 2)$, as

$$P(Y \le 2) = F_{XY}(\infty, 2) = (1 - 0)(1 - e^{-1}) = 0.632$$

For the components in parallel the probability that the combination fails in less than 2 years, $P(F_p \le 2)$, is obtained as

$$P(F_p \le 2) = P(X \le 2 \cap Y \le 2) = F_{XY}(2, 2) = (1 - e^{-0.8})(1 - e^{-1}) = 0.348$$

Now, for the components in series the probability that the combination fails in less than 2 years, $P(F_s \leq 2)$, is given as

$$P(F_s \leq 2) = P(X \leq 2 \cup Y \leq 2)$$
$$= 1 - P(X > 2 \cap Y > 2) = 1 - P(X > 2)P(Y > 2)$$
$$= 1 - [1 - F_{XY}(2, \infty)][1 - F_{XY}(\infty, 2)]$$
$$= 1 - e^{-0.8} e^{-1} = 0.835 \quad \square$$

2.5   Conditional Distribution and Density Functions

Letting $A = \{X \leq x\} = (-\infty, x]$ and $Y \in B$, the conditional probability distribution function, using $P(A|B) = P(A \cap B)/P(B)$, is defined as

$$F_X(x | Y \in B) = P(X \leq x | Y \in B) = \frac{P(X \leq x, Y \in B)}{P(Y \in B)} \qquad P(Y \in B) > 0$$

(2.5.1a)

which satisfies all of the properties of probability distribution functions. Also,

$$f_X(x | Y \in B) = \frac{dF_X(x | Y \in B)}{dx}$$

(2.5.1b)

is a conditional probability density function and it satisfies all the properties of a probability density function. The corresponding conditional probability function is given as

$$P(X = x | Y \in B) = \frac{P(X = x, Y \in B)}{P(Y \in B)} \qquad P(Y \in B) > 0 \quad (2.5.1c)$$

Example 2.5.1.   For the bivariate density function

$$f_{XY}(x, y) = x e^{-x(y+1)} u(x) u(y)$$

the conditional distribution function $F_X(x | Y \leq 1)$ is computed as

$$F_X(x | Y \leq 1) = P(X \leq x, Y \leq 1)/P(Y \leq 1)$$

$$= \frac{\{\int_0^x \int_0^1 t e^{-t(y+1)} \, dy \, dt\}}{\{\int_0^\infty \int_0^1 x e^{-x(y+1)} \, dy \, dx\}}$$

which reduces to

$$F_X(x | Y \leq 1) = (1 - 2e^{-x} + e^{-2x}) u(x) = (1 - e^{-x})^2 u(x)$$

Then the conditional density function is obtained, by taking the derivative, as

$$f_X(x \mid Y \le 1) = 2(e^{-x} - e^{-2x})u(x) = 2e^{-x}(1 - e^{-x})u(x)$$

Also, the conditional distribution function $F_X(x \mid Y \le 2)$ can be computed as

$$F_X(x \mid Y \le 2) = \tfrac{1}{2}(2 - 3e^{-x} + e^{-3x})u(x)$$

which illustrates that X is dependent on Y, and X and Y are not statistically independent. $\square$

The most useful conditional distribution function is conditioned on Y being equal to a particular value and is given as

$$F_{X \mid Y}(x \mid y) = F_X(x \mid Y = y) = P(X \le x \mid Y = y) = \frac{P(X \le x, Y = y)}{P(Y = y)} \quad (2.5.2)$$

which is referred to as point conditioning. For continuous random variables the denominator in Eq. (2.5.2) is 0 $[P(Y = y) = 0$ for a continuous random variable], which could make the conditional distribution function unbounded, but the numerator is also 0 $(P(X \le x, Y = y) = 0)$. $F_{X \mid Y}(x \mid y)$ is then obtained in a limiting manner. There is no problem for discrete random variables, since the probability of Y equaling any value for which the conditional distribution function is defined is nonzero. For X and Y jointly continuous random variables

$$P(X \le x \mid y \le Y \le y + \Delta y) = \frac{\int_{-\infty}^{x} \int_{y}^{y+\Delta y} f_{XY}(t, v) \, dv \, dt}{\int_{y}^{y+\Delta y} f_Y(v) \, dv}$$

where Δy is a small positive interval on the y axis. Using

$$\int_{a}^{b} g(z) \, dz = (b - a)g(c) \qquad a \le c \le b$$

which states that a continuous function must equal its average value somewhere in the interval (the mean-value theorem), yields

$$P(X \le x \mid y \le Y \le y + \Delta y) = \frac{\int_{-\infty}^{x} \Delta y f_{XY}(t, y') \, dt}{\Delta y f_Y(y'')} \qquad \begin{matrix} y \le y' \le y + \Delta y \\ y \le y'' \le y + \Delta y \end{matrix}$$

where the Δy's cancel. Now taking the limit as Δy goes to 0

$$F_{X \mid Y}(x \mid y) = \lim_{\Delta y \to 0} P(X \le x \mid y \le Y \le y + \Delta y) = \frac{\int_{-\infty}^{x} f_{XY}(t, y) \, dt}{f_Y(y)} \quad (2.5.3)$$

which is called the conditional distribution function of X given Y, and finally,

$$f_{X \mid Y}(x \mid y) = \frac{dF_{X \mid Y}(x \mid y)}{dx} = \frac{f_{XY}(x, y)}{f_Y(y)} \quad (2.5.4a)$$

which is called the conditional probability density function of X given Y. The form of Eq. (2.5.4a) is similar to the conditional probability of sets, as might have been expected. The corresponding conditional probability density function of Y given X is

$$f_{Y|X}(y|x) = \frac{dF_{Y|X}(y|x)}{dy} = \frac{f_{XY}(x,y)}{f_X(x)} \qquad (2.5.4b)$$

Also, the conditional probability function of Y given X is

$$P(Y=j|X=i) = \frac{P(Y=j, X=i)}{P(X=i)} \qquad (2.5.5)$$

which is the same form as the conditional probability of sets.

For the bivariate Gaussian density function $f_{XY}(x, y)$ of Eq. (2.4.5) and the marginal density function $f_Y(y)$ of Eq. (2.4.6b), the conditional density function $f_{X|Y}(x|y)$ is obtained as

$$f_{X|Y}(x|y) = \frac{f_{XY}(x,y)}{f_Y(y)}$$

$$= \frac{1}{\sqrt{2\pi(1-\rho^2)}} \exp\left[\frac{-(x^2-2\rho xy+y^2)}{2(1-\rho^2)} + \frac{y^2}{2}\right]$$

or

$$f_{X|Y}(x|y) = \frac{1}{\sqrt{2\pi(1-\rho^2)}} \exp\left[\frac{-(x-\rho y)^2}{2(1-\rho^2)}\right] \qquad -\infty < x < \infty \qquad (2.5.6)$$

which is a single-variable Gaussian density function with $\mu = \rho y$ and $\sigma^2 = 1 - \rho^2$. This conditional Gaussian density function is shown in Fig. 2.5.1 for

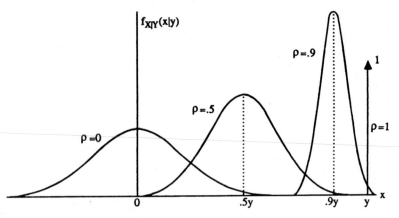

Fig. 2.5.1. Conditional Gaussian density functions.

several values of ρ (a measure of statistical dependence for the bivariate Gaussian random variables). For $\rho = 0$, the conditional density function is the normalized Gaussian density function of Eq. (2.4.6a). As $|\rho|$ increases to 1, the mean increases to y (for $\rho < 0$, the mean goes to $-y$) and the variance decreases to 0, which makes the height increase (to maintain unit area). This illustrates that as $|\rho|$ increases, the statistical dependence of X on Y increases, and when $\rho = \pm 1$, X and Y are totally dependent (x is known exactly if y is known).

Example 2.5.2. A bivariate Gaussian density function is given as

$$f_{XY}(x, y) = \frac{1}{4\pi} e^{-(5x^2 - 12xy + 8y^2)/8} \qquad -\infty < x < \infty \quad -\infty < y < \infty$$

where it is desired to find the marginal density functions and the conditional density functions. The density functions $f_X(x)$ and $f_{Y|X}(y|x)$ can be found together by writing Eq. (2.5.4b) as

$$f_{XY}(x, y) = f_{Y|X}(y|x)f_X(x)$$

and completing the square on the exponent of $f_{XY}(x, y)$ in y. This completed square will be the exponent for $f_{Y|X}(y|x)$ and the part that is left (only a function of x) is then the exponent for $f_X(x)$. Completing the square on the exponent (only the part in the parentheses) in y yields

$$(5x^2 - 12xy + 8y^2) = 8(y^2 - \tfrac{3}{2}xy) + 5x^2$$
$$= 8(y^2 - \tfrac{3}{2}xy + \tfrac{9}{16}x^2) - 8(\tfrac{9}{16}x^2) + 5x^2$$
$$= 8(y - \tfrac{3}{4}x)^2 + \tfrac{1}{2}x^2$$

After multiplying by $-$ and dividing by 8 the exponent for $f_{Y|X}(y|x)$ is $-(y - 3x/4)^2$ and the exponent for $f_X(x)$ is $-x^2/16$. These exponents can be separated to yield

$$f_{Y|X}(y|x)f_X(x) = \left(\frac{1}{\sqrt{\pi}} e^{-(y-3x/4)^2}\right)\left(\frac{1}{\sqrt{16\pi}} e^{-x^2/16}\right)$$

where the σ^2 (variance) terms have been inserted in the constant terms to match the exponents (without changing the overall expression). By associating the terms on the left of the equation with the appropriate term on the right, the conditional Gaussian density function is

$$f_{Y|X}(y|x) = \frac{1}{\sqrt{\pi}} e^{-(y-3x/4)^2} \qquad -\infty < y < \infty \quad -\infty < x < \infty$$

where the conditional mean of Y given x is $\tfrac{3}{4}x$ and the conditional variance is $\frac{1}{2}$. Also the marginal Gaussian density function is given as

$$f_X(x) = \frac{1}{\sqrt{16\pi}} e^{-x^2/16} \qquad -\infty < x < \infty$$

where the mean of X is 0 and the variance is 8.   □

By completing the square on the exponent of $f_{XY}(x, y)$ in x the density functions $f_{X|Y}(x|y)$ and $f_Y(y)$ can also be obtained.

Example 2.5.3. Consider the bivariate Gaussian density function of Example 2.5.2. Completing the square on the exponent of $f_{XY}(x, y)$ in x yields

$$(5x^2 - 12xy + 8y^2) = 5(x - \tfrac{6}{5}y)^2 + \tfrac{4}{5}y^2$$

From this

$$f_{X|Y}(x|y) = \frac{1}{\sqrt{8\pi/5}} e^{-(x-6y/5)^2/(8/5)} \qquad -\infty < x < \infty \quad -\infty < y < \infty$$

where the conditional mean of X given y is $\frac{6}{5}y$ and the conditional variance is $\frac{4}{5}$, and

$$f_Y(y) = \frac{1}{\sqrt{10\pi}} e^{-y^2/10} \qquad -\infty < y < \infty$$

where the mean of Y is 0 and the variance is 5. It should be noted that ρ is neither $\frac{3}{4}$ nor $\frac{6}{5}$ ($\rho = 0.95$) since the variances of X and Y are not 1.   □

Conditional probability functions can be manipulated in much the same way as conditional density functions. Consider the number of photons arriving at a photomultiplier tube which are Poisson distributed as given in Eq. (2.3.10). It is assumed that the photomultiplier tube is faulty and records correctly only a fraction p of the arriving photons. The probability function of the number of recorded photons, Y, will then be developed. The conditional probability of Y recorded photons given X received photons has a binomial probability assignment, Eq. (2.3.6), given as

$$P(Y = j | X = i) = C_j^i p^j (1-p)^{i-j} \qquad j = 0, 1, \ldots, i$$

Now, the unconditional probability of Y recorded photons is obtained by summing the joint probability of Y recorded photons and X received photons over all values of X, Eq. (1.4.4). This is expressed as

$$P(Y = j) = \sum_{i=j}^{\infty} P(Y = j | X = i) P(X = i) = \sum_{i=j}^{\infty} C_j^i p^j (1-p)^{i-j} \frac{a^i e^{-a}}{i!}$$

where the lower limit of the summation starts at j since $i \geq j$ (and $X \geq Y$).

Making the change of variable $k = i - j$, $P(Y = j)$ becomes

$$P(Y = j) = \frac{p^j a^j e^{-a}}{j!} \sum_{k=0}^{\infty} \frac{(1-p)^k a^k}{k!} = \frac{(pa)^j e^{-a} e^{a(1-p)}}{j!}$$

where the series has been recognized as $e^{a(1-p)}$. Finally,

$$P(Y = j) = \frac{(pa)^j e^{-pa}}{j!} \qquad j = 0, 1, \ldots$$

which is a Poisson probability function with parameter pa. The parameter of the Poisson probability function has been reduced by the factor p due to the faulty photomultiplier tube.

The extension from 2 to N random variables is a natural extension in vector form to any number of random variables as the N-dimensional vector $(X_1, X_2, \ldots, X_N) = \mathbf{X}$ (bold print indicates a vector or a matrix). The joint distribution function of $\mathbf{X}$ is given as

$$\begin{aligned} F_{\mathbf{X}}(\mathbf{x}) &= F_{X_1 X_2 \cdots X_N}(x_1, x_2, \ldots, x_N) \\ &= P(X_1 \le x_1, X_2 \le x_2, \ldots, X_N \le x_N) \\ &= P(\mathbf{X} \le \mathbf{x}) \end{aligned} \qquad (2.5.7)$$

with the corresponding probability density function as

$$\begin{aligned} f_{\mathbf{X}}(\mathbf{x}) &= f_{X_1 X_2 \cdots X_N}(x_1, x_2, \ldots, x_N) \\ &= \frac{\partial^N F_{X_1 X_2 \cdots X_N}(x_1, x_2, \ldots, x_N)}{\partial x_1 \, \partial x_2 \cdots x_N} \end{aligned} \qquad (2.5.8)$$

In a similar manner, a joint probability function is given as

$$P(\mathbf{X} = \mathbf{x}) = P(X_1 = x_1, X_2 = x_2, \ldots, X_N = x_N) \qquad (2.5.9)$$

which give the probabilities of discrete points in the N-dimensional space.

Probabilities of regions in N-space can be computed by appropriate integrals of the joint density function or by appropriate sums of the joint probability function. Even though they are straightforward generalizations of the previous concepts, evaluation of these expressions is more involved due to the number of integrals or sums involved.

Marginal distribution functions are obtained by setting the values of all the random variables, except the ones in the marginal distribution function, equal to infinity. The marginal density functions or the marginal probability functions are obtained by integrating or summing the joint density functions or probability functions over the entire range of the random variables not included in the function. Conditional distribution, density, and probability functions are defined as for the two-dimensional case, with the

N-dimensional functions replacing the two-dimensional ones. Statistical independence is defined as in Eq. (1.4.7) with the sets replaced by the distribution, density, or probability functions.

The main interest in N-dimensional random vectors will be in regard to N-dimensional Gaussian random vectors, which will be considered in Chapter 4. The importance of this type of random vector is the same as in the single-variable case, in that it models a large number of engineering applications (which in part is due to the central limit theorem).

PROBLEMS

2.1.1. For the probability assignment $P(X = i) = (\frac{1}{2})^i$, $i = 1, 2, \ldots$, determine $P(X \le 3)$, $P(X > 4)$, and $F_X(x)$.

2.1.2. For the probability assignment $P(a \le X \le b) = (b - a)/2\pi$, $0 \le a \le b < 2\pi$, with $A = \{X : 0 \le X \le \pi/3\}$ and $B = \{X : \pi/3 \le X \le \pi\}$, determine $A \cup B$, $A \cap B$, and show that $P(A \cup B) = P(A) + P(B)$ even though A and B are not disjoint.

2.1.3. For $F_X(x) = (1 - e^{-x})u(x)$, determine $P(1 < X \le 2)$ and $P(X > 3)$.

2.1.4. For $F_X(x) = [1 - 1/(x + 1)]u(x)$, determine $P(1 < X \le 2)$ and $P(X > 3)$.

2.1.5. Determine a and b for $F_X(x) = (a + b e^{-x^2/2c})u(x)$ to be a distribution function, where X is a continuous random variable.

2.1.6. Determine a and b for $F_X(x) = a \tan^{-1}(x/c) + b$ to be a distribution function, where X is a continuous random variable.

2.1.7. For $F_X(x) = (1 - e^{-x})u(x)$, determine $f_X(x)$.

2.1.8. For $F_X(x) = [1 - 1/(x + 1)]u(x)$, determine $f_X(x)$.

2.1.9. For the probability assignment $P(X = i) = p^i$, $i = 1, 2, \ldots, 0 < p < 1$, determine the values to which p is restricted.

2.1.10. Determine b such that $P(X = i) = bc^i/i!$, $i = 0, 1, \ldots, c > 0$ is a probability assignment.

2.1.11. Determine $f_X(x)$ for $F_X(x) = (\frac{2}{3} - \frac{1}{2}e^{-2x})u(x) + \frac{1}{3}u(x - 1)$.

2.1.12. Determine $F_X(x)$ for $f_X(x) = e^{-3x}u(x) + \frac{2}{3}\delta(x - \frac{1}{2})$.

2.1.13. Plot and label $f_X(x)$ for $F_X(x)$ given in Fig. P2.1.13.

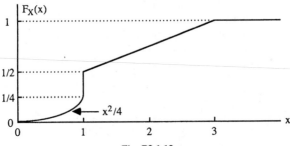

Fig. P2.1.13.

2.1.14. Plot and label $F_X(x)$ for $f_X(x)$ given in Fig. P2.1.14.

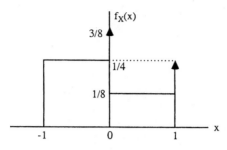

Fig. P2.1.14.

2.1.15. Determine a and $P(-\frac{1}{2} < X \leq \frac{1}{2})$ for $f_X(x)$ given in Fig. P2.1.15.

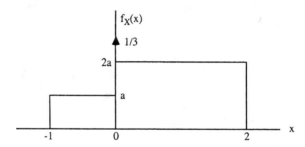

Fig. P2.1.15.

2.1.1.6. Determine a and $P(-\frac{1}{2} < X \leq \frac{1}{2})$ for $f_X(x)$ given in Fig. P2.1.16.

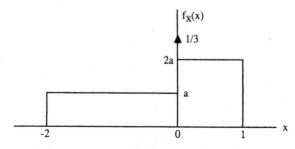

Fig. P2.1.16.

2.1.17. Express $P[(X-3)^2 > 4]$ in terms of $F_X(\ )$, where X is a continuous random variable.

2.1.18. Express $P[X^2 + 4X < 5]$ in terms of $F_X(\ )$, where X is a continuous random variable.

2.2.1. Determine $P(1 < X \le 10)$, where X is a Gaussian random variable with mean $\mu = 2$ and variance $\sigma^2 = 16$.

2.2.2. Determine $P(1 < X \le 15)$, where X is a Gaussian random variable with mean $\mu = 5$ and variance $\sigma^2 = 64$.

2.2.3. Determine the mean μ and the variance σ^2 where X is a Gaussian random variable when $P(X < 1) = P(X > 13) = Q(2)$.

2.2.4. Determine the mean μ and the variance σ^2 where X is a Gaussian random variable when $P(X < 3) = P(X > 15) = Q(3)$.

2.2.5. Determine a where $P(X < a) = Q(2)$ and X is a Gaussian random variable with mean $\mu = 13$ and variance $\sigma^2 = 16$.

2.2.6. Determine a where $P(X < a) = Q(1.2)$ and X is a Gaussian random variable with mean $\mu = 9$ and variance $\sigma^2 = 25$.

2.2.7. Determine the cutoffs for grades in terms of μ and σ when grading on a Gaussian curve where it is desired to have 10% A, 10% F, 20% B, 20% D, and 40% C.

2.2.8. Determine the cutoffs for grades in terms of μ and σ when grading on a Gaussian curve where it is desired to have 8% A, 8% F, 20% B, 20% D, and 44% C.

2.3.1. Determine $F_X(x)$ for the two-sided exponential probability density function $f_X(x) = \frac{1}{2} \exp(-|x|)$, $-\infty < x < \infty$.

2.3.2. The failure time X of an electronic system is modeled by Eqs. (2.3.1a) and (2.3.1b), where the probability that the failure time exceeds 100 months is e^{-2}. Determine the probability that the failure time is less than 30 months and the time T such that the probability is 0.2 that the failure time is less than T.

2.3.3. Information is transmitted in blocks of 7 bits with the probability of bit error $p = 0.1$ and the capability of correcting single errors. Thus, the block is in error only if two or more bit errors are made. Determine $P(0$ bit errors in block), $P(1$ bit error in block), and $P($block error).

2.3.4. Information is transmitted in blocks of 7 bits with the probability of bit error $p = 0.2$ and the capability of correcting single and double errors. Thus, the block is in error only if three or more bit errors are made. Determine $P(0$ bit errors in block), $P(1$ bit error in block), $P(2$ bit errors in block), and $P($block error).

2.3.5. If the numbers of photons counted in a photomultiplier tube are Poisson distributed where $P(0$ photons$) = 0.2$, determine the parameter of the Poisson probability function and $P(0, 1,$ or 2 photons).

2.3.6. If the numbers of photons counted in a photomultiplier tube are Poisson distributed where $P(0$ or 1 photon$) = 0.3$, determine the parameter of the Poisson probability function and $P(0, 1,$ or 2 photons).

2.4.1. For $F_{XY}(x, y) = (1 - e^{-x})(1 - e^{-2y})$, $x \ge 0$, $y \ge 0$, determine $f_{XY}(x, y)$ and $P(1 < X \le 3, 1 < Y \le 2)$.

2.4.2. For $f_{XY}(x, y) = x + y$, $0 \le x \le 1$, $0 \le y \le 1$, determine $F_{XY}(x, y)$ and $P(0 < X \le \frac{1}{2}, \frac{1}{2} < Y \le 1)$.

2.4.3. For $f_{XY}(x, y) = \frac{3}{2}(xy^2 + x)$, $0 \le x \le 1$, $0 \le y \le 1$ and correspondingly $F_{XY}(x, y) = \frac{1}{4}(x^2 y^3 + 3x^2 y)$, $0 \le x \le 1$, $0 \le y \le 1$, determine $f_X(x)$, $f_Y(y)$, $F_X(x)$, $F_Y(y)$, and whether X and Y are statistically independent.

2.4.4. For $f_{XY}(x, y) = x e^{-x(y+1)} u(x) u(y)$ and correspondingly $F_{XY}(x, y) = [1 - e^{-x} - (1/(y+1))(1 - e^{-x(y+1)})] u(x) u(y)$, determine $f_X(x)$, $f_Y(y)$, $F_X(x)$, $F_Y(y)$, and whether X and Y are statistically independent.

2.4.5. For $f_{XY}(x, y) = xy$, $0 \le x \le 1$, $0 \le y \le 2$, determine $P(X + Y > 1)$.

2.4.6. For $f_{XY}(x, y) = xy$, $0 \le x \le 2$, $0 \le y \le 1$, determine $P(X - Y < 1)$.

2.4.7. For $f_{XY}(x, y) = \frac{4}{3}xy$, $1 \le x \le 2$, $0 \le y \le 1$, determine $P(X < 2Y + 1)$.

2.4.8. For $f_{XY}(x, y) = \frac{4}{3}xy$, $1 \le x \le 2$, $0 \le y \le 1$, determine $P(Y > 2X - 3)$.

2.4.9. Determine the probability that a 200-Ω 10% resistor is within 5% tolerance of 200 Ω and the probability that the sum of two 100-Ω 10% resistors is within 5% tolerance of 200 Ω. The resistors are assumed to be statistically independent and uniformly distributed over the 10% tolerance range.

2.4.10. Determine the probability that a 200-Ω 10% resistor is within 4% tolerance of 200 Ω and the probability that the sum of two 100-Ω 10% resistors is within 4% tolerance of 200 Ω. The resistors are assumed to be statistically independent and uniformly distributed over the 10% tolerance range.

2.4.11. Determine the probability that a 300-Ω 10% resistor is within 5% tolerance of 300 Ω and the probability that the sum of a 100-Ω 10% resistor and a 200-Ω 10% resistor is within 5% tolerance of 300 Ω. The resistors are assumed to be statistically independent and uniformly distributed over the 10% tolerance range.

2.4.12. If the failure time of statistically independent electronic components is modeled by the exponential random variable where the probability that the failure time of component 1 exceeds 100 months is e^{-2} and the probability that the failure time of component 2 exceeds 100 months is e^{-3}, determine the probability that the failure time is less than 30 months when the two components are in series.

2.4.13. If the failure time of statistically independent electronic components is modeled by the exponential random variable where the probability that the failure time of component 1 exceeds 100 months is e^{-2} and the probability that the failure time of component 2 exceeds 100 months is e^{-3}, determine the probability that the failure time is less than 30 months when the two components are in parallel.

2.4.14. If the failure time of statistically independent electronic components is modeled by the exponential random variable where the probability that the failure time of a single component exceeds 100 months is e^{-4}, determine the time T such that the probability is 0.2 that the failure time is less than T when two of these components are in series.

2.4.15. If the failure time of statistically independent electronic components is modeled by the exponential random variable where the probability that the failure time of a single component exceeds 100 months is e^{-4}, determine the time T such that the probability is 0.2 that the failure time is less than T when two of these components are in parallel.

2.5.1. For the bivariate Gaussian density function

$$f_{XY}(x, y) = \frac{1}{2\pi} e^{-(2x^2 - 6xy + 5y^2)/2}, \quad -\infty < x < \infty, \ -\infty < y < \infty,$$

determine $f_X(x)$ and $f_{Y|X}(y|x)$.

2.5.2. For the bivariate Gaussian density function

$$f_{XY}(x, y) = \frac{1}{2\pi} e^{-(2x^2 - 6xy + 5y^2)/2}, \quad -\infty < x < \infty, \ -\infty < y < \infty,$$

determine $f_Y(y)$ and $f_{X|Y}(x|y)$.

2.5.3. For the bivariate Gaussian density function

$$f_{XY}(x, y) = \frac{1}{16\pi} e^{-(4x^2 - 4xy + 5y^2)/64}, \quad -\infty < x < \infty, \ -\infty < y < \infty,$$

determine $f_X(x)$ and $f_{Y|X}(y|x)$.

2.5.4. For the bivariate Gaussian density function

$$f_{XY}(x, y) = \frac{1}{16\pi} e^{-(4x^2 - 4xy + 5y^2)/64}, \quad -\infty < x < \infty, \ -\infty < y < \infty,$$

determine $f_Y(y)$ and $f_{X|Y}(x|y)$.

2.5.5. For the probability density function and corresponding distribution function of Problem 2.4.4, determine $F_Y(1|X \le 1)$.

2.5.6. For the probability density function and corresponding distribution function of Problem 2.4.4, determine $F_Y(1|X \le 2)$.

Functions of Random Variables

3

3.1 One-to-One Transformation of Random Variables

This chapter deals with the situation of a random variable X that undergoes a transformation (change) to produce a new random variable Y. The random variable X is described only in a statistical sense in terms of its distribution, density, or probability function. Thus, the problem encountered here is to develop procedures to obtain the distribution, density, or probability function of the new random variable Y. This description of Y will be a function of the distribution, density, or probability function of X and the transformation.

In many situations the actual choice of random variables to work with is somewhat arbitrary. For example, the time units used in describing a random occurrence can be seconds, milliseconds, microseconds, or many other possible units, where the choice is irrelevant to the solution of the problem. Many electrical circuits can be described equally well in terms of random currents, random voltages, random powers, or random energies. The calculations on any of these random circuit quantities should be equivalent if the underlying random phenomenon does not change. For a problem that is equally well described by random current or power in a 1-Ω resistor, the probability that a positive current is between 2 and 5 A should be the same as the probability that the power is between 4 and 25 W.

The basic principle behind all transformations of variables is that the probabilities of equivalent events are conserved. For the case of a single random variable X that undergoes a transformation $g(\ )$ to another single random variable Y, this relationship is given as

$$y = g(x) \tag{3.1.1}$$

89

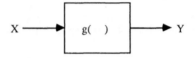

Fig. 3.1.1. Transformation of a single random variable.

which is depicted in Fig. 3.1.1. The input random variable X is described by $F_X(x)$ or $f_X(x)$ [or $P(X=x)$] and the transformed (output) variable by $F_Y(y)$ or $f_Y(y)$ [or $P(Y=y)$]. Thus, given some random variable X with $F_X(x)$ or $f_X(x)$ [or $P(X=x)$] and the transformation $y=g(x)$, it is desired to evaluate $F_Y(y)$ or $f_Y(y)$ [or $P(Y=y)$] for the random variable Y. If $F_Y(y)$ can be obtained from $F_X(x)$, $f_Y(y)$ is simply its derivative, and since $F_X(x)$ is obtainable from $f_X(x)$, $f_Y(y)$ can be expressed in terms of $f_X(x)$.

Now, using the definition of the distribution function and expressing Y in terms of X,

$$F_Y(y) = P(Y \le y) = P[g(X) \le y] \qquad (3.1.2a)$$

which is true for all values. The double notation used here, where the capital letter indicates the random variable and the lower case letter indicates the value that the random variable takes on, implies, from Eq. (3.1.1), that $Y = g(X)$. For $g(x)$ a monotonically increasing function, $g^{-1}(y) = h(y)$ exists and Eq. (3.1.2a) can be written

$$F_Y(y) = P[X \le h(y)] = F_X[h(y)] \qquad (3.1.2b)$$

Since $g(x)$ is a monotonically increasing function, the inequality in Eq. (3.1.2b) is the same as in Eq. (3.1.2a). If $g(x)$ is a monotonically nondecreasing function (not strictly monotonically increasing) there are flat portions of $g(x)$ which yield multiple values of x for a single y (x cannot be uniquely expressed in terms of y).

Example 3.1.1. Consider the example where $y = e^x$ [which is a monotonically increasing function, i.e., $e^x < a$ if and only if $x < \ln(a)$ for all a] and

$$F_X(x) = (1 - e^{-x})u(x)$$

Then, $x = \ln(y) = h(y)$ and

$$F_Y(y) = [1 - e^{-\ln(y)}]u(y-1) = \left(1 - \frac{1}{y}\right)u(y-1)$$

The range of the transformed random variable Y is obtained from the range of the input random variable and the transformation $g(x)$. Here, for

$x = 0$, $y = e^0 = 1$ and for $x = \infty$, $y = e^\infty = \infty$, thus $1 \leq y < \infty$. Also,

$$f_Y(y) = \frac{dF_Y(y)}{dy} = \left(\frac{1}{y^2}\right) u(y-1) \qquad \square$$

An expression for the density function of $f_Y(y)$ is obtained by differentiating Eq. (3.1.2b), with the aid of the chain rule, as

$$f_Y(y) = f_X(x)\big|_{x=h(y)} \frac{dh(y)}{dy} = f_X(h(y)) \frac{dh(y)}{dy} \qquad (3.1.3)$$

Thus, the transformed density function is equal to the input density function, with the old variable replaced by the appropriate function of the new variable, times the derivative of the inverse function (function of transformed variable) with respect to the transformed variable. On inspection of Eq. (3.1.3) it can be seen that it is equivalent to the change of variables required for a single-variable integration, changing from an integration on x to one on y, i.e., $f_Y(y)\, dy = f_X(x)\, dx = f_X(h(y))\, dh(y)$.

Equation (3.1.3) could have been obtained by expressing Eq. (3.1.2b) as the integral

$$F_Y(y) = \int_{-\infty}^{h(y)} f_X(x)\, dx \qquad (3.1.4)$$

and differentiating this integral. The differentiation of an integral, to obtain Eq. (3.1.3), is a special case of Leibnitz's rule for differentiating an integral, which states that if $v(x, t)$ is continuous in x and t

$$\frac{d}{dx} \int_{s(x)}^{r(x)} v(x, t)\, dt = v(x, r(x)) \frac{dr(x)}{dx} - v(x, s(x)) \frac{ds(x)}{dx}$$

$$+ \int_{s(x)}^{r(x)} \frac{\partial v(x, t)}{\partial x}\, dt \qquad (3.1.5)$$

If $g(x)$ is a monotonically decreasing function, the inequality in Eq. (3.1.2b) is reversed to yield

$$F_Y(y) = P[X \geq h(y)] = 1 - F_X[h(y)] \qquad (3.1.6a)$$

or in the form of Eq. (3.1.4)

$$F_Y(y) = \int_{h(y)}^{\infty} f_X(x)\, dx \qquad (3.1.6b)$$

Differentiating Eq. (3.1.6a) using the chain rule or differentiating Eq. (3.1.6b) using Leibnitz's rule gives

$$f_Y(y) = f_X(h(y))\left[-\frac{dh(y)}{dy} \right] \qquad (3.1.7)$$

for $g(x)$ a monotonically decreasing function. Combining Eqs. (3.1.3) and (3.1.7) for a monotonic or one-to-one transformation results in

$$f_Y(y) = f_X(x)|_{x=h(y)} \left| \frac{dh(y)}{dy} \right| = f_X(h(y)) \left| \frac{dh(y)}{dy} \right| \qquad (3.1.8)$$

Example 3.1.2. Consider the same density function as in Example 3.1.1, $f_X(x) = e^{-x} u(x)$, with the transformation $y = e^{-x} = g(x)$, $x = -\ln(y) = h(y)$. The transformed density function is obtained as

$$f_Y(y) = e^{-[-\ln(y)]} \left| -\frac{1}{y} \right| = y \left(\frac{1}{y} \right)$$

or

$$f_Y(y) = 1 \qquad 0 < y \le 1$$

$$= 0 \qquad \text{otherwise} \qquad \square$$

A very useful transformation of variables is the linear transformation $y = ax + b = g(x)$, where a and b are constants with $a \ne 0$. For this transformation, $x = (y-b)/a = h(y)$, $|dh(y)/dy| = 1/|a|$, and

$$f_Y(y) = \frac{1}{|a|} f_X \left[\frac{y-b}{a} \right] \qquad (3.1.9)$$

Example 3.1.3. Consider the case where X is a normalized (standardized) Gaussian random variable ($\mu_x = 0$ and $\sigma_x^2 = 1$). The density function of X is then

$$f_X(x) = \frac{1}{\sqrt{2\pi}} e^{-x^2/2}$$

With the linear transformation $y = ax + b$ with $a \ne 0$

$$f_Y(y) = \frac{1}{\sqrt{2\pi a^2}} e^{-(y-b)^2/2a^2}$$

which shows that Y is also Gaussian with $\mu_y = b$ and $\sigma_y^2 = a^2$. $\qquad \square$

It is possible, therefore, to transform normalized Gaussian random variables, by a suitable choice of a and b, into Gaussian random variables with any prescribed μ and σ^2. Conversely, it is possible to transform Gaussian random variables with any μ and σ^2 to normalized Gaussian random variables, i.e., $y = (x - \mu)/\sigma$. This is exactly what was done to use the Q function in Chapter 2.

Example 3.1.4. Consider another example where the density function is given as $f_X(x) = e^{-2|x|}$, $-\infty < x < \infty$, and the transformation as $y = e^x = g(x)$. The density function of Y is obtained in two parts since the absolute value represents the two functions $|x| = x$, $x \geq 0$, and $|x| = -x$, $x < 0$. Here, $f_X(x) = e^{-2x}$, $x \geq 0$, and $f_X(x) = e^{+2x}$, $x < 0$. With the inverse transformation $x = \ln(y) = h(y)$, $f_Y(y)$ is obtained, using Eq. (3.1.8), as

$$f_Y(y) = e^{-2\ln(y)} \left| \frac{1}{y} \right| = \frac{1}{y^2} \left| \frac{1}{y} \right| = \frac{1}{y^3} \qquad y \geq 1$$

$$= e^{+2\ln(y)} \left| \frac{1}{y} \right| = (y^2) \left| \frac{1}{y} \right| = y \qquad 0 < y < 1 \qquad \square$$

For discrete random variables with the conservation of probability (probability of equivalent events conserved), the input probability function and the transformed probability function are set equal [similar to Eq. (3.1.2a)] to yield

$$P(Y = y) = P[X = h(y)] \tag{3.1.10}$$

where $Y = g(X)$ and $X = h(Y)$.

Example 3.1.5. Consider the example of the Poisson random variable where, from Eq. (2.3.10),

$$P(X = x) = \frac{a^x e^{-a}}{x!} \qquad x = 0, 1, 2, \ldots \quad a > 0$$

$$= 0 \qquad \text{otherwise}$$

and the transformation $y = bx = g(x)$ with b a positive integer. With $x = y/b = h(y)$, the transformed probability function is then

$$P(Y = y) = \frac{a^{y/b} e^{-a}}{(y/b)!} \qquad y = 0, b, 2b, \ldots \quad a > 0 \qquad \square$$

An alternative problem to determining $f_Y(y)$ given $f_X(x)$ and $y = g(x)$ is to determine the transformation $y = g(x)$ given the input density $f_X(x)$ and the output density $f_Y(y)$. This problem is useful in determining a specific density (distribution or probability) function from a given density function. The most common application is to obtain different random variables from random variables uniformly distributed over the interval from 0 to 1. The reason for this is that it is relatively easy to generate uniform random numbers (actually pseudorandom numbers) over the interval from 0 to 1 on digital computers of varying word lengths. Equation (3.1.8) can be used to solve for the desired transformation, but this requires solution of a differential equation. A simpler approach is to set the two distribution functions equal (for continuous random variables),

$$F_X(x) = F_Y(y) \tag{3.1.11}$$

to obtain y as a function of x, which yields a monotonically nondecreasing

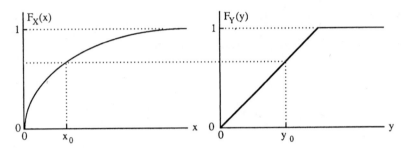

Fig. 3.1.2. Integral transform of variables.

transformation. This expression is shown graphically in Fig. 3.1.2 and is sometimes referred to as the integral transform. This figure shows two distribution functions, one for X and one for Y, plotted side by side. The vertical axis on the left is the distribution function of X and the vertical axis on the right the distribution function of Y, both of which range from 0 to 1. When these distribution functions are set equal, the values on the vertical axes are equal, which is represented by the horizontal dashed line. For a given common value of the distribution functions there are a value of x and a value of y, labeled x_0 and y_0, that correspond to this distribution function value. This relationship between x_0 and y_0 and in general between x and y determines the transformation.

Example 3.1.6. Consider the random variable U (input random variable) that is uniformly distributed from 0 to 1, which is given as

$$f_U(u) = 1 \qquad 0 \le u \le 1$$
$$= 0 \qquad \text{otherwise}$$

and the transformed random variable X (output random variable) that is Rayleigh distributed as

$$f_X(x) = x \exp(-x^2/2) \qquad x \ge 0$$
$$= 0 \qquad\qquad\quad x < 0$$

Using Eq. (3.1.11),

$$F_U(u) = \int_0^u (1)\, dt = \int_0^x v \exp(-v^2/2)\, dv = F_X(x)$$

or

$$u = 1 - \exp(-x^2/2)$$

(do not forget the lower limits). Solving for x yields the desired transformation

$$x = \sqrt{-2\ln(1-u)}$$

Also, the transformation

$$x = \sqrt{-2\ln(u)}$$

will work, since, if U is uniformly distributed over the interval 0 to 1, so is $1 - U$. Using the first version of the transformation, if $u = 0.2$ (the probability of being less than or equal to 0.2 is 0.2 since U is uniformly distributed from 0 to 1), $x = 0.67$ (the probability of the Rayleigh random variable X being less than or equal to 0.67 is 0.2). Likewise, for $u = 0.5$, $x = 1.18$ and for $u = 0.8$, $x = 1.79$.   □

Consider another example of the integral transform with continuous random variables.

Example 3.1.7.   Let U be a uniform random variable from 0 to 1 again, but let X be a continuous random variable with the density function

$$f_X(x) = 6x/5 \qquad\quad 0 \le x < 1$$

$$= 6(2-x)^2/5 \qquad 1 \le x \le 2$$

$$= 0 \qquad\qquad\quad \text{otherwise}$$

which is shown in Fig. 3.1.3. Since the density function for X is described by two different functions, the transformation will also be described by two

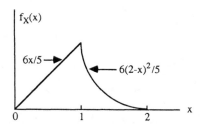

Fig. 3.1.3. Transformed density function.

different functions. Using Eq. (3.1.11) and with $F_U(u) = u$, $0 \le u \le 1$, for $0 \le x < 1$

$$u = \int_0^x \frac{6t}{5}\, dt = \frac{3t^2}{5}\bigg|_{t=0}^{t=x} = \frac{3x^2}{5}$$

or solving for x

$$x = \sqrt{5u/3} \qquad 0 \le u < 3/5$$

where the plus sign in front of the square root was chosen to yield the correct range of x. Over the range $1 \le x \le 2$

$$u = \frac{3}{5} + \int_{1}^{x} \frac{6}{5}(2-t)^2 \, dt = \frac{3}{5} - \frac{2}{5}(2-t)^3 \Big|_{t=1}^{t=x}$$

$$= \tfrac{3}{5} - \tfrac{2}{5}(2-x)^3 + \tfrac{2}{5} = 1 - \tfrac{2}{5}(2-x)^3$$

where the $\frac{3}{5}$ is the probability of being in the interval from 0 to 1 (since the distribution function is a cumulative probability). Solving for x yields

$$x = 2 - \sqrt[3]{\tfrac{5}{2}(1-u)} \qquad \tfrac{3}{5} \le u \le 1 \qquad \square$$

An example of obtaining discrete random variables from uniform random variables will now be considered.

Example 3.1.8.   It is desired to obtain Bernoulli random variables from uniform random variables. From Eq. (2.3.5),

$$P(X = x) = 1 - p \qquad x = 0$$

$$= p \qquad x = 1$$

$$= 0 \qquad \text{otherwise}$$

The distribution functions for this transformation are shown in Fig. 3.1.4.

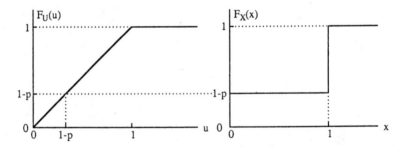

Fig. 3.1.4. Bernoulli random variable transformation.

For this transformation, $P(X = 0) = 1 - p = P(X \le x)$ for all x in the range $0 \le x < 1$, since the only value in this range with nonzero probability is 0. All values of u for which $F_U(u) \le 1 - p$ correspond to the single point $X = 0$. Also, the values of u for $1 - p < F_U(u) \le 1$ (which has probability p) are transformed into $X = 1$. Finally, since $F_U(u) = u$, $0 \le u \le 1$, the transformation is

$$x = 0 \qquad u \le 1 - p$$

$$= 1 \qquad u > 1 - p$$

This transformation illustrates a monotonically nondecreasing transformation where u cannot be uniquely expressed in terms of x. An equivalent transformation is

$$x = 0 \qquad u \geq p$$
$$= 1 \qquad u < p$$

since $P(X = 0) = 1 - p$ and $P(X = 1) = p$. $\square$

This transformation for Bernoulli random variables from uniform random variables is useful for generating random bits for communication systems and computer simulations.

Now consider two procedures for obtaining binomial random variables from uniform random variables.

Example 3.1.9. For the binomial random variable of Fig. 2.3.3,

$$P(Y = y) = C_y^5 (0.4)^y (0.6)^{5-y} \qquad y = 0, 1, 2, 3, 4, 5$$
$$= 0 \qquad\qquad\qquad \text{otherwise}$$

($N = 5$ and $p = 0.4$). The binomial variable Y can be obtained from the uniform random variables

$$x_i = 0 \qquad u_i \leq 0.6$$
$$= 1 \qquad u_i > 0.6 \quad i = 1, 2, 3, 4, 5$$

as

$$y = x_1 + x_2 + x_3 + x_4 + x_5 \qquad (3.1.12a)$$

since the X_i's are Bernoulli random variables. As an alternative, the binomial random variable can be obtained from one uniform random variable by using the integral transform directly. With the aid of the distribution function values of Fig. 2.3.3b

$$y = 0 \qquad u \leq 0.08$$
$$= 1 \qquad 0.08 < u \leq 0.34$$
$$= 2 \qquad 0.34 < u \leq 0.68$$
$$= 3 \qquad 0.68 < u \leq 0.91$$
$$= 4 \qquad 0.91 < u \leq 0.99$$
$$= 5 \qquad 0.99 < u \leq 1 \qquad (3.1.12b)$$

Even though the first way of generating the binomial random variable requires the sum of five uniform random variables, it is conceivably easier to implement than the second way due to the testing required to partition U.   □

Poisson random variables can be obtained from uniform random variables in a manner similar to Eq. (3.1.12b) (this is true for all discrete random variables), but would require an infinite partition (in practice this could be reduced to a large finite number) of U. Since Poisson random variables are important discrete random variables, an alternative method for obtaining Poisson random variables will now be given. Letting the Poisson random variable Y be the number of events (photons counted in a photomultiplier tube) occurring in a time interval of length T with the probability function given as

$$P(Y = k) = \frac{(aT)^k e^{-aT}}{k!} \qquad k = 0, 1, 2, \ldots \quad a > 0 \qquad (3.1.13)$$

If X_i is the time between events, Y would be the number of X_i's in the interval T. Now,

$$F_{X_i}(x_i) = P(X_i \le x_i) = P \text{ (at least one event in interval of duration } x_i)$$

$$= 1 - P \text{ (no events in interval of duration } x_i)$$

and using Eq. (3.1.13)

$$F_{X_i}(x_i) = 1 - e^{-ax_i} \qquad 0 \le x_i < \infty$$

The density function is obtained, by differentiating $F_{X_i}(x_i)$, as

$$f_{X_i}(x_i) = a e^{-ax_i} \qquad 0 \le x_i < \infty$$

which is an exponential density function. The exponential random variable X_i can be obtained from the uniform (over the interval from 0 to 1) random variable U_i, using the integral transform, as

$$x_i = -\ln(u_i)/a \qquad i = 1, 2, \ldots$$

The Poisson random variable Y is then the number of X_i's in the interval T, i.e., Y is the largest integer such that

$$\sum_{i=1}^{y} x_i \le T$$

The integral transform is then a convenient method of obtaining random variables with other density functions from the uniform random variable. This method is applicable as long as $F_X(x)$ can be evaluated in closed form. Unfortunately, for a Gaussian random variable its distribution function cannot be evaluated in closed form, and the integral transform cannot be used for obtaining Gaussian random variables. It is possible, though, to obtain pairs of Gaussian random variables from pairs of uniform random variables. Performing transformations on multiple random variables is more complicated than on single random variables, but due to the importance of Gaussian random variables, transformations on multiple random variables are considered in the next section.

3.2   One-to-One Transformation of Random Vectors

The method for manipulating one-to-one transformations of random vectors (multiple random variables) is entirely analogous to that for single random variables, with vector notation. The expression developed should be similar to Eq. (3.1.8) for the single-variable case, where the density functions are joint density functions and the derivative replaced by derivatives with respect to all of the variables of the vector.

Given the pair of random variables X_1 and X_2 which are jointly distributed with the probability density function $f_{X_1 X_2}(x_1, x_2)$, define two new random variables Y_1 and Y_2 by the bivariate one-to-one transformation

$$y_1 = g_1(x_1, x_2) \qquad y_2 = g_2(x_1, x_2)$$

A one-to-one transformation implies that a unique inverse exists, and this inverse is given as

$$x_1 = h_1(y_1, y_2) \qquad x_2 = h_2(y_1, y_2)$$

For the two-variable case, in general, two nonlinear equations are solved to obtain x_1 and x_2 [h_1 does not come directly from $y_1 = g_1(x_1, x_2)$]. In vector form

$$\mathbf{y} = \mathbf{g}(\mathbf{x}) \tag{3.2.1}$$

where

$$(y_1, y_2) = (g_1(x_1, x_2), g_2(x_1, x_2))$$

and

$$\mathbf{x} = \mathbf{g}^{-1}(\mathbf{y}) = \mathbf{h}(\mathbf{y}) \tag{3.2.2}$$

To determine the joint density function of Y_1 and Y_2 consider

$$F_{\mathbf{Y}}(\mathbf{y}) = F_{Y_1 Y_2}(y_1, y_2) = P(Y_1 \leq y_1, Y_2 \leq y_2)$$

$$= P[g_1(X_1, X_2) \leq y_1, g_2(X_1, X_2) \leq y_2]$$

$$= \iint\limits_{\mathbf{g}(\mathbf{x}) \leq \mathbf{y}} f_{X_1 X_2}(x_1, x_2) \, dx_1 \, dx_2 = \int \cdots \int\limits_{\mathbf{g}(\mathbf{x}) \leq \mathbf{y}} f_{\mathbf{X}}(\mathbf{x}) \, d\mathbf{x}$$

where $g(x) \le y$ means that each component of $g(x)$ is less than the corresponding component of y, i.e., for two components $g_1(x_1, x_2) \le y_1$ and $g_2(x_1, x_2) \le y_2$. Taking the derivative of the integral in this form with the constrained limits is extremely difficult, but with the proper change of variables it becomes a simple matter to take the derivative. The variables are changed so that the limits on the integrals are the limits for a distribution function; i.e., each limit goes from $-\infty$ to the appropriate y. Letting

$$\gamma = g(x) \qquad (\gamma_1, \gamma_2) = (g_1(x_1, x_2), g_2(x_1, x_2))$$

which yields

$$x = h(\gamma) \qquad (x_1, x_2) = (h_1(\gamma_1, \gamma_2), h_2(\gamma_1, \gamma_2))$$

and from multivariate calculus the differential volume dx is given in terms of the absolute value of the Jacobian of the change of variables and the differential volume $d\gamma$ as

$$dx = |J_h(\gamma)| \, d\gamma$$

The Jacobian of the change of variables is the determinant of the matrix $\{\partial h_i(\gamma)/\partial \gamma_j\}$ (a square matrix of all the partial derivatives of all the inverse transformations) or

$$J_h(\gamma) = |\{\partial h_i(\gamma)/\partial \gamma_j\}| \qquad (3.2.3)$$

This Jacobian which is due to the change of variables on the integration will be illustrated shortly. After this change of variables

$$F_{Y_1 Y_2}(y_1, y_2) = \int \cdots \int_{\gamma \le y} f_X(h(\gamma))|J_h(\gamma)| \, d\gamma$$

$$= \int_{-\infty}^{y_2} \int_{-\infty}^{y_1} f_{X_1 X_2}(h_1(\gamma_1, \gamma_2), h_2(\gamma_1, \gamma_2))|J_{h_1 h_2}(\gamma_1, \gamma_2)| \, d\gamma_1 \, d\gamma_2$$

The derivative of this integral is easy, since the derivative of an integral, whose lower limit is a constant and whose upper limit is the variable of the derivative, is the argument of the integral evaluated at the upper limit. The bivariate density function is obtained as

$$f_{Y_1 Y_2}(y_1, y_2) = \frac{\partial^2 F_{Y_1 Y_2}(y_1, y_2)}{\partial y_1 \, \partial y_2}$$

$$= f_{X_1 X_2}(h_1(y_1, y_2), h_2(y_1, y_2))|J_{h_1 h_2}(y_1, y_2)|$$

or

$$f_Y(y) = f_X(x)|_{x = h(y)}|J_h(y)| = f_X(h(y))|J_h(y)| \qquad (3.2.4a)$$

where $|\ |$ indicates magnitude and for two variables the Jacobian is given as

$$J_{\mathbf{h}}(\mathbf{y}) = J_{h_1 h_2}(y_1, y_2) = \begin{vmatrix} \dfrac{\partial h_1}{\partial y_1} & \dfrac{\partial h_1}{\partial y_2} \\[2mm] \dfrac{\partial h_2}{\partial y_1} & \dfrac{\partial h_2}{\partial y_2} \end{vmatrix} \tag{3.2.4b}$$

It can be observed that for a single variable Eq. (3.2.4) reduces to Eq. (3.1.8), i.e., a single-variable density function and a single derivative. If h_1 is a function only of y_1, h_2 is a function only of y_2, and X_1 and X_2 are statistically independent, Eq. (3.2.4b) reduces to the product

$$J_{\mathbf{h}}(\mathbf{y}) = \left(\frac{\partial h_1}{\partial y_1}\right)\left(\frac{\partial h_2}{\partial y_2}\right)$$

and Eq. (3.2.4a) is completely separable as

$$f_{\mathbf{Y}}(\mathbf{y}) = f_{X_1}(h_1(y_1)) \left|\frac{\partial h_1}{\partial y_1}\right| f_{X_2}(h_2(y_2)) \left|\frac{\partial h_2}{\partial y_2}\right|$$

$$= f_{Y_1}(y_1) f_{Y_2}(y_2)$$

Thus, Y_1 and Y_2 are statistically independent and Eq. (3.1.8) (for single-variable transformations) could have been used on each variable. For these cases Eq. (3.2.4) is consistent with the single-variable transformation.

The main reason for considering vector transformations was to develop a transformation to obtain Gaussian random variables from uniform random variables. The transformation that yields pairs of uniform random variables from pairs of Gaussian random variables will now be considered. This is the transformation from rectangular to polar coordinates, i.e., from the random variables X and Y to the random variables R and Θ, which is given as

$$r = \sqrt{x^2 + y^2} = g_1(x, y)$$

$$\theta = \tan^{-1}\left(\frac{y}{x}\right) = g_2(x, y)$$

(in this example X and Y correspond to the input random variables X_1 and X_2 and R and Θ correspond to the output random variables Y_1 and Y_2), and the input density function is the bivariate Gaussian given as

$$f_{XY}(x, y) = \frac{1}{2\pi} e^{-(x^2+y^2)/2} \qquad -\infty < x < \infty \quad -\infty < y < \infty$$

The Gaussian random variables X and Y are statistically independent and normalized (mean 0 and variance 1). Now, the inverse transformation is

$$x = r \cos \theta = h_1(r, \theta)$$

$$y = r \sin \theta = h_2(r, \theta)$$

and the Jacobian of the transformation is obtained as

$$J_{h_1 h_2}(r, \theta) = \begin{vmatrix} \dfrac{\partial h_1}{\partial r} & \dfrac{\partial h_1}{\partial \theta} \\ \dfrac{\partial h_2}{\partial r} & \dfrac{\partial h_2}{\partial \theta} \end{vmatrix} = \begin{vmatrix} \cos \theta & -r \sin \theta \\ \sin \theta & r \cos \theta \end{vmatrix} = r$$

This result justifies the relationship of the differential surfaces in rectangular and polar coordinates, $dx\, dy = r\, dr\, d\theta$. The joint density function for R and Θ is then given as

$$f_{R\Theta}(r, \theta) = f_{XY}(r \cos \theta, r \sin \theta) |J_{h_1 h_2}(r, \theta)|$$

$$= \frac{1}{2\pi} e^{-(r^2 \cos^2 \theta + r^2 \sin^2 \theta)/2} (r)$$

and finally

$$f_{R\Theta}(r, \theta) = \frac{r}{2\pi} e^{-r^2/2} \qquad 0 \le r < \infty \quad 0 \le \theta < 2\pi$$

where the ranges for r and θ are obtained from the rectangular-to-polar transformation and the ranges of x and y.

The marginal density functions for R and Θ are obtained by integrating out the unwanted variable. It is easily verified that

$$f_R(r) = r e^{-r^2/2} \qquad r \ge 0$$

and

$$f_\Theta(\theta) = \frac{1}{2\pi} \qquad 0 \le \theta < 2\pi$$

Since the joint density function $f_{R\Theta}(r, \theta)$ is the product of the marginal density functions $f_R(r)$ and $f_\Theta(\theta)$, the random variables R and Θ are statistically independent. R is a Rayleigh random variable with parameter $b = 1$ (obtained as the square root of the sum of the squares of two independent normalized Gaussian random variables) and Θ is a uniform random variable over the interval from 0 to 2π. Both R and Θ can be obtained directly from uniform random variables by using the integral transform. The transformation for the Rayleigh random variable has been done previously and in terms of the variables used here

$$r = \sqrt{-2 \ln(1 - u_1)}$$

where

$$f_{U_i}(u_i) = 1 \qquad 0 \le u_i < 1 \quad i = 1, 2$$

$$= 0 \qquad \text{otherwise}$$

Likewise, the transformation for the uniform random variable, which is a linear transformation from the uniform 0 to 1 random variable, is

$$\theta = 2\pi u_2$$

This development has shown that two uniform random variables can be obtained from two Gaussian random variables, but since the transformation is reversible, two Gaussian random variables can be obtained from two uniform random variables. If this transformation were performed in the forward manner the Jacobian would require the derivatives of $r = (x^2 + y^2)^{1/2}$ and $\theta = \tan^{-1}(y/x)$ with respect to x and y.

The Jacobians for the forward and reverse transformation are related as

$$J_h(\mathbf{y}) = \frac{1}{J_g(\mathbf{x})}\bigg|_{\mathbf{x} = h(\mathbf{y})} \qquad \text{or} \qquad J_g(\mathbf{x}) = \frac{1}{J_h(\mathbf{y})}\bigg|_{\mathbf{y} = g(\mathbf{x})}$$

For the case here

$$dr\, d\theta = \frac{1}{r}\bigg|_{r = \sqrt{x^2 + y^2}} dx\, dy = \frac{dx\, dy}{\sqrt{x^2 + y^2}}$$

In conclusion, the statistically independent random variables R and Θ are obtained from the statistically independent uniform random variables U_1 and U_2 as

$$r = \sqrt{-2\ln(1 - u_1)} \tag{3.2.5a}$$

$$\theta = 2\pi u_2 \tag{3.2.5b}$$

Then the statistically independent Gaussian random variables X and Y are obtained from R and Θ as

$$x = r\cos\theta \tag{3.2.6a}$$

$$y = r\sin\theta \tag{3.2.6b}$$

Combining these two steps yields

$$x = \sqrt{-2\ln(1 - u_1)}\,\cos(2\pi u_2) \tag{3.2.7a}$$

$$y = \sqrt{-2\ln(1 - u_1)}\,\sin(2\pi u_2) \tag{3.2.7b}$$

This method of obtaining Gaussian random variables is called the Box-Muller method. Even though it was not possible to obtain a single Gaussian random variable from a single uniform random variable, pairs of Gaussian random variables could be obtained from pairs of uniform random variables.

The linear transformation of Eq. (3.1.9) can be used to obtain Gaussian random variables with any desired μ and σ^2 from the normalized Gaussian random variables of Eq. (3.2.7).

An alternative procedure for obtaining statistically independent normalized Gaussian random variables X and Y from the statistically independent 0 to 1 uniform random variables U_1 and U_2 is now given. Obtain the random variables V_1 and V_2 from the transformation

$$v_1 = 2u_1 - 1 \qquad v_2 = 2u_2 - 1$$

and obtain the random variable S from

$$s = v_1^2 + v_2^2$$

Now if $s \geq 1$ discard the current v_1 and v_2 and get a new v_1, v_2 pair. When $s < 1$ the statistically independent normalized Gaussian random variables X and Y are obtained from

$$x = v_1\sqrt{-2\ln(s)/s} \qquad (3.2.8a)$$

$$y = v_2\sqrt{-2\ln(s)/s} \qquad (3.2.8b)$$

The advantage of Eq. (3.2.8) is that it does not require the calculations of the sine and cosine, but its disadvantage is that it requires approximately 27% more U_1, U_2 pairs. The derivation of Eq. (3.2.8) would present the interested student with a challenge.

Consider an example of a two-dimensional linear transformation.

Example   3.2.1. Determine $f_{Y_1Y_2}(y_1, y_2)$ for $f_{X_1X_2}(x_1, x_2) = [1/(2\pi)]\exp[-(x_1^2+x_2^2)/2]$, $-\infty < x_1 < \infty$, $-\infty < x_2 < \infty$, and the linear transformation $y_1 = x_1 + x_2$ and $y_2 = 3x_1 + 2x_2$. Solving $y_1 = x_1 + x_2 = g_1(x_1, x_2)$ and $y_2 = 3x_1 + 2x_2 = g_2(x_1, x_2)$ for x_1 and x_2 yields $x_1 = y_2 - 2y_1 = h_1(y_1, y_2)$ and $x_2 = 3y_1 - y_2 = h_2(y_1, y_2)$. The Jacobian of the transformation, using Eq. (3.2.4b), is then

$$J_{h_1h_2}(y_1, y_2) = \begin{vmatrix} \dfrac{\partial(y_2-2y_1)}{\partial y_1} & \dfrac{\partial(y_2-2y_1)}{\partial y_2} \\ \dfrac{\partial(3y_1-y_2)}{\partial y_1} & \dfrac{\partial(3y_1-y_2)}{\partial y_2} \end{vmatrix} = \begin{vmatrix} -2 & 1 \\ 3 & -1 \end{vmatrix} = -1$$

Finally, $f_{Y_1Y_2}(y_1, y_2)$ is obtained, using Eq. (3.2.4a), as

$$f_{Y_1Y_2}(y_1, y_2) = \frac{1}{2\pi} e^{-((y_2-2y_1)^2+(3y_1-y_2)^2)/2}$$

$$= \frac{1}{2\pi} e^{-(13y_1^2-10y_1y_2+2y_2^2)/2} \qquad -\infty < y_1 < \infty \quad -\infty < y_2 < \infty \qquad \square$$

3.3   Non-One-to-One Transformation

For a transformation that is not one-to-one, the transformation will be broken up into transformations each of which is one-to-one. Given the X_i's, $i = 1, \ldots, k$, jointly distributed random variables with joint density function $f_{\mathbf{X}}(\mathbf{x})$, define k new random variables Y_i such that $y_i = g_i(\mathbf{x})$, $i = 1, \ldots, k$, or $\mathbf{y} = \mathbf{g}(\mathbf{x})$. Let A be the k-dimensional space on $\mathbf{X}$ and B the k-dimensional space on $\mathbf{Y}$. Now partition A as shown in Fig. 3.3.1 such that $A_i \cap A_j = \varnothing$, $i \neq j = 1, \ldots, n$, $A_1 \cup A_2 \cup \cdots \cup A_n = A$, and $x_i = h_{ij}(\mathbf{y})$, $j = 1, \ldots, n$, $i = 1, \ldots, k$, or $\mathbf{x} = \mathbf{h}_j(\mathbf{y})$, $j = 1, \ldots, n$, defines a one-to-one transformation of each A_j onto B.

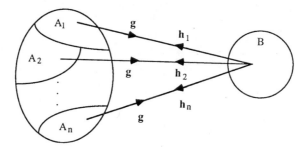

Fig. 3.3.1. Partitioning for non-one-to-one transformation.

The density function of $\mathbf{y}$ is given as

$$f_{\mathbf{Y}}(\mathbf{y}) = \frac{\partial^k F_{\mathbf{Y}}(\mathbf{y})}{\partial y_1 \cdots \partial y_k} = \frac{\partial^k P(\mathbf{Y} \le \mathbf{y})}{\partial y_1 \cdots \partial y_k} = \frac{\partial^k P[\mathbf{g}(\mathbf{X}) \le \mathbf{y}]}{\partial y_1 \cdots \partial y_k}$$

Let $C = \{\mathbf{g}(\mathbf{X}) \le \mathbf{y}\}$ and $C \subset A$, then

$$C = C \cap A = C \cap \left(\bigcup_{j=1}^{n} A_j \right) = \bigcup_{j=1}^{n} (C \cap A_j)$$

Since the $(C \cap A_j)$'s are mutually exclusive

$$f_{\mathbf{Y}}(\mathbf{y}) = \frac{\partial^k}{\partial y_1 \cdots \partial y_k} \left[\sum_{j=1}^{n} P(\mathbf{g}(\mathbf{X}) \le \mathbf{y}, \mathbf{X} \in A_j) \right]$$

or

$$f_{\mathbf{Y}}(\mathbf{y}) = \frac{\partial^k}{\partial y_1 \cdots \partial y_k} \left[\sum_{j=1}^{n} \int_{\substack{\mathbf{g}(\mathbf{x}) \le \mathbf{y} \\ \mathbf{x} \in A_j}} \cdots \int f_{\mathbf{X}}(\mathbf{x}) \, d\mathbf{x} \right]$$

Letting $\boldsymbol{\gamma} = \mathbf{g}(\mathbf{x})$ and $\mathbf{x} = \mathbf{h}_j(\boldsymbol{\gamma})$ for $\mathbf{x} \in A_j$, this change of variables yields

$dx = |J_{h_j}(\gamma)| \, d\gamma$. Thus

$$f_Y(y) = \frac{\partial^k}{\partial y_1 \cdots \partial y_k} \left[\sum_{j=1}^{n} \int_{-\infty}^{y_1} \cdots \int_{-\infty}^{y_k} f_X(\mathbf{h}_j(\gamma))|J_{h_j}(\gamma)| \, d\gamma \right]$$

and finally

$$f_Y(y) = \sum_{j=1}^{n} f_X(\mathbf{h}_j(y))|J_{h_j}(y)| \tag{3.3.1}$$

which is a direct extension of Eq. (3.2.4) by summing each one-to-one transformation.

Consider the squaring transformation where $y = x^2$. This operation can be found by operating in the nonlinear region of a diode and can be used to generate some forms of amplitude modulation. This transformation is not one-to-one and in fact is a two-to-one transformation (e.g., both -2 and $+2$ transform into $+4$). Using Eq. (3.3.1), $n = 2$, $k = 1$, $A = \{-\infty < x < \infty\}$, $B = \{0 \le y < \infty\}$, $A_1 = \{0 \le x < \infty\}$, and $A_2 = \{-\infty < x < 0\}$. Then,

$$x = +\sqrt{y} = h_1(y) \qquad \text{and} \qquad x = -\sqrt{y} = h_2(y)$$

which yields

$$|J_{h_1}(y)| = |\tfrac{1}{2}y^{-1/2}| = \frac{1}{2\sqrt{y}}$$

and

$$|J_{h_2}(y)| = |-\tfrac{1}{2}y^{-1/2}| = \frac{1}{2\sqrt{y}}$$

Thus, the squaring transformation yields

$$f_Y(y) = \frac{1}{2\sqrt{y}} [f_X(\sqrt{y}) + f_X(-\sqrt{y})] \qquad 0 < y < \infty \tag{3.3.2}$$

This expression can be derived directly from Eq. (3.1.2a) as

$$F_Y(y) = P(X^2 \le y) = P(-\sqrt{y} \le X \le \sqrt{y})$$
$$= F_X(x = \sqrt{y}) - F_X(x = -\sqrt{y}) \qquad y > 0$$

(this assumes there is no discrete probability at $x = -\sqrt{y}$). The density function of Y is obtained, by using the chain rule for differentiating $F_Y(y)$ or using Leibnitz's rule on the equivalent integral, as

$$f_Y(y) = f_X(\sqrt{y}) \frac{d(\sqrt{y})}{dy} - f_X(-\sqrt{y}) \frac{d(-\sqrt{y})}{dy} \qquad y > 0$$

$$= \frac{1}{2\sqrt{y}} [f_X(\sqrt{y}) + f_X(-\sqrt{y})] \qquad y > 0$$

which is Eq. (3.3.2).

Example 3.3.1.   Consider the squaring transformation on a Gaussian random variable. For X a normalized Gaussian random variable

$$f_X(x) = \frac{1}{\sqrt{2\pi}} e^{-x^2/2} \qquad -\infty < x < \infty$$

The density function of the squared random variable Y is, from Eq. (3.3.2), given as

$$f_Y(y) = \frac{1}{\sqrt{2\pi y}} e^{-y/2} \qquad 0 < y < \infty \qquad \square$$

Another non-one-to-one transformation is the cosine transformation given as $y = \cos(x) = g(x)$, which yields the random variable Y. If X is a random variable distributed over the interval from 0 to 2π, the cosine transforms two values of X into one value of Y. For $0 \le x < \pi$ the inverse transformation is

$$x = \cos^{-1}(y) = h_1(y)$$

and for $\pi \le x < 2\pi$ the inverse transformation is

$$x = 2\pi - \cos^{-1}(y) = h_2(y)$$

The density function of Y, using Eq. (3.3.1), is obtained as

$$f_Y(y) = f_X(\cos^{-1}(y)) \left| \frac{d(\cos^{-1}(y))}{dy} \right| + f_X(2\pi - \cos^{-1}(y)) \left| \frac{d(2\pi - \cos^{-1}(y))}{dy} \right|$$

which reduces to

$$f_Y(y) = [f_X(\cos^{-1}(y)) + f_X(2\pi - \cos^{-1}(y))] \frac{1}{\sqrt{1-y^2}} \qquad (3.3.3)$$

Example 3.3.2.   Consider the cosine transform on the random variable X which is uniformly distributed over the interval from 0 to 2π. Then,

$$f_X(x) = \frac{1}{2\pi} \qquad 0 \le x < 2\pi$$

$$= 0 \qquad \text{otherwise}$$

and $f_Y(y)$, using Eq. (3.3.3), reduces to

$$f_Y(y) = \frac{1}{\pi\sqrt{1-y^2}} \qquad -1 \le y \le 1$$

$$= 0 \qquad \text{otherwise}$$

This is the density function of the random variable that is the cosine of a uniform random phase and is called an arcsine random variable. $\square$

The same density function of Example 3.3.2 can be shown to hold for the sine of a uniform random phase. For either the cosine or the sine, with a random phase uniformly distributed over any continuous interval of an integer multiple of length 2π (or appropriately defined integer multiple of π), the cosine or the sine random variable has an arcsine density function. This is true since as the number of terms in Eq. (3.3.1), n, (multiple of π) increases, the constant in the uniform phase density function decreases by the same factor n, leaving the density function of the cosine or the sine unaltered.

3.4 Sum of Random Variables

One of the most important functions of random variables is their sum. The sum of two random variables will be considered first, and the results generalized for the sum of any number of random variables. This generalization can be obtained as an iterative procedure, where the density function for the sum of three random variables is developed from the sum of the third and the previously developed sum of the first two, etc.

Consider the random variable Z obtained from the sum

$$z = x + y = g_1(x, y)$$

This transformation does not fit the mold of transformations that have been considered previously, since it is a transformation from two random variables to one random variable. In addition the inverse function is ill-defined. The density function of Z can be obtained by using conditional density functions, but the approach used here will be to define a second random variable W with the transformation $w = g_2(x, y)$ such that the pair $z = g_1(x, y)$ and $w = g_2(x, y)$ form a one-to-one transformation. The inverse functions $x = h_1(w, z)$ and $y = h_2(w, z)$ are determined, and $f_{WZ}(w, z)$ obtained from Eq. (3.2.4) for a two-dimensional transformation. The desired density function $f_Z(z)$ is then a marginal density function and is obtained by integrating $f_{WZ}(w, z)$ over all values of w. Since the desired result does not involve w, there are many possible valid choices for w. To facilitate this development a simple transformation is chosen as

$$w = x = g_2(x, y)$$

which makes it easy to determine the inverse transformation as

$$x = w = h_1(w, z) \qquad y = z - w = h_2(w, z)$$

The Jacobian for this transformation is

$$J_{h_1 h_2}(w, z) = \begin{vmatrix} \dfrac{\partial h_1(w, z)}{\partial w} & \dfrac{\partial h_1(w, z)}{\partial z} \\[2mm] \dfrac{\partial h_2(w, z)}{\partial w} & \dfrac{\partial h_2(w, z)}{\partial z} \end{vmatrix} = \begin{vmatrix} 1 & 0 \\ -1 & 1 \end{vmatrix} = 1$$

which yields

$$f_{WZ}(w, z) = f_{XY}(x, y)\big|_{x = h_1 = w, \, y = h_2 = z - w} = f_{XY}(w, z - w)$$

Then the marginal density function for Z can be expressed as

$$f_Z(z) = \int_{-\infty}^{\infty} f_{XY}(w, z - w)\, dw = \int_{-\infty}^{\infty} f_{XY}(x, z - x)\, dx \qquad (3.4.1)$$

where the second integral is written in terms of one of the original variables, since in this case w and x are dummy variables of the integration. This integral can be viewed as averaging the joint density function over all combinations of x and y with the constraint that $y = z - x$.

For X and Y statistically independent random variables, the joint density function factors into the product of the marginal density functions, and Eq. (3.4.1) reduces to

$$f_Z(z) = \int_{-\infty}^{\infty} f_X(x) f_Y(z - x)\, dx \qquad (3.4.2a)$$

which is known as a convolution integral. This integral can be thought of as obtaining the area of the product of two functions, one of which is as given and the other is shifted and rotated, with the area being a function of how much the second function is shifted, which is z. By interchanging X and Y in the above derivation, the alternative form of the convolution integral is given as

$$f_Z(z) = \int_{-\infty}^{\infty} f_X(z - y) f_Y(y)\, dy \qquad (3.4.2b)$$

The convolution integral is also of importance in linear system analysis, where the output of a linear system is given as the convolution of the input with the impulse response of the system.

Several examples will be given to illustrate the evaluation of the convolution integral of Eq. (3.4.2).

Example 3.4.1. For X and Y statistically independent normalized Gaussian random variables, the density functions are given as

$$f_X(x) = \frac{1}{\sqrt{2\pi}}\, e^{-x^2/2} \qquad -\infty < x < \infty$$

and

$$f_Y(y) = \frac{1}{\sqrt{2\pi}} e^{-y^2/2} \qquad -\infty < y < \infty$$

The density function of the sum $Z = X + Y$ can be expressed, using Eq. (3.4.2a), as

$$f_Z(z) = \int_{-\infty}^{\infty} \frac{1}{\sqrt{2\pi}} e^{-x^2/2} \frac{1}{\sqrt{2\pi}} e^{-(z-x)^2/2} \, dx$$

and by completing the square in the exponent on x, becomes

$$f_Z(z) = \frac{1}{\sqrt{4\pi}} e^{-z^2/2} \int_{-\infty}^{\infty} \frac{1}{\sqrt{2\pi(\frac{1}{2})}} e^{-(x-z/2)^2/2(1/2)} \, dx$$

The integral is 1 since it is over the entire range of a Gaussian density function (with mean $z/2$ and variance $\frac{1}{2}$). The density function of Z reduces to

$$f_Z(z) = \frac{1}{\sqrt{4\pi}} e^{-z^2/4} \qquad -\infty < z < \infty$$

Thus, Z is also Gaussian with mean 0, but the variance has increased from 1 to 2. ☐

The sum of Gaussian random variables with nonzero means and nonunity variances will be generalized in Chapter 4. Setting up the integral in Example 3.4.1 was easy since both variables in the sum ranged over $-\infty$ to ∞. When the limits of one or both of the variables are finite, care has to be taken to ensure the correct limits.

Next consider the sum of two random variables with semi-infinite ranges.

Example 3.4.2. Let X and Y be statistically independent exponential random variables with

$$f_X(x) = e^{-x} \qquad x \geq 0$$
$$= 0 \qquad \text{otherwise}$$

and

$$f_Y(y) = e^{-y} \qquad y \geq 0$$
$$= 0 \qquad \text{otherwise}$$

The product terms $f_X(x)$ and $f_Y(z-x)$ are shown plotted on the same axis in Fig. 3.4.1 for $z > 0$. The shifted and rotated density function for Y has its peak value at $x = z$ (due to the shift) and drops off to the left (due to the rotation). The convolution integral gives the area of the product of the two functions for all values of z. From Fig. 3.4.1 it can be seen that the

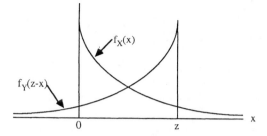

Fig. 3.4.1. Convolution of two exponential density functions.

product is zero for $z < 0$ (the functions do not overlap). For $z \geq 0$ the limits of integration are from 0 to z (product is nonzero over this range), and the density function of Z is evaluated as

$$f_Z(z) = \int_0^z e^{-x} e^{-(z-x)} \, dx = e^{-z} \int_0^z dx = z \, e^{-z}$$

which is a gamma density function. Combining the ranges gives

$$f_Z(z) = z \, e^{-z} \qquad z \geq 0$$

$$= 0 \qquad \text{otherwise} \qquad \square$$

The limits on the convolution integral are the limits (z replaced by t) in most convolution integrals for the output of a linear system, since the input function usually starts at 0 and goes to ∞ and the impulse response of a real system starts at 0 and goes to ∞.

The next example is one with finite limits for both density functions of the sum.

Example 3.4.3. For X and Y statistically independent consider

$$f_X(x) = 1 \qquad 0 \leq x \leq 1$$

$$= 0 \qquad \text{otherwise}$$

and

$$f_Y(y) = y/2 \qquad 0 \leq y \leq 2$$

$$= 0 \qquad \text{otherwise}$$

The alternative form of the convolution integral where x is shifted and rotated, Eq. (3.4.2b), will be used here. The product terms $f_X(z-y)$ and $f_Y(y)$ are shown plotted on the same axis for $0 \leq z < 1$ in Fig. 3.4.2a and for $1 \leq z < 2$ in Fig. 3.4.2b. From Fig. 3.4.2 it can be seen that the leading edge of the square pulse (shifted and rotated pulse) is always z no matter where it is drawn and the trailing edge is always $z - 1$. For $z < 0$ the square

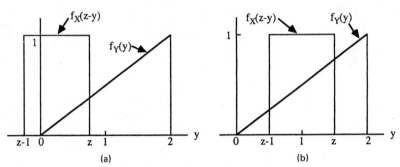

Fig. 3.4.2. Convolution of a square and a triangular density function: (a) $0 \leq z < 1$; (b) $1 \leq z < 2$.

pulse is to the left of the triangular pulse, and since there is no overlap $f_Z(z) = 0$. Likewise, for $z - 1 > 2$ or $z > 3$ the square pulse is to the right of the triangular pulse, there is no overlap, and again $f_Z(z) = 0$. For $0 \leq z < 1$, Fig. 3.4.2a, the limits of integration are from 0 to z (product is nonzero over this range), and the density function of Z is evaluated as

$$f_Z(z) = \int_0^z (1)\left(\frac{y}{2}\right) dy = \frac{z^2}{4}$$

When $1 \leq z < 2$, Fig. 3.4.2b, the limits of integration are from $z - 1$ to z (product is nonzero over this range), and the density function of Z is evaluated as

$$f_Z(z) = \int_{z-1}^z (1)\left(\frac{y}{2}\right) dy = \frac{2z - 1}{4}$$

The last range $2 \leq z \leq 3$, not shown, is the case of the square pulse partially overlapping the triangular pulse on the right. The limits of integration are from $z - 1$ to 2 and the density function of Z is evaluated as

$$f_Z(z) = \int_{z-1}^2 (1)\frac{y}{2} dy = \frac{-z^2 + 2z + 3}{4}$$

Note that the integrand is the same for all of the ranges. Combining all the ranges, $f_Z(z)$ is given as

$$
\begin{aligned}
f_Z(z) &= 0 & z &< 0 \\[4pt]
&= \frac{z^2}{4} & 0 &\leq z < 1 \\[4pt]
&= \frac{2z - 1}{4} & 1 &\leq z < 2 \\[4pt]
&= \frac{-z^2 + 2z + 3}{4} & 2 &\leq z \leq 3 \\[4pt]
&= 0 & z &> 3
\end{aligned}
$$

Even though the equalities are not included at all of the end points of the different segments $f_Z(z)$ is a continuous function (this is not true if there is a discrete probability at these points).   □

Now consider the sum of uniformly distributed random variables. Let X_i, $i = 1, 2, 3$, be statistically independent uniform random variables from 0 to 1, where

$$f_{X_i}(x_i) = 1 \qquad 0 \le x_i < 1 \quad i = 1, 2, 3$$

$$= 0 \qquad \text{otherwise}$$

The density function for the random variable Z_2, where $z_2 = x_1 + x_2$, can be determined as

$$f_{Z_2}(z_2) = z_2 \qquad 0 \le z_2 \le 1$$

$$= 2 - z_2 \qquad 1 \le z_2 \le 2$$

$$= 0 \qquad \text{otherwise}$$

and the density function for the random variable Z_3, where $z_3 = z_2 + x_3 = x_1 + x_2 + x_3$, determined as

$$f_{Z_3}(z_3) = \tfrac{1}{2}z_3^2 \qquad 0 \le z_3 \le 1$$

$$= \tfrac{1}{2}(-2z_3^2 + 6z_3 - 3) \qquad 1 \le z_3 \le 2$$

$$= \tfrac{1}{2}(3 - z_3)^2 \qquad 2 \le z_3 \le 3$$

$$= 0 \qquad \text{otherwise}$$

The density function for Z_2 is shown in Fig. 3.4.3a and the density function for Z_3 in Fig. 3.4.3b. The density function of a uniform random variable is far from looking Gaussian, but the density function of the sum of uniform random variables, even for just three random variables, as shown in Fig. 3.4.3b, starts to look Gaussian. This tendency, as stated earlier, is an illustration of the central limit theorem.

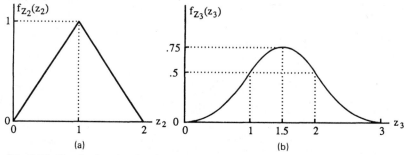

Fig. 3.4.3. Density function for the sum of uniform random variables: (a) two uniforms; (b) three uniforms.

Appendix B gives derivations for the density function for the sum Z_N of N statistically independent random variables uniformly distributed from 0 to 1, the distribution function for this sum, and for a normalized version of this sum W_N obtained as $W_N = (Z_N - N/2)/\sqrt{N/12}$. The normalized sum W_N has zero mean and variance 1 to facilitate direct comparison with the normalized Gaussian density function. This comparison is made in Fig. B.1 for several values of N to illustrate the central limit theorem. If Gaussian random variables are approximated by summing up uniform random variables, a good question is, what value of N should be used? One such generator uses $N = 12$, but this seems to be more of a choice to eliminate the square root in W_N than to make a good approximation to Gaussian random variables. Care should be taken not to blindly invoke the central limit theorem.

Consider the sum of two discrete random variables. The discrete version of convolution [of Eq. (3.4.2)] for the sum random variable Z obtained as $Z = X + Y$, in terms of the probability functions $P(X = i)$ and $P(Y = j)$ where X and Y are statistically independent, is given as

$$P(Z = k) = \sum_{i=-\infty}^{\infty} P(X = i)P(Y = k - i) \qquad (3.4.3a)$$

and

$$P(Z = k) = \sum_{j=-\infty}^{\infty} P(X = k - j)P(Y = j) \qquad (3.4.3b)$$

Example 3.4.4. Let X and Y be statistically independent binomial random variables, where $N = 3$ and $p = 0.4$ for X and $N = 2$ and $p = 0.4$ for Y. The probability functions are given, using Eq. (2.3.6), as

$$P(X = i) = C_i^3 (0.4)^i (0.6)^{3-i} \qquad i = 0, 1, 2, 3$$

$$P(Y = j) = C_j^2 (0.4)^j (0.6)^{2-j} \qquad j = 0, 1, 2$$

The product terms $P(X = i)$ and $P(Y = k - i)$ are shown plotted on the same axis in Fig. 3.4.4 for $0 \le k \le 1$. From this figure it is seen that the

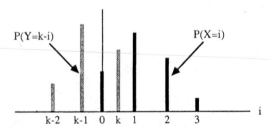

Fig. 3.4.4. Convolution of two binomial probability functions.

product is 0 except for $k = 0, 1, 2, 3, 4, 5$ (as would be expected for the sum of two integers). The probabilities $P(Z = k)$, $k = 0, 1, 2, 3, 4, 5$, are calculated as

$$P(Z = 0) = P(X = 0)P(Y = 0) = (0.216)(0.36) = 0.07776$$

$$P(Z = 1) = P(X = 1)P(Y = 0) + P(X = 0)P(Y = 1)$$

$$= (0.432)(0.36) + (0.216)(0.48) = 0.2592$$

$$P(Z = 2) = P(X = 2)P(Y = 0) + P(X = 1)P(Y = 1) + P(X = 0)P(Y = 2)$$

$$= (0.288)(0.36) + (0.432)(0.48) + (0.216)(0.16) = 0.3456$$

$$P(Z = 3) = P(X = 3)P(Y = 0) + P(X = 2)P(Y = 1) + P(X = 1)P(Y = 2)$$

$$= (0.064)(0.36) + (0.288)(0.48) + (0.432)(0.16) = 0.2304$$

$$P(Z = 4) = P(X = 3)P(Y = 1) + P(X = 2)P(Y = 2)$$

$$= (0.064)(0.48) + (0.288)(0.16) = 0.0768$$

$$P(Z = 5) = P(X = 3)P(Y = 2) = (0.064)(0.16) = 0.01024$$

In this case the probability function for Z turns out to be binomial with $N = 5$ and $p = 0.4$ or

$$P(Z = k) = C_k^5 (0.4)^k (0.6)^{5-k} \qquad k = 0, 1, 2, 3, 4, 5$$

$$= 0 \qquad\qquad \text{otherwise} \qquad \square$$

Example 3.4.5. Let p be different for the binomial random variables of Example 3.4.4. With $N = 3$ and $p = 0.4$ for X and $N = 2$ and $p = 0.2$ for Y the probability function for Y is given as

$$P(Y = j) = C_j^2 (0.2)^j (0.8)^{2-j} \qquad j = 0, 1, 2$$

In the same manner as in Example 3.4.4 the probabilities of the random variable Z, where $z = x + y$, are obtained as $P(Z = 0) = 0.13824$, $P(Z = 1) = 0.3456$, $P(Z = 2) = 0.3312$, $P(Z = 3) = 0.1504$, $P(Z = 4) = 0.032$, and $P(Z = 5) = 0.00256$. For this to be a binomial probability distribution, the binomial random variable W would have $N = 5$ and a value of p obtained from $P(W = 5) = p^5 = 0.00256$ or $p = 0.3031$. With $p = 0.3031$, $P(W = 0) = 0.1643$, $P(W = 1) = 0.3574$, $P(W = 2) = 0.3110$, $P(W = 3) = 0.1353$, and $P(W = 4) = 0.0294$. Thus, $P(Z = k)$ is not a binomial probability function and Z is not a binomial random variable. $\quad \square$

It will be shown in Section 4.3 that the only way for the sum of two statistically independent binomial random variables to be a binomial random variable is for the parameter p to be the same for both binomial random variables in the sum.

Consider the sum of two statistically independent Poisson random variables whose probability functions are given as

$$P(X = i) = \frac{e^{-a}a^i}{i!} \qquad i = 0, 1, 2, \ldots$$

$$P(Y = j) = \frac{e^{-b}b^j}{j!} \qquad j = 0, 1, 2, \ldots$$

The probability function of the sum random variable Z, where $z = x + y$, is obtained by convolution as

$$P(Z = k) = \sum_{i=0}^{k} P(X = i)P(Y = k - i) = \sum_{i=0}^{k} \left[\frac{e^{-a}a^i}{i!}\right]\left[\frac{e^{-b}b^{k-i}}{(k-i)!}\right]$$

$$= e^{-(a+b)} \sum_{i=0}^{k} \frac{a^i b^{k-i}}{i!(k-i)!} = \frac{e^{-(a+b)}}{k!} \sum_{i=0}^{k} C_i^k a^i b^{k-i}$$

Using the binomial theorem of Eq. (2.3.7) on the summation yields

$$P(Z = k) = \frac{e^{-(a+b)}(a+b)^k}{k!}$$

Thus the sum of two Poisson random variables is also a Poisson random variable with the parameter $a + b$.

The density function of the sum of random variables is important, as has been stated, but there are others that deserve some consideration. Additional transformations are considered in the next section.

3.5 Special Transformations

Consider the product Z of the random variables X and Y given by the transformation $z = xy = g_1(x, y)$. The density function for the product can be obtained in a manner similar to that for the sum. As before, choose the random variable W where $w = x = g_2(x, y)$. This yields the inverse transformation as

$$x = w = h_1(w, z) \qquad y = z/w = h_2(w, z)$$

The Jacobian of this transformation is

$$J_{h_1 h_2}(w, z) = \begin{vmatrix} \dfrac{\partial h_1}{\partial w} & \dfrac{\partial h_1}{\partial z} \\ \dfrac{\partial h_2}{\partial w} & \dfrac{\partial h_2}{\partial z} \end{vmatrix} = \begin{vmatrix} 1 & 0 \\ \dfrac{-z}{w^2} & \dfrac{1}{w} \end{vmatrix} = \frac{1}{w}$$

Then the joint density function of W and Z becomes

$$f_{WZ}(w, z) = f_{XY}\left(w, \frac{z}{w}\right)\left|\frac{1}{w}\right|$$

and the marginal density function of Z is obtained as

$$f_Z(z) = \int_{-\infty}^{\infty} \frac{1}{|x|} f_{XY}\left(x, \frac{z}{x}\right) dx \qquad (3.5.1)$$

where w has been replaced by x. For X and Y statistically independent the density function of the product reduces to

$$f_Z(z) = \int_{-\infty}^{\infty} \frac{1}{|x|} f_X(x) f_Y\left(\frac{z}{x}\right) dx \qquad (3.5.2a)$$

The alternative form for $f_Z(z)$ is

$$f_Z(z) = \int_{-\infty}^{\infty} \frac{1}{|y|} f_X\left(\frac{z}{y}\right) f_Y(y) \, dy \qquad (3.5.2b)$$

Example 3.5.1. Consider the product of the random variables X and Y which are statistically independent and uniformly distributed on the interval from 0 to 1. The density functions for the integral of Eq. (3.5.2a) are given as

$$f_X(x) = 1 \qquad 0 < x \le 1$$
$$= 0 \qquad \text{otherwise}$$

$$f_Y\left(\frac{z}{x}\right) = 1 \qquad 0 < z/x \le 1$$

$$= 0 \qquad \text{otherwise}$$

The range for the second variable can be written as $0 < z \le x$ with $x \ge 0$, and the range of x values for which both density functions are nonzero is $0 < z \le x \le 1$. Thus, the range of integration on x is from z to 1, with the range of z from 0 to 1. The density function of the product random variable Z is evaluated as

$$f_Z(z) = \int_z^1 \frac{1}{x} \, dx = \ln(x)\Big|_{x=z}^{x=1} = -\ln(z)$$

or

$$f_Z(z) = -\ln(z) \qquad 0 < z \le 1$$
$$= 0 \qquad \text{otherwise} \qquad \square$$

Next, consider the division of the two random variables X and Y to produce Z which is given by the transformation $z = x/y = g_1(x, y)$. Now choose the random variable W where $w = y = g_2(x, y)$, yielding the inverse transformation

$$x = wz = h_1(w, z) \qquad y = w = h_2(w, z)$$

with the corresponding Jacobian

$$J_{h_1 h_2}(w, z) = \begin{vmatrix} z & w \\ 1 & 0 \end{vmatrix} = -w$$

The density function of Z becomes

$$f_Z(z) = \int_{-\infty}^{\infty} |y| f_{XY}(zy, y) \, dy \qquad (3.5.3)$$

where w has been replaced by y. For X and Y statistically independent this reduces to

$$f_Z(z) = \int_{-\infty}^{\infty} |y| f_X(zy) f_Y(y) \, dy \qquad (3.5.4a)$$

where the alternative form is

$$f_Z(z) = \frac{1}{z^2} \int_{-\infty}^{\infty} |x| f_X(x) f_Y\left(\frac{x}{z}\right) dx \qquad (3.5.4b)$$

Example 3.5.2.   Consider the division of the random variable X by the random variable Y when X and Y are statistically independent normalized Gaussian random variables, where

$$f_{XY}(x, y) = \frac{1}{2\pi} e^{-(x^2 + y^2)/2} \qquad -\infty < x < \infty \quad -\infty < y < \infty$$

The density function of this division random variable Z is obtained, using Eq. (3.5.4a), as

$$f_Z(z) = \int_{-\infty}^{\infty} |y| \frac{1}{2\pi} e^{-(z^2 y^2 + y^2)/2} \, dy$$

Since the integrand is even

$$f_Z(z) = \int_{0}^{\infty} \frac{y}{\pi} e^{-(z^2 + 1)y^2/2} \, dy$$

or

$$f_Z(z) = \frac{1}{\pi(z^2 + 1)} \qquad -\infty < z < \infty$$

which is called a Cauchy density function.   □

Two additional useful transformations will be considered. The first is the random variable Z that is the maximum of the two random variables X and Y. This transformation is expressed as

$$z = \max(x, y)$$

If both X and Y are less than or equal to some value z, then the random variable Z is less than or equal to this same value z, and conversely, if either X is greater than z or Y is greater than z, then Z is greater than this same value z. The distribution function for Z can be obtained from the joint distribution function for X and Y using this result, i.e., that $Z \leq z$ if and only if $X \leq z$ and $Y \leq z$, which implies

$$F_Z(z) = P(Z \leq z) = P(X \leq z, Y \leq z) = F_{XY}(z, z)$$

or in integral form

$$F_{XY}(z, z) = \int_{-\infty}^{z} \int_{-\infty}^{z} f_{XY}(x, y) \, dx \, dy$$

The density function of Z is obtained by differentiating this expression. To facilitate this, let the inner integral be

$$g(y, z) = \int_{-\infty}^{z} f_{XY}(x, y) \, dx$$

to give

$$F_Z(z) = F_{XY}(z, z) = \int_{-\infty}^{z} g(y, z) \, dy$$

Using Leibniz's rule, Eq. (3.1.5), for differentiating this integral, the density function of the maximum random variable becomes

$$f_Z(z) = \frac{dF_{XY}(z, z)}{dz} = g(z, z) + \int_{-\infty}^{z} \frac{\partial g(y, z)}{\partial z} \, dy$$

or

$$f_Z(z) = \int_{-\infty}^{z} f_{XY}(x, z) \, dx + \int_{-\infty}^{z} f_{XY}(z, y) \, dy \tag{3.5.5}$$

If X and Y are statistically independent, Eq. (3.5.5) reduces to

$$f_Z(z) = F_X(z)f_Y(z) + f_X(z)F_Y(z) \tag{3.5.6}$$

which could have been obtained by differentiating $F_{XY}(z, z) = F_X(z)F_Y(z)$ directly.

Example 3.5.3.   Consider the maximum of the random variables X and Y, which are statistically independent and uniformly distributed from 0 to

1. The distribution functions of these random variables with the arguments replaced by z are given as

$$F_X(z) = F_Y(z) = 0 \qquad z < 0$$
$$= z \qquad 0 \le z \le 1$$
$$= 1 \qquad z > 1$$

The distribution for the maximum of these two random variables is then

$$F_Z(z) = 0 \qquad z < 0$$
$$= z^2 \qquad 0 \le z \le 1$$
$$= 1 \qquad z > 1$$

and the corresponding density function

$$f_Z(z) = 2z \qquad 0 \le z \le 1$$
$$= 0 \qquad \text{otherwise}$$

This density function could also have been obtained directly from Eq. (3.5.6).   □

The other transformation is the random variable Z that is the minimum of the two random variables X and Y. This transformation is expressed as

$$z = \min(x, y)$$

In this case, Z is greater than some value z if and only if both X and Y are greater than the same value z. This implies

$$P(Z > z) = P(z < X < \infty, z < Y < \infty)$$

which in terms of the joint distribution function is

$$P(Z > z) = F_{XY}(\infty, \infty) - F_{XY}(\infty, z) - F_{XY}(z, \infty) + F_{XY}(z, z)$$
$$= 1 - F_Y(z) - F_X(z) + F_{XY}(z, z)$$

Since $F_Z(z) = 1 - P(Z > z)$

$$F_Z(z) = F_X(z) + F_Y(z) - F_{XY}(z, z)$$

Using the results of Eq. (3.5.5) for the last term, the density function of the minimum random variable is

$$f_Z(z) = f_X(z) + f_Y(z) - \int_{-\infty}^{z} f_{XY}(x, z)\, dx - \int_{-\infty}^{z} f_{XY}(z, y)\, dy \qquad (3.5.7)$$

If X and Y are statistically independent, Eq. (3.5.7) reduces to

$$f_Z(z) = f_X(z) + f_Y(z) - F_X(z)f_Y(z) - f_X(z)F_Y(z)$$

or

$$f_Z(z) = [1 - F_X(z)]f_Y(z) + f_X(z)[1 - F_Y(z)] \qquad (3.5.8)$$

Example 3.5.4. Consider the minimum of the random variables X and Y, which are statistically independent and exponentially distributed. The density functions are given as

$$f_X(x) = a e^{-ax} \qquad x \geq 0$$
$$= 0 \qquad \text{otherwise}$$
$$f_Y(y) = b e^{-by} \qquad y \geq 0$$
$$= 0 \qquad \text{otherwise}$$

and the corresponding distribution functions as

$$F_X(x) = 1 - e^{-ax} \qquad x \geq 0$$
$$= 0 \qquad \text{otherwise}$$
$$F_Y(y) = 1 - e^{-by} \qquad y \geq 0$$
$$= 0 \qquad \text{otherwise}$$

Then the density function of the minimum random variable, using Eq. (3.5.8), can be written as

$$f_Z(z) = (e^{-az})(be^{-bz}) + (a e^{-az})(e^{-bz})$$

or

$$f_Z(z) = (a + b) e^{-(a+b)z} \qquad z \geq 0$$
$$= 0 \qquad \text{otherwise}$$

The minimum random variable Z is also exponential with parameter the sum of the parameters of the random variables X and Y. □

Conceptually, the extension of these results to the maximum or minimum of N random variables is straightforward, especially N statistically independent random variables, which is a common assumption. These results are useful in determining the distribution function of time to failure of systems in reliability theory. A system described by a parallel reliability configuration, as in Fig. 1.4.5b, operates as long as any of the components operate, and its time to failure is the maximum of the times to failure of the components. Similarly, a system described by a series reliability configuration, as in Fig. 1.4.5a, fails if any of the components fail, and its time to failure is the minimum of the times to failure of the components.

Define the maximum and minimum random variables Y and Z in terms of the transformations as

$$y = \max(x_1, x_2, \ldots, x_N)$$

and

$$z = \min(x_1, x_2, \ldots, x_N)$$

where $X_1, X_2, \ldots, X_N$ has joint distribution function $F_{X_1 X_2 \cdots X_N}(x_1, x_2, \ldots, x_N)$. As in the two-variable case, $Y \le y$ if and only if $X_1 \le y, X_2 \le y, \ldots, X_N \le y$ are simultaneously satisfied, which yields

$$F_Y(y) = F_{X_1 X_2 \cdots X_N}(y, y, \ldots, y)$$

and $Z \ge z$ if and only if $X_1 > z, X_2 > z, \ldots, X_N > z$ are simultaneously satisfied to yield

$$1 - F_Z(z) = P(X_1 > z, X_2 > z, \ldots, X_N > z)$$

For $X_1, X_2, \ldots, X_N$ statistically independent, these expressions reduce to

$$F_Y(y) = \prod_{i=1}^{N} F_{X_i}(y) \tag{3.5.9}$$

and

$$F_Z(z) = 1 - \prod_{i=1}^{N} [1 - F_{X_i}(z)] \tag{3.5.10}$$

For N identically distributed random variables $f_{X_i}(x_i) = f_X(x)$, $i = 1, \ldots, N$, the density function of the maximum random variable becomes

$$f_Y(y) = N[F_X(y)]^{N-1} f_X(y) \tag{3.5.11}$$

Likewise, for the minimum random variable

$$f_Z(z) = N[1 - F_X(z)]^{N-1} f_X(z) \tag{3.5.12}$$

A common assumption in reliability theory for a density function describing time to failure is an exponential density function.

Example 3.5.5. For N statistically independent and identically distributed exponential random variables, where

$$f_{X_i}(x_i) = a e^{-ax_i} \qquad x_i \ge 0 \quad i = 1, \ldots, N$$
$$= 0 \qquad\qquad \text{otherwise}$$

the density function for the maximum random variable of these N random variables, using Eq. (3.5.11), becomes

$$f_Y(y) = N[1 - e^{-ay}]^{N-1} a\, e^{-ay} \qquad y \geq 0$$

$$= 0 \qquad\qquad\qquad\qquad \text{otherwise}$$

and the density function for the minimum random variable, using Eq. (3.5.12), becomes

$$f_Z(z) = Na\, e^{-Naz} \qquad z \geq 0$$

$$= 0 \qquad\qquad\qquad \text{otherwise}$$

The density function for the minimum random variable is exponential with the parameter equal to the sum of the parameters for the X_i's, even if the X_i's do not all have the same parameter.   □

PROBLEMS

3.1.1. For $y = 1/x$ where $f_X(x) = 2/x^3$, $1 \leq x < \infty$, determine $f_Y(y)$. (Include range.)

3.1.2. For $y = 1/x^2$ where $f_X(x) = 1/x^2$, $1 \leq x < \infty$, determine $f_Y(y)$. (Include range.)

3.1.3. For $y = \ln(x)$ where $f_X(x) = 2/x^3$, $1 \leq x < \infty$, determine $f_Y(y)$. (Include range.)

3.1.4. For $y = e^{2x}$ where $f_X(x) = \frac{1}{2} e^{-|x|}$, $-\infty < x < \infty$, determine $f_Y(y)$. (Include range.)

3.1.5. For the uniform random variable U with $f_U(u) = 1$, $0 \leq u \leq 1$, determine the transformation to obtain the random variable X with $f_X(x) = \frac{1}{2} e^{-|x|}$, $-\infty < x < \infty$.

3.1.6. For the uniform random variable U with $f_U(u) = 1$, $0 \leq u \leq 1$, determine the transformation to obtain the random variable X with $f_X(x) = 1 - |x|$, $-1 \leq x \leq 1$.

3.1.7. For the uniform random variable U with $f_U(u) = 1$, $0 \leq u \leq 1$, determine the transformation to obtain the random variable X with $f_X(x) = \frac{2}{3}x$, $0 \leq x \leq 1$, and $f_X(x) = \frac{2}{3}$, $1 \leq x \leq 2$.

3.1.8. For the uniform random variable U with $f_U(u) = 1$, $0 \leq u \leq 1$, determine the transformation to obtain the random variable X with $f_X(x) = a\, e^{-ax}$, $0 \leq x < \infty$.

3.1.9. For the uniform random variable U with $f_U(u) = 1$, $0 \leq u \leq 1$, determine the transformation to obtain the random variable X with $f_X(x) = 1/(x+1)^2$, $0 \leq x < \infty$.

3.1.10. Determine the density function of the conductance of a 1-Ω (uniformly distributed) 10% resistor.

3.1.11. Determine the density function of the impedance of a 1 millihenry (uniformly distributed) 10% inductor at an angular frequency of 10^3 rad/s.

3.1.12. Determine the density function of the impedance of a 0.1 μF (uniformly distributed) 10% capacitor at an angular frequency of 5×10^6 rad/s.

3.2.1. For $f_{X_1 X_2}(x_1, x_2) = \exp(-x_1 - x_2)$, $0 \le x_1 < \infty$, $0 \le x_2 < \infty$ and the transformation $y_1 = x_1/(x_1 + x_2)$ and $y_2 = x_1 + x_2$, determine $f_{Y_1 Y_2}(y_1, y_2)$. (Include ranges.)

3.2.2. For $f_{X_1 X_2}(x_1, x_2) = [1/(6\pi)] e^{-(5x_1^2 - 2x_1 x_2 + 2x_2^2)/18}$, $-\infty < x_1 < \infty$, $-\infty < x_2 < \infty$ and the transformation $y_1 = (x_1 + x_2)/3$ and $y_2 = (x_2 - 2x_1)/3$, determine $f_{Y_1 Y_2}(y_1, y_2)$. (Include ranges.)

3.2.3. For $f_{X_1 X_2}(x_1, x_2) = x_1 e^{-x_1}$, $0 \le x_1 < \infty$, $0 \le x_2 \le 1$ and the transformation $y_1 = x_1 x_2$ and $y_2 = x_1 - x_1 x_2$, determine $f_{Y_1 Y_2}(y_1, y_2)$. (Include ranges.)

3.2.4. Determine the Jacobian, $J_{xyz}(r, \theta, \phi)$, of the transformation from rectangular to spherical coordinates, from $x, y,$ and z to $r, \theta,$ and ϕ, where

$$r = \sqrt{x^2 + y^2 + z^2}, \ \theta = \tan^{-1}\left(\frac{y}{x}\right), \text{ and } \phi = \cos^{-1}\left(\frac{z}{\sqrt{x^2 + y^2 + z^2}}\right).$$

The inverse transformation is given as $x = r \sin \phi \cos \theta$, $y = r \sin \phi \sin \theta$, and $z = r \cos \phi$.

3.2.5. Derive Eq. (3.2.8).

3.3.1. For $f_X(x) = (1/\sqrt{2\pi}) \exp[-(x-2)^2/2]$, $-\infty < x < \infty$, and the transformation $y = x^2$, determine $f_Y(y)$. (Include range.)

3.3.2. For $f_X(x) = 1/[\pi(x^2 + 1)]$, $-\infty < x < \infty$, and the transformation $y = |x - 1|$, determine $f_Y(y)$. (Include range.)

3.4.1. For the statistically independent random variables X and Y with $f_X(x) = 1$, $0 \le x \le 1$, and $f_Y(y) = e^{-y}$, $0 \le y < \infty$, determine $f_Z(z)$ where $z = x + y$.

3.4.2. For the statistically independent random variables X and Y with $f_X(x) = e^{-x}$, $0 \le x < \infty$, and $f_Y(y) = \frac{1}{2} e^{-|y|}$, $-\infty < y < \infty$, determine $f_Z(z)$ where $z = x + y$.

3.4.3. For the statistically independent random variables X and Y with $f_X(x) = \frac{1}{2} e^{-|x|}$, $-\infty < x < \infty$, and $f_Y(y) = 1$, $1 \le y \le 2$, determine $f_Z(z)$ where $z = x + y$.

3.4.4. For the statistically independent random variables X and Y with $f_X(x) = 1$, $1 \le x \le 2$, and $f_Y(y) = e^{-(y-1)}$, $1 \le y < \infty$, determine $f_Z(z)$ where $z = x + y$.

3.4.5. For the statistically independent random variables X and Y with $f_X(x) = e^{-x}$, $0 \le x < \infty$, and $f_Y(y) = y e^{-y}$, $0 \le y < \infty$, determine $f_Z(z)$ where $z = x + y$.

3.4.6. For the statistically independent random variables X and Y with $f_X(x) = x e^{-x}$, $0 \le x < \infty$, and $f_Y(y) = \frac{1}{2} y^2 e^{-y}$, $0 \le y < \infty$, determine $f_Z(z)$ where $z = x + y$.

3.4.7. For the statistically independent random variables X and Y with $z = x - y$, develop an expression for $f_Z(z)$ similar to Eq. (3.4.2a).

3.4.8. Develop Eq. (3.4.2b).

3.4.9. For the statistically independent random variables X and Y with $P(X = i) = C_i^3 (0.3)^i (0.7)^{3-i}$, $i = 0, 1, 2, 3$, and $P(Y = j) = C_j^3 (0.3)^j (0.7)^{3-j}$, $j = 0, 1, 2, 3$, determine $P(Z = k)$ where $z = x + y$.

3.4.10. For the statistically independent random variables X and Y with $P(X = i) = C_i^2 (0.3)^i (0.7)^{2-i}$, $i = 0, 1, 2$, and $P(Y = j) = C_j^3 (0.3)^j (0.7)^{3-j}$, $j = 0, 1, 2, 3$, determine $P(Z = k)$ where $z = x + y$.

3.4.11. For the statistically independent random variables X and Y with $P(X = i) = 2^i e^{-2}/i!$, $i = 0, 1, 2, \ldots$, and $P(Y = j) = 2^j e^{-2}/j!$, $j = 0, 1, 2, \ldots$, determine $P(Z = 3)$ where $z = x + y$.

3.4.12. For the statistically independent random variables X and Y with $P(X = i) = 3^i e^{-3}/i!$, $i = 0, 1, 2, \ldots$, and $P(Y = j) = 2^j e^{-2}/j!$, $j = 0, 1, 2, \ldots$, determine $P(Z = 4)$ where $z = x + y$.

3.4.13. Determine the probability that the sum of three 100-Ω (uniformly distributed) 10% resistors is within 5% tolerance of 300 Ω.

3.4.14. Determine the probability that the sum of three 100-Ω (uniformly distributed) 10% resistors is within 4% tolerance of 300 Ω.

3.5.1. Determine the density function of the maximum of three statistically independent uniform random variables (over 0 to 1) and determine the probability that the maximum is greater than 0.75.

3.5.2. Determine the density function of the minimum of three statistically independent uniform random variables (over 0 to 1) and determine the probability that the minimum is greater than 0.25.

3.5.3. If the failure time of statistically independent electronic components is modeled by the exponential random variable where $f_{X_i}(x_i) = 0.02\, e^{-0.02 x_i}$, $x_i \geq 0$, determine the density function of the failure time when three components are in series. Also determine the probability that the failure time is less than 30 months.

3.5.4. If the failure time of statistically independent electronic components is modeled by the exponential random variable where $f_{X_i}(x_i) = 0.02\, e^{-0.02 x_i}$, $x_i \geq 0$, determine the density function of the failure time when three components are in parallel. Also determine the probability that the failure time is less than 30 months.

3.5.5. Develop Eq. (3.5.4b).

Statistical Averages

4.1 Expected Value

The statistical average, or expected value, of a random variable X is an average based on the modeled probability density function $f_X(x)$. The expected value can intuitively be thought of as the value the random variable is expected to take on, the most likely value, or the value that is the median. Even though these statements are true in many cases, there are exceptions to all of them. In fact, the expected value of a random variable may not be a possible value of the random variable; e.g., the expected value of a Bernoulli random variable with $p = \frac{1}{2}$ is $\frac{1}{2}$, although the only values for the random variable are 0 and 1. A relative frequency interpretation of the expected value is the value to which the average of independent observations of the random variable would converge as the number of observations becomes large.

The expected value of a random variable X is then defined as

$$E(X) = \bar{x} = \int_{-\infty}^{\infty} x f_X(x) \, dx \qquad (4.1.1)$$

This expected value is also called the mean value or first moment, and is a constant or parameter of the density function. In mechanics the expected value corresponds to the centroid of the geometric figure or mass. It should be noted here that sometimes the expected value does not exist (may be infinite).

Example 4.1.1. For the random variable X uniformly distributed on the interval from a to b, the expected value is calculated as

$$E(X) = \int_a^b x \left(\frac{1}{b-a}\right) dx = \left(\frac{1}{b-a}\right)\left(\frac{x^2}{2}\right)\Bigg|_{x=a}^{x=b} = \frac{b+a}{2}$$

which is the midpoint of the interval, as might have been expected. ☐

For the Gaussian random variable X with parameters μ and σ^2, where

$$f_X(x) = \frac{1}{\sqrt{2\pi\sigma^2}} e^{-(x-\mu)^2/2\sigma^2} \qquad -\infty < x < \infty$$

the expected value of X is determined as

$$E(X) = \int_{-\infty}^{\infty} x \frac{1}{\sqrt{2\pi\sigma^2}} e^{-(x-\mu)^2/2\sigma^2} dx$$

$$= \int_{-\infty}^{\infty} \frac{x-\mu}{\sqrt{2\pi\sigma^2}} e^{-(x-\mu)^2/2\sigma^2} dx + \mu \int_{-\infty}^{\infty} \frac{1}{\sqrt{2\pi\sigma^2}} e^{-(x-\mu)^2/2\sigma^2} dx$$

$$= -\frac{\sigma}{\sqrt{2\pi}} e^{-(x-\mu)^2/2\sigma^2} \Bigg|_{x=-\infty}^{x=\infty} + \mu(1) = -0 + 0 + \mu = \mu$$

The first integral could have been noted to be 0 since it is an integral of an odd function, and the second integral is 1 since it is over the entire range of a Gaussian density function. Thus,

$$E(X) = \mu \qquad (4.1.2)$$

which illustrates that the parameter μ is appropriately called the mean. Manipulating the integration into a form such that the integral of the density function equaling 1 can be utilized is a useful technique.

Example 4.1.2. For the special case of the gamma random variable, where $a = 1$ and $b = n$, a nonnegative integer, the density function, Eq. (2.3.4a), is given as

$$f_X(x) = \frac{x^n}{n!} e^{-x} \qquad x \geq 0$$

$$= 0 \qquad \text{otherwise}$$

Since all density functions must integrate to 1,

$$\int_0^{\infty} \frac{x^n}{n!} e^{-x} dx = 1$$

for all nonnegative integers n. Now the expected value of X is obtained as

$$E(X) = \int_0^{\infty} x \left(\frac{x^n}{n!}\right) e^{-x} dx = \int_0^{\infty} \frac{x^{n+1}}{n!} e^{-x} dx$$

Matching up the factorial term with the exponent of x, where $(n+1)! = (n+1)n!$, yields

$$E(X) = (n+1) \int_0^\infty \frac{x^{n+1}}{(n+1)!} e^{-x} dx = (n+1) \int_0^\infty \frac{x^m}{m!} e^{-x} dx = (n+1)(1)$$

since $m = n+1$ is a positive integer and the integral is over the entire range of a gamma density function. Thus, the mean of this gamma random variable is

$$E(X) = n+1 \qquad \square$$

Equation (4.1.1) is valid for both continuous and discrete random variables, but a more useful expression can be developed for discrete random variables. For discrete random variables

$$f_X(x) = \sum_{k=-\infty}^{\infty} P(X = x_k) \delta(x - x_k)$$

and

$$E(X) = \int_{-\infty}^{\infty} x \sum_{k=-\infty}^{\infty} P(X = x_k) \delta(x - x_k) \, dx$$

or the expected value for discrete random variables is given by the sum

$$E(X) = \sum_{k=-\infty}^{\infty} x_k P(X = x_k) \tag{4.1.3}$$

For discrete random variables, the integral of the values the random variable takes on times the density function is replaced by the summation of the values the random variable takes on times the probability function. Equation (4.1.3) is similar to the empirical average $\sum x_k(n_k/N)$, involving relative frequencies.

Example 4.1.3. For the Bernoulli random variable

$$P(X = k) = p^k (1-p)^{1-k} \qquad k = 0,1$$

the mean is obtained as

$$E(X) = \sum_{k=0}^{1} k[p^k (1-p)^{1-k}] = 0(1-p) + 1(p) = p \qquad \square$$

In Example 4.1.3 for $0 < p < 1$, the mean value never occurs, i.e., never is a value of the random variable.

Example 4.1.4. The mean of the binomial random variable is evaluated in a manner similar to the mean of the gamma random variable, but with a manipulation to obtain the sum of the probability function (rather than the integral of the density function), which is 1. For the binomial probability function

$$P(Y = k) = C_k^N p^k (1-p)^{N-k} \qquad k = 0, 1, \ldots, N$$

$$= 0 \qquad \qquad \text{otherwise}$$

and

$$\sum_{k=0}^{N} P(Y = k) = \sum_{k=0}^{N} C_k^N p^k (1-p)^{N-k} = 1$$

which is true since it is a probability function, and can be shown by using the binomial theorem. The mean of the binomial random variable is obtained as

$$E(Y) = \sum_{k=0}^{N} k C_k^N p^k (1-p)^{N-k} = \sum_{k=1}^{N} k C_k^N p^k (1-p)^{N-k}$$

since the term $k = 0$ is 0. Now,

$$kC_k^N = k \frac{N!}{k![N-k]!} = \frac{N!}{[k-1]![N-k]!} = N \frac{(N-1)!}{[k-1]![N-k]!}$$

$$= N C_{k-1}^{N-1}$$

and the expected value becomes

$$E(Y) = N \sum_{k=1}^{N} C_{k-1}^{N-1} p^k (1-p)^{N-k}$$

For the change of variable $j = k - 1$

$$E(Y) = Np \sum_{j=0}^{N-1} C_j^{N-1} p^j (1-p)^{N-1-j}$$

where the summation is 1 since it is the sum of a binomial probability function (N replaced by $N-1$) over the entire range, and finally

$$E(Y) = Np \qquad \square$$

Since moments other than the first moment or mean value are of importance, the expected value of $Y = g(X)$ is considered. Transformations of random variables were considered in Chapter 3 so that the density function of Y could be obtained from the density function of X and $g(x)$ and the mean or expected value of Y then obtained from $f_Y(y)$. This approach is more involved than necessary if only the expected value of Y is desired. This expected value can be calculated without obtaining the density function of Y by considering

$$E(Y) = \int_{-\infty}^{\infty} y f_Y(y)\, dy = \int_{-\infty}^{\infty} y f_X(h(y)) \left| \frac{\partial h(y)}{\partial y} \right| dy$$

and with the change of variables $y = g(x)$ or $x = h(y)$, $dx = |\partial h(y)/\partial y|\, dy$, to yield

$$E[g(X)] = \int_{-\infty}^{\infty} g(x) f_X(x)\, dx \qquad (4.1.4)$$

Even if $g(x)$ is not a monotonic function, this expression is still valid and the integration is over the entire range of x, but obtaining it is more involved. Calculating $E[g(X)]$ by Eq. (4.1.4) or by first determining $f_Y(y)$ and calculating $E(Y)$ is equivalent for $Y = g(X)$. For example, if X represents the voltage across a 1-Ω resistor and Y represents the power in the same resistor, the average power can be obtained by averaging the power (integral of power times the density function of the power) or by averaging the voltage squared (integral of voltage squared times the density function of the voltage).

Equation (4.1.4) is valid for both continuous and discrete random variables, but a more useful expression for discrete random variables can be developed as

$$E[g(X)] = \int_{-\infty}^{\infty} g(x) \sum_{k=-\infty}^{\infty} P(X = x_k) \delta(x - x_k)\, dx$$

or the expected value of $g(X)$ reduces to

$$E[g(X)] = \sum_{k=-\infty}^{\infty} g(x_k) P(X = x_k) \qquad (4.1.5)$$

Equation (4.1.4) enables the calculation of $E[g(X)]$ directly from the density function of X, and Eq. (4.1.5) enables this calculation directly from the probability function of X.

Expectation is a linear operation since expectation is an integration, which is a linear operation. This is expressed as

$$E[ag(X) + bh(X)] = \int_{-\infty}^{\infty} [ag(x) + bh(x)] f_X(x)\, dx$$

$$= a \int_{-\infty}^{\infty} g(x) f_X(x)\, dx + b \int_{-\infty}^{\infty} h(x) f_X(x)\, dx$$

or

$$E[ag(X) + bh(X)] = aE[g(X)] + bE[h(X)] \qquad (4.1.6a)$$

A useful special case of this is for $h(X) = 1$, which yields

$$E(aX + b) = aE(X) + b \qquad (4.1.6b)$$

and in addition, when $a = 0$,

$$E(b) = b$$

or the expected value of a constant is that constant.

The expected values of additional important functions will now be considered. The nth moment of X, $g(X) = X^n$, is given as

$$E(X^n) = \int_{-\infty}^{\infty} x^n f_X(x)\, dx \qquad (4.1.7)$$

The most common of this type is that for $n = 2$, the second moment, which is also called the mean square value of X, and $[E(X^2)]^{1/2}$ is the rms value of X. Another class of important moments consists of the central moments, i.e., the moments taken about the mean value $E(X) = \bar{x}$, which is a constant [$E(X)$ is not a function of X]. The nth central moment, $g(X) = (X - \bar{x})^n$, is defined as

$$E[(X - \bar{x})^n] = \int_{-\infty}^{\infty} (x - \bar{x})^n f_X(x)\, dx \qquad (4.1.8)$$

The most important central moment is the second central moment, which is called the variance and is given as

$$\mathrm{Var}(X) = E[(X - \bar{x})^2] = \int_{-\infty}^{\infty} (x - \bar{x})^2 f_X(x)\, dx = \sigma_x^2 \qquad (4.1.9a)$$

Expanding the squared term

$$\mathrm{Var}(X) = \int_{-\infty}^{\infty} (x^2 - 2\bar{x}x + \bar{x}^2) f_X(x)\, dx = E(X^2) - 2\bar{x}E(X) + \bar{x}^2(1)$$

yields

$$\mathrm{Var}(X) = E(X^2) - [E(X)]^2 \qquad (4.1.9b)$$

which is an alternative form for computing the variance and is sometimes more convenient. If X represents a random voltage across a 1-Ω resistor, $E(X)$ represents the dc component, $E(X^2)$ represents the total (dc plus ac) power, and $\mathrm{Var}(X)$ represents the ac power. Equation (4.1.9a) represents finding the ac power by first subtracting the dc component in the voltage and then determining the power, while Eq. (4.1.9b) represents obtaining the ac power by subtracting the dc power from the total power. In mechanics the variance corresponds to the moment of inertia about the centroid of the geometric figure or mass. The square root of the variance

$$\sigma = \sqrt{\text{Var}(X)}$$

is called the standard deviation and is a measure of the spread about the mean of the density function of the random variable.

For discrete random variables Eqs. (4.1.7), (4.1.8), and (4.1.9a) can be expressed in terms of sums of the probability function in a straightforward manner. Because of its importance, the variance for a discrete random variable is given here as

$$\text{Var}(X) = \sum_{k=-\infty}^{\infty} (x_k - \bar{x})^2 P(X = x_k) \tag{4.1.10}$$

From Eq. (4.1.9a), it can be seen that $\text{Var}(X) \geq 0$ since the integrand is nonnegative over the entire range, and from Eq. (4.1.9b), $E(X^2) \geq [E(X)]^2$. The only time that the mean square value is equal to the mean value squared, $E(X^2) = [E(X)]^2$, is, using Eq. (4.1.9b), when $\text{Var}(X) = 0$. This implies that $X = E(X)$, a single constant, and that $f_X(x) = \delta(x - E(X))$. In this case, if X is a voltage, there is no ac component.

Example 4.1.5. For the random variable X of Example 4.1.1 that is uniformly distributed on the interval from a to b, the variance is calculated, using Eq. (4.1.9a), as

$$\text{Var}(X) = \int_a^b \left(x - \frac{b+a}{2}\right)^2 \frac{1}{b-a}\, dx = \frac{1}{3(b-a)}\left(x - \frac{b+a}{2}\right)^3 \Bigg|_{x=a}^{x=b}$$

$$= \frac{1}{3(b-a)}\left[\frac{(b-a)^3}{8} - \frac{(a-b)^3}{8}\right]$$

or

$$\text{Var}(X) = \frac{(b-a)^2}{12}$$

which is a function of the difference of the values of a and b; i.e., the variance is a function only of the interval width and not of the location of the interval.   □

For the Gaussian random variable X with parameters μ and σ^2,

$$\text{Var}(X) = \int_{-\infty}^{\infty} (x - \mu)^2 \frac{1}{\sqrt{2\pi\sigma^2}}\, e^{-(x-\mu)^2/2\sigma^2}\, dx$$

and integrating by parts, with $dv = (x - \mu) \exp[-(x-\mu)^2/(2\sigma^2)]\, dx/\sigma^2$ and

$$u = \sigma^2(x - \mu),$$

$$\text{Var}(X) = -\frac{\sigma^2(x-\mu)}{\sqrt{2\pi\sigma^2}} e^{-(x-\mu)^2/2\sigma^2} \Big|_{x=-\infty}^{x=\infty}$$

$$+ \sigma^2 \int_{-\infty}^{\infty} \frac{1}{\sqrt{2\pi\sigma^2}} e^{-(x-\mu)^2/2\sigma^2} \, dx$$

which, since the last integral is an integral of a Gaussian density function over its entire range and equals 1, reduces to

$$\text{Var}(X) = \sigma^2 \qquad (4.1.11)$$

The parameter σ^2 is appropriately called the variance.

Example 4.1.6. For the gamma random variable of Example 4.1.2 where

$$f_X(x) = \frac{x^n}{n!} e^{-x} \qquad x \geq 0$$

the variance is more easily found by using Eq. (4.1.9b). The mean square value of X is obtained as

$$E(X^2) = \int_0^{\infty} x^2 \frac{x^n}{n!} e^{-x} \, dx = \int_0^{\infty} \frac{x^{n+2}}{n!} e^{-x} \, dx$$

Matching up the factorial term with the exponent of x, where $(n+2)! = (n+2)(n+1)n!$ and with $m = n+2$, yields

$$E(X^2) = (n+2)(n+1) \int_0^{\infty} \frac{x^m}{m!} e^{-x} \, dx = (n+2)(n+1)(1) = (n+2)(n+1)$$

since the integral is over the entire range of a gamma density function. Using Eq. (4.1.9b), the previously calculated mean from Example 4.1.2, $E(X) = n+1$, and the mean square value $E(X^2)$, the variance, is

$$\text{Var}(X) = (n+2)(n+1) - (n+1)^2 = n+1 \qquad \square$$

Now consider the calculation of the variance for discrete random variables.

Example 4.1.7. For the Bernoulli random variable of Example 4.1.3

$$E(X^2) = (0)^2(1-p) + (1)^2(p) = p$$

and

$$\text{Var}(X) = p - (p)^2 = p(1-p) \qquad \square$$

Neither expression for the variance, Eq. (4.1.9b) or Eq. (4.1.10), can be used straightforwardly to obtain the variance for the binomial random variable. A moment that is useful in this case is the second factorial moment $E[X(X-1)]$, which is a special case of the nth factorial moment $E[X(X-1)\cdots(X-n+1)]$. The factorial moments are easier to calculate than the standard moments for discrete random variables that take on equally spaced values. Since expectation is a linear operation, the second factorial moment and the mean square value are related by

$$E(X^2)=E[X(X-1)]+E(X)$$

and the variance given in terms of the second factorial moment and the mean as

$$\text{Var}(X)=E[X(X-1)]+E(X)-[E(X)]^2 \qquad (4.1.12)$$

Example 4.1.8.   The second factorial moment for the binomial random variable of Example 4.1.4 can be calculated as

$$E[X(X-1)]=\sum_{k=0}^{N}k(k-1)C_k^N p^k(1-p)^{N-k}=\sum_{k=2}^{N}k(k-1)C_k^N p^k(1-p)^{N-k}$$

since the terms $k=0$ and $k=1$ are 0. Now

$$k(k-1)C_k^N=k(k-1)\frac{N!}{k![N-k]!}=\frac{N!}{[k-2]![N-k]!}$$

$$=N(N-1)\frac{(N-2)!}{[k-2]![N-k]!}=N(N-1)C_{k-2}^{N-2}$$

which shows the useful cancellation of the factorial moments, and the second factorial moment becomes

$$E[X(X-1)]=N(N-1)\sum_{k=2}^{N}C_{k-2}^{N-2}p^k(1-p)^{N-k}$$

For the change of variables $j=k-2$

$$E[X(X-1)]=N(N-1)p^2\sum_{j=0}^{N-2}C_j^{N-2}p^j(1-p)^{N-2-j}$$

where the summation is 1 since it is the sum of a binomial probability function (N replaced by $N-2$) over the entire range, and

$$E[X(X-1)]=N(N-1)p^2$$

The variance of the binomial random variable is then

$$\text{Var}(X)=N(N-1)p^2+Np-(Np)^2$$

or

$$\text{Var}(X)=Np(1-p) \qquad \square$$

A useful property for the variance is

$$\text{Var}(aX + b) = E\{[aX + b - E(aX + b)]^2\}$$
$$= E\{[aX + b - aE(X) - b]^2\}$$
$$= E\{a^2[X - E(X)]^2\}$$

or

$$\text{Var}(aX + b) = a^2 \, \text{Var}(X) \qquad (4.1.13)$$

which is not a function of the additive constant b. This emphasizes the fact that the variance is unaffected by a shift in mean value, and is still a nonnegative value because of the multiplication by a^2.

Using Eqs. (4.1.6b) and (4.1.13), a random variable Y with mean μ and variance σ^2 can be obtained from the random variable X with mean 0 and variance 1 as $Y = \pm\sigma X + \mu$ (as was shown in Section 3.1).

Example 4.1.9. Determine a and b for $Y = aX + b$ such that $E(X) = 3$, $E(Y) = 10$, $\text{Var}(X) = 2$, and $\text{Var}(Y) = 32$. Using Eq. (4.1.6b), $E(Y) = a(3) + b = 10$ or $b = 10 - 3a$, and using Eq. (4.1.13), $\text{Var}(Y) = a^2(2) = 32$ or $a = \pm 4$. The two solutions are $a = 4$, $b = -2$ and $a = -4$, $b = 22$. □

4.2 Characteristic Function

A moment of particular interest obtained with $g(X) = e^{j\omega X}$, where $j = \sqrt{-1}$, is called the characteristic function and is defined as

$$\phi_X(\omega) = E(e^{j\omega X}) = \int_{-\infty}^{\infty} e^{j\omega x} f_X(x) \, dx \qquad -\infty < \omega < \infty \qquad (4.2.1)$$

which is effectively the Fourier transform of the density function $f_X(x)$. The only difference is the sign of the exponent, which is of little consequence as long as the inverse transform has the opposite sign. The density function can be obtained from the inverse transform as

$$f_X(x) = \frac{1}{2\pi} \int_{-\infty}^{\infty} e^{-j\omega x} \phi_X(\omega) \, d\omega \qquad (4.2.2)$$

The discrete version of the characteristic function is given as

$$\phi_X(\omega) = \sum_{k=-\infty}^{\infty} e^{j\omega x_k} P(X = x_k) \qquad (4.2.3)$$

From Fourier transform theory a function and its transform form a unique pair, which means that the density function (or distribution or probability function) is completely specified by its characteristic function. The other expected values that have been considered do not fully characterize the density functions; e.g., many different density functions may have the same mean and the same variance.

Another moment closely related to the characteristic function is the moment generating function defined as

$$M_X(\nu) = E(e^{\nu X}) = \int_{-\infty}^{\infty} e^{\nu x} f_X(x)\, dx \qquad -\infty < \nu < \infty \qquad (4.2.4)$$

which is the same as the characteristic function with the j (imaginary value) in the exponent removed. The characteristic function will be used here since it is essentially a Fourier transform and it always exists (has finite absolute value). The moment generating function does not exist in some cases. The absolute value of the characteristic function can be bounded as

$$|\phi_x(\omega)| = \left| \int_{-\infty}^{\infty} e^{j\omega x} f_X(x)\, dx \right| \le \int_{-\infty}^{\infty} |e^{j\omega x} f_X(x)|\, dx$$

since the absolute value of an integral is less than or equal to the integral of the absolute value, and

$$|e^{j\omega x} f_X(x)| = |e^{j\omega x}| |f_X(x)| = (1) f_X(x)$$

to yield

$$|\phi_X(\omega)| \le \int_{-\infty}^{\infty} f_X(x)\, dx = 1$$

This proves the existence of $\phi_X(\omega)$ and bounds its magnitude by 1. The upper bound is achieved at $\omega = 0$, i.e., $\phi_X(0) = 1$, since $\phi_X(0) = E(e^{j0X}) = E[1] = 1$.

One of the main reasons for considering the characteristic function is that moments can be computed from it by differentiation (without integration of the density function). This relationship can be developed by considering

$$\frac{d^n[E(e^{j\omega X})]}{d\omega^n} = E\left[\frac{d^n(e^{j\omega X})}{d\omega^n} \right] = E[(jX)^n e^{j\omega X}]$$

since the expectation is an integration and interchanging differentiation and integration is valid when the function is bounded. Evaluating this expression at $\omega = 0$ and dividing by $(j)^n$ yields

$$E(X^n) = (-j)^n \frac{d^n \phi_X(\omega)}{d\omega^n} \bigg|_{\omega=0} \qquad (4.2.5)$$

The corresponding expression for the moment generating function is

$$E(X^n) = \frac{d^n M_X(\nu)}{d\nu^n}\bigg|_{\nu=0} \tag{4.2.6}$$

Example 4.2.1. The characteristic function for the exponential random variable with

$$f_X(x) = a\, e^{-ax} \qquad x \geq 0 \qquad a > 0$$

$$= 0 \qquad\qquad \text{otherwise}$$

is determined as

$$\phi_X(\omega) = \int_0^\infty e^{j\omega x}(a\, e^{-ax})\, dx = \int_0^\infty a\, e^{-(a-j\omega)x}\, dx = \frac{a}{a - j\omega}$$

From this, the mean is obtained as

$$\frac{d\phi_X(\omega)}{d\omega} = \frac{d[a(a-j\omega)^{-1}]}{d\omega} = [a(j)(a-j\omega)^{-2}]$$

and

$$E(X) = (-j)\frac{d\phi_X(\omega)}{d\omega}\bigg|_{\omega=0} = \frac{1}{a}$$

Likewise, the second moment is obtained as

$$\frac{d^2\phi_X(\omega)}{d\omega^2} = \frac{d^2[a(a-j\omega)^{-1}]}{d\omega^2} = [a(-2)(a-j\omega)^{-3}]$$

and

$$E(X^2) = (-j)^2 \frac{d^2\phi_X(\omega)}{d\omega^2}\bigg|_{\omega=0} = \frac{2}{a^2}$$

The variance is then

$$\text{Var}(X) = \frac{2}{a^2} - \left(\frac{1}{a}\right)^2 = \frac{1}{a^2} \qquad \square$$

Since the Gaussian random variable is one of the most important random variables, the Gaussian characteristic function is one of the most important characteristic functions. The characteristic function of the Gaussian random variable with mean μ and variance σ^2 can be developed as

$$\phi_X(\omega) = \int_{-\infty}^\infty e^{j\omega x}\left\{\frac{1}{\sqrt{2\pi\sigma^2}}\exp\left[\frac{-(x-\mu)^2}{2\sigma^2}\right]\right\} dx$$

$$= \int_{-\infty}^\infty \frac{1}{\sqrt{2\pi\sigma^2}}\exp\left[\frac{-(x^2 - 2\mu x + \mu^2 - j2\sigma^2\omega x)}{2\sigma^2}\right] dx$$

Completing the square of the exponent in x yields

$$\phi_X(\omega) = \exp\left(j\mu\omega - \frac{\sigma^2\omega^2}{2}\right) \int_{-\infty}^{\infty} \frac{1}{\sqrt{2\pi\sigma^2}} \exp\left[\frac{-(x-\mu-j\sigma^2\omega)^2}{2\sigma^2}\right] dx$$

and finally, since the integral is over the entire range of a Gaussian density function and equal to 1,

$$\phi_X(\omega) = \exp(j\mu\omega - \sigma^2\omega^2/2) \qquad (4.2.7)$$

The bell-shaped curve is easily recognized as the Gaussian density function, but the characteristic function of Eq. (4.2.7) is just as Gaussian. Any characteristic function of this form is Gaussian with the mean and variance associated with the imaginary and real parts of the exponent, respectively.

For the Gaussian random variable X with characteristic function given in Eq. (4.2.7) (mean μ and variance σ^2), when $Y = aX + b$ the characteristic function of Y is obtained as

$$\phi_Y(\omega) = E(e^{j\omega Y}) = E(e^{j\omega(aX+b)}) = e^{j\omega b} E(e^{j\omega aX})$$

and with $\omega' = a\omega$

$$\phi_Y(\omega) = e^{j\omega b} E(e^{j\omega' X}) = e^{j\omega b} \exp\left[j\mu\omega' - \frac{\sigma^2(\omega')^2}{2}\right]$$

$$= e^{j\omega b} \exp\left(j\mu a\omega - \frac{\sigma^2 a^2\omega^2}{2}\right) = \exp\left[j\omega(a\mu+b) - \frac{(a^2\sigma^2)\omega^2}{2}\right]$$

Since this is a Gaussian characteristic function, Y is a Gaussian random variable with mean $a\mu + b$ and variance $a^2\sigma^2$.

Example 4.2.2.   For the gamma random variable with density function, from Eq. (2.3.4a) with $b = n$,

$$f_X(x) = \frac{a^{n+1}x^n}{n!} e^{-ax} \qquad x \geq 0$$

$$= 0 \qquad\qquad \text{otherwise}$$

the characteristic function can be determined as

$$\phi_X(\omega) = \int_0^{\infty} e^{j\omega x}\left(\frac{a^{n+1}x^n}{n!}\right) e^{-ax} dx = \int_0^{\infty} \frac{a^{n+1}x^n}{n!} e^{-(a-j\omega)x} dx$$

and letting $c = a - j\omega$

$$\phi_X(\omega) = \frac{a^{n+1}}{c^{n+1}} \int_0^{\infty} \frac{c^{n+1}x^n}{n!} e^{-cx} dx = \left(\frac{a}{c}\right)^{n+1}(1) = \left(\frac{a}{c}\right)^{n+1}$$

since the integral is over the entire density function. The characteristic function simplifies to

$$\phi_X(\omega) = \left(\frac{a}{a-j\omega}\right)^{n+1} = \left(1 - \frac{j\omega}{a}\right)^{-n-1} \tag{4.2.8}$$

Using Eq. (4.2.5), the mean is obtained as

$$\frac{d\phi_X(\omega)}{d\omega} = \frac{d[(1-j\omega/a)^{-n-1}]}{d\omega} = (-n-1)\left(1 - \frac{j\omega}{a}\right)^{-n-2}\left(\frac{-j}{a}\right)$$

and

$$E(X) = (-j)\frac{d\phi_X(\omega)}{d\omega}\bigg|_{\omega=0} = \frac{n+1}{a}$$

Likewise, the mean square value is obtained as

$$\frac{d^2\phi_X(\omega)}{d\omega^2} = \frac{d^2[(1-j\omega/a)^{-n-1}]}{d\omega^2} = (-n-1)(-n-2)\left(1 - \frac{j\omega}{a}\right)^{-n-3}\left(\frac{-j}{a}\right)^2$$

and

$$E(X^2) = (-j)^2\frac{d^2\phi_X(\omega)}{d\omega^2}\bigg|_{\omega=0} = \frac{(n+1)(n+2)}{a^2}$$

From this the variance is

$$\text{Var}(X) = \frac{(n+1)(n+2)}{a^2} - \left(\frac{n+1}{a}\right)^2 = \frac{n+1}{a^2} \qquad \square$$

Now consider the evaluation of the characteristic function for a discrete random variable.

Example 4.2.3. The characteristic function of the binomial random variable is obtained as

$$\phi_Y(\omega) = \sum_{k=0}^{N} e^{j\omega k}C_k^N p^k(1-p)^{N-k} = \sum_{k=0}^{N} C_k^N(p\,e^{j\omega})^k(1-p)^{N-k}$$

and using the binomial theorem

$$\phi_Y(\omega) = [p\,e^{j\omega} + (1-p)]^N \tag{4.2.9}$$

The mean can be obtained as

$$\frac{d\phi_Y(\omega)}{d\omega} = \frac{d\{[p\,e^{j\omega} + (1-p)]^N\}}{d\omega} = N[p\,e^{j\omega} + (1-p)]^{N-1}(jp\,e^{j\omega})$$

and

$$E(Y) = (-j)\frac{d\phi_Y(\omega)}{d\omega}\bigg|_{\omega=0} = Np$$

Likewise, the mean square value is obtained as

$$\frac{d^2\phi_Y(\omega)}{d\omega^2} = \frac{d^2\{[p\,e^{j\omega}+(1-p)]^N\}}{d\omega^2}$$

$$= N(N-1)[p\,e^{j\omega}+(1-p)]^{N-2}(jp\,e^{j\omega})^2$$

$$+ N[p\,e^{j\omega}+(1-p)]^{N-1}(jp\,e^{j\omega})(j)$$

and

$$E(Y^2) = (-j)^2 \frac{d^2\phi_Y(\omega)}{d\omega^2}\bigg|_{\omega=0} = N(N-1)p^2 + Np$$

From this the variance is

$$\mathrm{Var}(Y) = N(N-1)p^2 + Np - (Np)^2 = Np(1-p) \qquad \square$$

Since the binomial random variable takes on equally spaced values, the factorial moments may be more appropriate. The factorial moments can be obtained from the probability generating function, defined for discrete random variables as

$$G(z) = E(z^X) = \sum_{k=-\infty}^{\infty} z^k P(X=k) \tag{4.2.10}$$

and the nth factorial moment in terms of this as

$$E[X(X-1)\cdots(X-n+1)] = \frac{d^n G(z)}{dz^n}\bigg|_{z=1} \tag{4.2.11}$$

The probability generating function is essentially the z transform, but with z replaced by z^{-1}.

Example 4.2.4.   The probability generating function for the binomial random variable Y is evaluated as

$$G(z) = \sum_{k=0}^{N} z^k C_k^N p^k (1-p)^{N-k} = \sum_{k=0}^{N} C_k^N (zp)^k (1-p)^{N-k} = (pz+1-p)^N$$

Then

$$E(X) = \frac{dG(z)}{dz}\bigg|_{z=1} = \frac{d[(pz+1-p)^N]}{dz}\bigg|_{z=1} = N(pz+1-p)^{N-1}(p)\big|_{z=1} = Np$$

and

$$E[X(X-1)] = \frac{d^2 G(z)}{dz^2}\bigg|_{z=1} = \frac{d^2[(pz+1-p)^N]}{dz^2}\bigg|_{z=1}$$

$$= N(N-1)(pz+1-p)^{N-2}(p)^2\big|_{z=1} = N(N-1)p^2 \qquad \square$$

Even for discrete random variables the characteristic function will be used almost exclusively here. A listing of the mean, variance, and characteristic function for a large collection of continuous and discrete random variables is given in Appendix C.

4.3 Multiple Random Variables

Statistical expectations are easily extended to multiple random variables by the generalization defined as

$$E[g(X_1, X_2, \ldots, X_N)]$$

$$= \int_{-\infty}^{\infty} \cdots \int_{-\infty}^{\infty} g(x_1, x_2, \ldots, x_N)$$

$$\times f_{X_1 X_2 \cdots X_N}(x_1, x_2, \cdots, x_N) \, dx_1 \, dx_2 \cdots dx_N \qquad (4.3.1a)$$

or in vector notation as

$$E[g(\mathbf{X})] = \int_{-\infty}^{\infty} \cdots \int_{-\infty}^{\infty} g(\mathbf{x}) f_{\mathbf{X}}(\mathbf{x}) \, d\mathbf{x} \qquad (4.3.1b)$$

As in the single-variable case, vector expectations are linear, which results in

$$E\left[\sum_{i=1}^{N} a_i g_i(\mathbf{X}) \right] = \sum_{i=1}^{N} a_i E[g_i(\mathbf{X})] \qquad (4.3.2)$$

A special case of Eq. (4.3.2) arises when $g_i(\mathbf{X})$ is a function only of X_i. The integration for evaluating $E[g_i(X_i)]$ is accomplished by integrating over all other x_j, $j \neq i$, where these integrations reduce to the marginal density function $f_{X_i}(x_i)$. This expected value is then the single integral given as

$$E[g_i(X_i)] = \int_{-\infty}^{\infty} g_i(x_i) f_{X_i}(x_i) \, dx_i$$

For $E[g_i(X_i)]$, $\mathbf{X}$ is replaced by X_i in Eq. (4.3.2) and the expectation on the right involves only one integration. Equation (4.3.2) is valid for both continuous and discrete random variables. An important special case of this is

$$E\left[\sum_{i=1}^{N} a_i X_i \right] = \sum_{i=1}^{N} a_i E(X_i) \qquad (4.3.3)$$

For the statistically independent random variables X_1 and X_2, a useful property is that the expected value of the product of functions of these random variables is equal to the product of the expected values of each of these functions. Consider $E[g_1(X_1)g_2(X_2)]$, which is expressed as

$$E[g_1(X_1)g_2(X_2)] = \int_{-\infty}^{\infty} \int_{-\infty}^{\infty} g_1(x_1)g_2(x_2)f_{X_1X_2}(x_1, x_2)\, dx_1\, dx_2$$

and for statistical independence

$$E[g_1(X_1)g_2(X_2)] = \int_{-\infty}^{\infty} \int_{-\infty}^{\infty} g_1(x_1)g_2(x_2)f_{X_1}(x_1)f_{X_2}(x_2)\, dx_1\, dx_2$$

$$= \left[\int_{-\infty}^{\infty} g_1(x_1)f_{X_1}(x_1)\, dx_1 \right]\left[\int_{-\infty}^{\infty} g_2(x_2)f_{X_2}(x_2)\, dx_2 \right]$$

or

$$E[g_1(X_1)g_2(X_2)] = E[g_1(X_1)]E[g_2(X_2)]$$

The converse of this is not necessarily true; i.e., the expected value of a product equaling the product of expected values does not imply that the random variables are statistically independent. If this expression is true, all of the above integrals are still equal, but the double integral involving $f_{X_1X_2}(x_1, x_2)$ equaling the double integral involving $f_{X_1}(x_1)f_{X_2}(x_2)$ does not necessarily make $f_{X_1X_2}(x_1, x_2)$ equal $f_{X_1}(x_1)f_{X_2}(x_2)$, which is required for statistical independence. Two integrals being equal does not necessarily imply that their integrands are equal (all density functions integrate to 1 and the density functions are not equal). In general for X_i, $i = 1, 2, \ldots, N$, mutually statistically independent random variables, this factorization holds and

$$E\left[\prod_{i=1}^{N} g_i(X_i) \right] = \prod_{i=1}^{N} E[g_i(X_i)] \qquad (4.3.4)$$

Again, the expected value of the product being equal to the product of the expected values does not necessarily imply that the random variables are mutually statistically independent. The proof of Eq. (4.3.4) is the same as the proof for two random variables, but with N instead of two integrals.

Much of statistical analysis involves taking a sample of random variables and summing the sample values. The density function of the sum of N random variables could be obtained by performing $N - 1$ convolutions, as was shown in Section 3.4; but if only the mean and variance of this sum are desired, obtaining the density function of the sum would be a lot of unnecessary work. The mean of the sum of N random variables can be obtained from Eq. (4.3.3) as

$$E\left(\sum_{i=1}^{N} X_i \right) = \sum_{i=1}^{N} E(X_i) \qquad (4.3.5)$$

Also, the variance of the sum can be obtained, using Eq. (4.1.9b) and the expected value of the sum, Eq. (4.3.5), as

$$\text{Var}\left(\sum_{i=1}^{N} X_i\right) = E\left\{\left[\sum_{i=1}^{N} X_i - E\left(\sum_{i=1}^{N} X_i\right)\right]^2\right\} = E\left\{\left[\sum_{i=1}^{N} X_i - \sum_{i=1}^{N} E(X_i)\right]^2\right\}$$

$$= E\left\{\left[\sum_{i=1}^{N} (X_i - E(X_i))\right]^2\right\}$$

$$= E\left\{\sum_{i=1}^{N}\sum_{j=1}^{N} [X_i - E(X_i)][X_j - E(X_j)]\right\}$$

where a summation squared can always be written as a double summation with two different indices. The expectation cannot be brought inside the squared term, but it can be brought inside the double summation to yield

$$\text{Var}\left(\sum_{i=1}^{N} X_i\right) = \sum_{i=1}^{N}\sum_{j=1}^{N} E\{[X_i - E(X_i)][X_j - E(X_j)]\}$$

The expected value in the double summation yields different terms for $i = j$ and $i \neq j$. Thus, the double summation is broken up into a single summation of equal terms and a double summation of unequal terms as

$$\text{Var}\left(\sum_{i=1}^{N} X_i\right) = \sum_{i=1}^{N} E\{[X_i - E(X_i)]^2\}$$

$$+ \sum_{i=1}^{N}\sum_{\substack{j=1 \\ j \neq i}}^{N} E\{[X_i - E(X_i)][X_j - E(X_j)]\} \qquad (4.3.6)$$

The terms in the single summation should be recognized as the variances $\text{Var}(X_i)$, $i = 1, 2, \ldots, N$, and the terms in the double summation will now be defined as covariances. The covariance of the two random variables X_i and X_j is defined as

$$\text{Cov}(X_i, X_j) = E\{[X_i - E(X_i)][X_j - E(X_j)]\} \qquad (4.3.7a)$$

which can be put in an alternative form (as was the variance) as

$$\text{Cov}(X_i, X_j) = E(X_i X_j) - E(X_j)E(X_i) - E(X_i)E(X_j) + E(X_i)E(X_j)$$

or

$$\text{Cov}(X_i, X_j) = E(X_i X_j) - E(X_i)E(X_j) \qquad (4.3.7b)$$

From Eq. (4.3.7) it can be seen that $\text{Cov}(X_i, X_i) = \text{Var}(X_i)$ and $\text{Cov}(X_i, X_j) = \text{Cov}(X_j, X_i)$ since the order of terms in a product is irrelevant. The variance of a sum of random variables is expressed in terms of the sum of variances and covariances of the random variables as

$$\text{Var}\left(\sum_{i=1}^{N} X_i\right) = \sum_{i=1}^{N} \text{Var}(X_i) + \sum_{i=1}^{N} \sum_{\substack{j=1 \\ j \neq i}}^{N} \text{Cov}(X_i, X_j) \qquad (4.3.8)$$

From Eq. (4.3.4), if the random variables X_i, $i = 1, 2, \ldots, N$, are mutually statistically independent, $E(X_iX_j) = E(X_i)E(X_j)$, $i \neq j = 1, 2, \ldots, N$; and from Eq. (4.3.7b), $\text{Cov}(X_i, X_j) = 0$, $i \neq j = 1, 2, \ldots, N$. If $\text{Cov}(X_i, X_j) = 0$, X_i and X_j are said to be uncorrelated. For the random variables X_i, $i = 1, 2, \ldots, N$, uncorrelated, which is a weaker statement than statistical independence, Eq. (4.3.8) reduces to

$$\text{Var}\left(\sum_{i=1}^{N} X_i\right) = \sum_{i=1}^{N} \text{Var}(X_i) \qquad (4.3.9)$$

or the variance of the sum equals the sum of the variances if the random variables are uncorrelated. Equation (4.3.9) also holds if the random variables are mutually statistically independent.

Example 4.3.1. Determine $\text{Var}(Y)$ when $Y = 2X_1 - 3X_2$ with $\text{Var}(X_1) = 5$, $\text{Var}(X_2) = 6$, $\text{Cov}(X_1, X_2) = 4$, and $E(X_1) = E(X_2) = 0$. Now,

$$\text{Var}(Y) = \text{Var}(2X_1 - 3X_2) = 4\,\text{Var}(X_1) - 12\,\text{Cov}(X_1, X_2) + 9\,\text{Var}(X_2)$$

$$= 4(5) - 12(4) + 9(6) = 26 \qquad \square$$

The first term in Eq. (4.3.7b), $E(X_iX_j)$, is called the correlation of the random variables X_i and X_j. If $E(X_1X_2) = E(X_1)E(X_2)$

$$\text{Cov}(X_1, X_2) = E(X_1X_2) - E(X_1)E(X_2) = 0$$

and if $\text{Cov}(X_1, X_2) = 0$

$$0 = E(X_1X_2) - E(X_1)E(X_2)$$

or

$$E(X_1X_2) = E(X_1)E(X_2)$$

Thus $E(X_1X_2) = E(X_1)E(X_2)$ is equivalent to $\text{Cov}(X_1, X_2) = 0$ or

$$E(X_1X_2) = E(X_1)E(X_2) \Leftrightarrow \text{Cov}(X_1, X_2) = 0 \qquad (4.3.10)$$

An equivalent definition of X_1 and X_2 being uncorrelated is that $E(X_1X_2) = E(X_1)E(X_2)$. As was observed from Eqs. (4.3.4) and (4.3.7b), if X_1 and X_2 are statistically independent then X_1 and X_2 are uncorrelated, but since the converse of Eq. (4.3.4) was not true, if X_1 and X_2 are uncorrelated then X_1 and X_2 are not necessarily statistically independent. This is represented as

$$X_1 \text{ and } X_2 \text{ statistically independent} \Rightarrow \text{Cov}(X_1, X_2) = 0 \qquad (4.3.11)$$

Since the converse of this is not true, the statement that random variables are uncorrelated is weaker than the statement that they are statistically independent.

An example is now considered to show that two random variables can be uncorrelated and not statistically independent.

Example 4.3.2. Consider the case with Z a uniform random variable where

$$f_Z(z) = \frac{1}{2\pi} \qquad 0 \le z < 2\pi$$

$$= 0 \qquad \text{otherwise}$$

and the two variables under consideration defined in terms of Z as

$$X = \sin(Z) \qquad Y = \cos(Z)$$

The expected value of X is given as

$$E(X) = E[\sin(Z)] = \int_0^{2\pi} \sin(z) \left(\frac{1}{2\pi}\right) dz = 0$$

and the expected value of Y as

$$E(Y) = E[\cos(Z)] = \int_0^{2\pi} \cos(z) \left(\frac{1}{2\pi}\right) dz = 0$$

Also, the expected value of XY is obtained as

$$E(XY) = E[\sin(Z)\cos(Z)] = \int_0^{2\pi} \sin(z)\cos(z) \left(\frac{1}{2\pi}\right) dz = 0$$

Thus, $\text{Cov}(X, Y) = 0$ and X and Y are uncorrelated. Now, the expected value of X^2 is given as

$$E(X^2) = E[\sin^2(Z)] = \int_0^{2\pi} \sin^2(z) \left(\frac{1}{2\pi}\right) dz = \frac{1}{2}$$

and the expected value of Y^2 as

$$E(Y^2) = E[\cos^2(Z)] = \int_0^{2\pi} \cos^2(z) \left(\frac{1}{2\pi}\right) dz = \frac{1}{2}$$

Also, the expected value of $X^2 Y^2$ is obtained as

$$E(X^2 Y^2) = E[\sin^2(Z)\cos^2(Z)] = \int_0^{2\pi} \sin^2(z) \cos^2(z) \left(\frac{1}{2\pi}\right) dz = \frac{1}{8}$$

Note that $E(X^2 Y^2) = \frac{1}{8} \neq (\frac{1}{2})(\frac{1}{2}) = E(X^2)E(Y^2)$, but if X and Y were statistically independent $E(X^2 Y^2)$ would equal $E(X^2)E(Y^2)$. An alternative way of observing that X and Y are not statistically independent is to observe that $X^2 + Y^2 = \sin^2(z) + \cos^2(z) = 1$, which implies that if $X = x$, Y is one of two values $Y = \pm\sqrt{1 - x^2}$. Thus, even though X and Y are uncorrelated, X and Y are not statistically independent.   □

Two additional definitions are useful at this point. The random variables X and Y are said to be orthogonal if and only if $E(XY) = 0$. If X and Y are both orthogonal and uncorrelated, either X or Y must have mean 0. The correlation coefficient of the random variables X and Y, denoted by ρ_{xy} or ρ, is defined as

$$\rho = \rho_{xy} = \frac{\text{Cov}(X, Y)}{\sqrt{\text{Var}(X)\,\text{Var}(Y)}} \tag{4.3.12}$$

which is a normalized version of the covariance. This is the same parameter that was used in Sections 2.4 and 2.5 in conjunction with the bivariate Gaussian density function, and it will be shown in Section 4.6 that $-1 \le \rho \le 1$.

Example 4.3.3. Determine $\text{Cov}(X, Y)$, ρ, and whether X and Y are uncorrelated when $f_{XY}(x, y) = x + y$, $0 \le x \le 1$, $0 \le y \le 1$. The marginal density functions are determined first

$$f_X(x) = \int_0^1 (x + y)\, dy = x + \frac{1}{2}$$

and

$$f_Y(y) = \int_0^1 (x + y)\, dx = y + \frac{1}{2}$$

The means are obtained from these marginal density functions as

$$E(X) = \int_0^1 x\left(x + \frac{1}{2}\right) dx = \frac{7}{12}$$

and

$$E(Y) = \int_0^1 y\left(y + \frac{1}{2}\right) dy = \frac{7}{12}$$

and the second moments as

$$E(X^2) = \int_0^1 x^2\left(x + \frac{1}{2}\right) dx = \frac{5}{12}$$

and

$$E(Y^2) = \int_0^1 y^2\left(y + \frac{1}{2}\right) dy = \frac{5}{12}$$

The variances are obtained as $\text{Var}(X) = E(X^2) - [E(X)]^2 = \frac{5}{12} - (\frac{7}{12})^2 = \frac{11}{144}$ and $\text{Var}(Y) = E(Y^2) - [E(Y)]^2 = \frac{5}{12} - (\frac{7}{12})^2 = \frac{11}{144}$. The correlation of X and Y is given as

$$E(XY) = \int_0^1 \int_0^1 xy(x+y) \, dx \, dy = \frac{1}{3}$$

and the covariance is $\text{Cov}(X, Y) = E(XY) - E(X)E(Y) = \frac{1}{3} - (\frac{7}{12})(\frac{7}{12}) = -\frac{1}{144}$. Finally, from Eq. (4.3.12), $\rho = -\frac{1}{11}$ and X and Y are correlated. $\square$

Equation (2.4.5) is the bivariate Gaussian density function of X and Y with the means 0 and the variances 1. The general bivariate Gaussian density function of X and Y has the five parameters μ_x, σ_x^2, μ_y, σ_y^2, and ρ [ρ_{xy} or $\text{Cov}(X, Y)$] and is given as

$$f_{XY}(x, y) = \frac{1}{2\pi\sigma_x\sigma_y\sqrt{1-\rho^2}}$$

$$\times \exp\left[\frac{-([(x-\mu_x)/\sigma_x]^2 - 2\rho[(x-\mu_x)/\sigma_x][(y-\mu_y)/\sigma_y] + [(y-\mu_y)/\sigma_y]^2)}{2[1-\rho^2]}\right]$$

$$-\infty < x < \infty \quad -\infty < y < \infty \qquad (4.3.13)$$

The corresponding marginal density functions are

$$f_X(x) = \frac{1}{\sqrt{2\pi\sigma_x^2}} \exp\left[\frac{-(x-\mu_x)^2}{2\sigma_x^2}\right] \quad -\infty < x < \infty$$

$$f_Y(y) = \frac{1}{\sqrt{2\pi\sigma_y^2}} \exp\left[\frac{-(y-\mu_y)^2}{2\sigma_y^2}\right] \quad -\infty < y < \infty$$

If X and Y are uncorrelated, $\text{Cov}(X, Y) = 0$ and $\rho = 0$, which implies, from Eq. (4.3.13), that $f_{XY}(x, y) = f_X(x)f_Y(y)$ or that X and Y are statistically independent. Therefore, uncorrelated and statistically independent are equivalent for Gaussian random variables. This is represented as

$$X \text{ and } Y \text{ statistically independent} \Leftrightarrow \text{Cov}(X, Y) = 0 \text{ (Gaussian)} \qquad (4.3.14)$$

Example 4.3.4. Determine a and b for $Y_1 = X_1$ and $Y_2 = aX_1 + bX_2$ such that $E(X_1) = E(X_2) = E(Y_1) = E(Y_2) = 0$, $\text{Var}(X_1) = \text{Var}(Y_1) = 2$, $\text{Var}(X_2) = 4$, $\text{Var}(Y_2) = 86$, $\text{Cov}(X_1, X_2) = 0$, and $\text{Cov}(Y_1, Y_2) = 10$. Since the means are 0

$$\text{Cov}(Y_1, Y_2) = E(Y_1 Y_2) = E[X_1(aX_1 + bX_2)] = aE(X_1^2) + bE(X_1 X_2)$$

$$= a \, \text{Var}(X_1) + b \, \text{Cov}(X_1, X_2) = a(2) + b(0) = 10$$

and $a = 5$. Again, since the means are 0

$$\text{Var}(Y_2) = E(Y_2^2) = E[(aX_1 + bX_2)^2] = E(a^2 X_1^2 + 2ab X_1 X_2 + b^2 X_2^2)$$

$$= a^2 \text{Var}(X_1) + 2ab \text{Cov}(X_1, X_2) + b^2 \text{Var}(X_2)$$

$$= a^2(2) + 2ab(0) + b^2(4) = 86$$

Solving gives $b = \pm 3$ and the two solutions are $a = 5$, $b = 3$ and $a = 5$, $b = -3$.   □

A second important use of the characteristic function, which is in the sum of statistically independent random variables, will now be considered. For $Z = X + Y$, where X and Y are statistically independent random variables, the characteristic function of Z is expressed as

$$\phi_Z(\omega) = E(e^{j\omega Z}) = E(e^{j\omega X + j\omega Y})$$

$$= E(e^{j\omega X} e^{j\omega Y})$$

Since X and Y are statistically independent, the expected value of a product is equal to the product of expected values, Eq. (4.3.4), so the characteristic function of Z becomes

$$\phi_Z(\omega) = E(e^{j\omega X}) E(e^{j\omega Y}) = \phi_X(\omega) \phi_Y(\omega) \qquad (4.3.15)$$

Thus, the characteristic function of a sum of two independent random variables is the product of the characteristic functions of the two random variables. This result is consistent with the results of Section 3.4, where the density function of the sum of two statistically independent random variables was the convolution of the two individual density functions. Since the characteristic function is a Fourier transform, a standard result of Fourier transform theory is that the transform of the convolution of two functions is the product of the Fourier transforms of the functions (likewise for Laplace and z transforms). This concept is also an important part of linear system theory, where the output of a linear system is the convolution of the input with the impulse response of the system, and the transformed output is the product of the transformed input and the transfer function (transform of the impulse response) of the system. In some cases working with the convolution may be easier and in other cases working the transform may be easier.

Consider Z to be the sum of the two Gaussian random variables X and Y. Let X be a Gaussian random variable with mean μ_x and variance σ_x^2, Y be a Gaussian random variable with mean μ_y and variance σ_y^2, and X and Y be statistically independent. From Eq. (4.2.7)

$$\phi_X(\omega) = \exp(j\omega\mu_x - \omega^2 \sigma_x^2/2)$$

and

$$\phi_Y(\omega) = \exp(j\omega\mu_y - \omega^2\sigma_y^2/2)$$

which yields

$$\phi_Z(\omega) = \exp[j\omega(\mu_x + \mu_y) - \omega^2(\sigma_x^2 + \sigma_y^2)/2]$$

Thus, Z is also Gaussian, with mean $\mu_z = \mu_x + \mu_y$ and variance $\sigma_z^2 = \sigma_x^2 + \sigma_y^2$. This procedure was much simpler than the convolution performed in Section 3.4.

This result can be generalized to the sum of N statistically independent Gaussian random variables, since the product of Gaussian characteristic functions yields a Gaussian characteristic function. If

$$Z = \sum_{i=1}^{N} X_i$$

where the X_i's are mutually statistically independent Gaussian random variables with means μ_i and variances σ_i^2, the characteristic function of Z is obtained as

$$\phi_Z(\omega) = \prod_{i=1}^{N} \phi_{X_i}(\omega) = \prod_{i=1}^{N} \exp\left(j\omega\mu_i - \frac{\omega^2\sigma_i^2}{2}\right)$$

or

$$\phi_Z(\omega) = \exp\left[j\omega\left(\sum_{i=1}^{N}\mu_i\right) - \frac{\omega^2}{2}\left(\sum_{i=1}^{N}\sigma_i^2\right)\right]$$

Then Z is Gaussian with mean and variance given as

$$\mu_Z = \sum_{i=1}^{N}\mu_i \qquad \sigma_Z^2 = \sum_{i=1}^{N}\sigma_i^2 \qquad (4.3.16)$$

This is much simpler than performing $N-1$ convolutions.

Example 4.3.5. Determine $f_Z(z)$ when $Z = X + Y$ for the statistically independent Cauchy random variables X and Y where $f_X(x) = (a/\pi)[1/(x^2 + a^2)]$, $-\infty < x < \infty$, with $\phi_X(\omega) = e^{-a|\omega|}$, and $f_Y(y) = (b/\pi)[1/(y^2 + b^2)]$, $-\infty < y < \infty$, with $\phi_Y(\omega) = e^{-b|\omega|}$. Using Eq. (4.3.15), the characteristic function of Z is obtained as $\phi_Z(\omega) = e^{-(a+b)|\omega|}$. Since $\phi_Z(\omega)$ is of the same form as $\phi_X(\omega)$, Z is a Cauchy random variable with parameter $a+b$. The density function of the sum is then $f_Z(z) = [(a+b)/\pi][1/(z^2 + (a+b)^2)]$, $-\infty < z < \infty$. $\square$

As an example with discrete random variables consider the sum of binomial random variables.

Example 4.3.6. Let Z be the sum of the statistically independent binomial random variables X and Y. If X has parameters N and p and Y has parameters M and p, the characteristic functions are given, from Eq. (4.2.9), as

$$\phi_X(\omega) = [p\,e^{j\omega} + (1-p)]^N$$

and

$$\phi_Y(\omega) = [p\,e^{j\omega} + (1-p)]^M$$

The characteristic function of $Z = X + Y$ is given as

$$\phi_Z(\omega) = [p\,e^{j\omega} + (1-p)]^{N+M} \qquad (4.3.17)$$

and Z is a binomial random variable with parameters $N + M$ and p.   □

This is consistent with the discrete convolution of Fig. 3.4.4, Example 3.4.4, where in that case $N = 3$, $M = 2$, and $p = 0.4$. The development of Eq. (4.3.17) by using convolution would present the interested student with a challenge.

The sum Z of two statistically independent binomial random variables X and Y is not a binomial random variable unless the parameter p is the same for both X and Y. To show this let X have parameters N and p_1 and Y have parameters M and p_2. Then Z has parameters $N + M$ and p. The mean of Z is the sum of the means of X and Y and is expressed as

$$E(Z) = E(X + Y) = E(X) + E(Y) = Np_1 + Mp_2 = (N+M)p$$

where the mean for a binomial random variable is given in Example 4.1.4. Since X and Y are statistically independent, the variance of Z is the sum of the variances of X and Y and is expressed as

$$\text{Var}(Z) = \text{Var}(X + Y) = \text{Var}(X) + \text{Var}(Y)$$
$$= Np_1(1 - p_1) + Mp_2(1 - p_2) = (N+M)p(1-p)$$

where the variance for a binomial random variable is given in Example 4.1.8. Solving for p in the mean equation and putting it into the variance equation yields

$$Np_1(1-p_1) + Mp_2(1-p_2) = (Np_1 + Mp_2)(N + M - Np_1 - Mp_2)/(N+M)$$

or multiplying by $N + M$

$$(N^2 + NM)p_1(1-p_1) + (NM + M^2)p_2(1-p_2)$$
$$= N^2 p_1(1-p_1) + NM[p_1(1-p_2) + p_2(1-p_1)] + M^2 p_2(1-p_2)$$

which reduces to

$$p_1(1-p_1)+p_2(1-p_2) = p_1(1-p_2)+p_2(1-p_1)$$

Finally, this gives that $p_2^2 - 2p_1 p_2 + p_1^2 = (p_2 - p_1)^2 = 0$. Thus $p_2 = p_1 = p$.

It can also be shown that the sum of N statistically independent Poisson random variables with parameters a_i, $i = 1, 2, \ldots, N$, is a Poisson random variable with parameter the sum of the a_i's (see Problem 4.3.14). This satisfies intuition, since if the Poisson random variables are the number of photons counted in N different photomultiplier tubes, the total number counted in all of the photomultiplier tubes is a Poisson random variable with the average value (parameter) equal to the sum of the individual average values.

4.4   *N*-Dimensional Gaussian

Observing Eq. (4.3.13), the two-dimensional Gaussian density function, gives an indication of how complex the density function would be for the N-dimensional case if written in this manner. However, it is much simpler to write this N-dimensional Gaussian density function in matrix notation. An introduction to matrix notation and manipulation is given in Appendix D. Letting the random vector $\mathbf{X}$ be an $N \times 1$ column vector of random variables, the transpose of $\mathbf{X}$ is a $1 \times N$ row vector given as $\mathbf{X}^T = (X_1, X_2, \ldots, X_N)$. The parameters of the N-dimensional Gaussian density function are then a mean vector (or vector of means) given as

$$\boldsymbol{\mu}_x^T = E(\mathbf{X}^T) = (E(X_1), E(X_2), \ldots, E(X_N)) = (\mu_1, \mu_2, \ldots, \mu_N)$$

and an $N \times N$ covariance matrix (matrix of variances and covariances) as

$$\boldsymbol{\Sigma}_x = E[(\mathbf{X}-\boldsymbol{\mu}_X)(\mathbf{X}-\boldsymbol{\mu}_X)^T] = \begin{bmatrix} \sigma_1^2 & \sigma_{12} & \cdots & \sigma_{1N} \\ \sigma_{21} & \sigma_2^2 & \cdots & \sigma_{2N} \\ \vdots & \vdots & & \vdots \\ \sigma_{N1} & \sigma_{N2} & \cdots & \sigma_N^2 \end{bmatrix}$$

Expanding out the product $(\mathbf{X}-\boldsymbol{\mu}_x)(\mathbf{X}-\boldsymbol{\mu}_x)^T$, the ijth term, $i \neq j$, can be seen to be $(X_i - \mu_i)(X_j - \mu_j)$, so that $E[(X_i - \mu_i)(X_j - \mu_j)] = \text{Cov}(X_i, X_j) = \sigma_{ij}$, $i \neq j$. As can be seen from the covariance matrix $\boldsymbol{\Sigma}_x$, the diagonal terms are the variances and the off-diagonal terms the covariances. Also, since $\sigma_{ij} = \sigma_{ji}$ the covariance matrix is symmetric. The N-dimensional Gaussian density function is written in terms of these vector and matrix parameters as

$$f_{\mathbf{X}}(\mathbf{x}) = \frac{1}{(2\pi)^{N/2}\sqrt{|\boldsymbol{\Sigma}_x|}} \exp\left[\frac{-(\mathbf{x}-\boldsymbol{\mu}_x)^T \boldsymbol{\Sigma}_x^{-1}(\mathbf{x}-\boldsymbol{\mu}_x)}{2}\right] \qquad (4.4.1)$$

where $|\Sigma_x|$ is the determinant of the covariance matrix. Since $(\mathbf{x}-\boldsymbol{\mu}_x)^T$ is a $1 \times N$ matrix, Σ_x^{-1} is an $N \times N$ matrix, and $(\mathbf{x}-\boldsymbol{\mu}_x)$ is an $N \times 1$ matrix, the matrix multiplication $(\mathbf{x}-\boldsymbol{\mu}_x)^T\Sigma_x^{-1}(\mathbf{x}-\boldsymbol{\mu}_x)$ is a 1×1 matrix or a scalar, and the argument of the exponent in Eq. (4.4.1) is a scalar. Also, the normalizing constant times the exponent is a scalar since the determinant is a scalar.

The corresponding N-dimensional Gaussian characteristic function (N-dimensional Fourier transform of the N-dimensional Gaussian random vector) is given as

$$\phi_{\mathbf{X}}(\boldsymbol{\omega}) = E[\exp(j\boldsymbol{\omega}^T\mathbf{X})] = E\left[\exp\left(j\sum_{i=1}^{N}\omega_i X_i\right)\right]$$

$$= \exp\left(j\boldsymbol{\omega}^T\boldsymbol{\mu}_x - \frac{\boldsymbol{\omega}^T\Sigma_x\boldsymbol{\omega}}{2}\right) \qquad (4.4.2)$$

The vector variable $\boldsymbol{\omega}$ of the transformation is an $N \times 1$ matrix. The matrix products $\boldsymbol{\omega}^T\boldsymbol{\mu}_x$ and $\boldsymbol{\omega}^T\Sigma_x\boldsymbol{\omega}$ are 1×1 matrices or scalars, so the argument of the exponent in the characteristic function is a scalar.

Several cases of interest for the N-dimensional Gaussian random vector will now be considered. The simplest case for the covariance matrix is when all of the variables are uncorrelated and have variance 1 or

$$\Sigma_x = \mathbf{I} = \begin{bmatrix} 1 & 0 & \cdots & 0 \\ 0 & 1 & \cdots & 0 \\ \vdots & \vdots & & \vdots \\ 0 & 0 & \cdots & 1 \end{bmatrix}$$

where $\mathbf{I}$ is called the identity matrix $(\mathbf{CC}^{-1} = \mathbf{C}^{-1}\mathbf{C} = \mathbf{I})$. The inverse of the covariance matrix $\Sigma_x^{-1} = \mathbf{I}$, and the quadratic form in the exponent of Eq. (4.4.1) becomes

$$(\mathbf{x}-\boldsymbol{\mu}_x)^T\Sigma_x^{-1}(\mathbf{x}-\boldsymbol{\mu}_x) = (\mathbf{x}-\boldsymbol{\mu}_x)^T\mathbf{I}(\mathbf{x}-\boldsymbol{\mu}_x) = (\mathbf{x}-\boldsymbol{\mu}_x)^T(\mathbf{x}-\boldsymbol{\mu}_x) = \sum_{i=1}^{N}(x_i-\mu_i)^2$$

Since the exponential of the sum is the product of exponentials

$$\exp\left[-\sum_{i=1}^{N}\frac{(x_i-\mu_i)^2}{2}\right] = \prod_{i=1}^{N}\exp\left[\frac{-(x_i-\mu_i)^2}{2}\right]$$

and for this case the joint Gaussian density function is

$$f_{\mathbf{X}}(\mathbf{x}) = \prod_{i=1}^{N}\frac{1}{\sqrt{2\pi}}\exp\left[\frac{-(x_i-\mu_i)^2}{2}\right] = \prod_{i=1}^{N}f_{X_i}(x_i)$$

Thus the random variables with $\Sigma_x = \mathbf{I}$ are statistically independent and all have variance 1.

For a second case let $X_1, X_2, \ldots, X_N$ be uncorrelated but of unequal variances or

$$
\Sigma_x = \begin{bmatrix} \sigma_1^2 & 0 & \cdots & 0 \\ 0 & \sigma_2^2 & \cdots & 0 \\ \vdots & \vdots & & \vdots \\ 0 & 0 & \cdots & \sigma_N^2 \end{bmatrix}
$$

The inverse of Σ_x can be obtained as

$$
\Sigma_x^{-1} = \begin{bmatrix} 1/\sigma_1^2 & 0 & \cdots & 0 \\ 0 & 1/\sigma_2^2 & \cdots & 0 \\ \vdots & \vdots & & \vdots \\ 0 & 0 & \cdots & 1/\sigma_N^2 \end{bmatrix}
$$

(which can be verified by checking $\Sigma_x \Sigma_x^{-1} = I$). The quadratic form in the exponent of Eq. (4.4.1) becomes

$$
(\mathbf{x} - \boldsymbol{\mu}_x)^T \Sigma_x^{-1} (\mathbf{x} - \boldsymbol{\mu}_x) = \sum_{i=1}^{N} \frac{1}{\sigma_i^2} (x_i - \mu_i)^2
$$

and the joint Gaussian density function in this case is

$$
f_{\mathbf{X}}(\mathbf{x}) = \prod_{i=1}^{N} \frac{1}{\sqrt{2\pi\sigma_i^2}} \exp\left[\frac{-(x_i - \mu_i)^2}{2\sigma_i^2} \right] = \prod_{i=1}^{N} f_{X_i}(x_i)
$$

which shows that if the X_i's are Gaussian and uncorrelated (diagonal covariance matrix) they are also statistically independent.

Example 4.4.1. A two-dimensional example of correlated Gaussian random variables is $\mathbf{X}^T = (X_1, X_2)$ with $\boldsymbol{\mu}_x^T = (0, 0)$ and

$$
\Sigma_x = \begin{bmatrix} 5 & 6 \\ 6 & 9 \end{bmatrix}
$$

The inverse of the covariance matrix is

$$
\Sigma_x^{-1} = \frac{1}{9} \begin{bmatrix} 9 & -6 \\ -6 & 5 \end{bmatrix}
$$

and $|\Sigma_x| = 9$. Now, the quadratic form in the exponent of Eq. (4.4.1) becomes

$$
\mathbf{x}^T \Sigma_x^{-1} \mathbf{x} = \frac{1}{9} [x_1 \ \ x_2] \begin{bmatrix} 9 & -6 \\ -6 & 5 \end{bmatrix} \begin{bmatrix} x_1 \\ x_2 \end{bmatrix} = \frac{1}{9} [9x_1 - 6x_2 \ \ \ -6x_1 + 5x_2] \begin{bmatrix} x_1 \\ x_2 \end{bmatrix}
$$

or $\mathbf{x}^T \Sigma_x^{-1} \mathbf{x} = (9x_1^2 - 12x_1 x_2 + 5x_2^2)/9$, and the joint Gaussian density function becomes

$$f_{\mathbf{X}}(\mathbf{x}) = f_{X_1 X_2}(x_1, x_2) = \frac{1}{6\pi} \exp\left[\frac{-(9x_1^2 - 12x_1 x_2 + 5x_2^2)}{18}\right] \qquad \square$$

A contour plot of constant probability density is obtained by setting the exponent of the N-dimensional Gaussian density function, Eq. (4.4.1), equal to a constant. For two random variables, as in Example 4.4.1, a contour plot of constant probability density can be represented in two dimensions. Information about the values of the variances and whether the variables are uncorrelated can be obtained from this contour plot. Several contour plots of equal constant probability density are shown in Fig. 4.4.1. As can be seen from Eq. (4.4.1) and Example 4.4.1, the contour plots are ellipses. In Fig. 4.4.1a the variables are uncorrelated and have equal variances and the ellipse reduces to a circle. For uncorrelated and unequal variances the constant probability contour is an ellipse, as seen in Fig. 4.4.1b, whose major and minor axes align with the x_1 and x_2 axes. In this case $\sigma_1^2 > \sigma_2^2$. Figure 4.4.1c shows a constant probability contour where the variables are correlated. As seen in this figure, the major and minor axes of the ellipse do not align with the x_1 and x_2 axes. The variances of the variables in Fig. 4.4.1c are not equal and $\sigma_2^2 > \sigma_1^2$. The constant probability contours of Fig. 4.4.1 are shown for zero means, but nonzero mean would just shift the center of the ellipses.

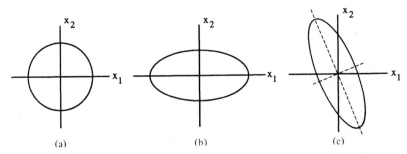

Fig. 4.4.1. Equal-probability contours for two Gaussian random variables: (a) uncorrelated equal variance; (b) uncorrelated unequal variance; (c) correlated unequal variance.

As seen in Example 4.4.1 and the preceding cases, the mean vector and the covariance matrix for a Gaussian random vector convey the same information as the joint density function, Equation (4.4.1), but the mean vector and covariance matrix are easier to work with.

Example 4.4.2. For the case where $\mathbf{X}^T = (X_1, X_2, X_3)$ is a Gaussian random vector with $\boldsymbol{\mu}^T = (1, 2, 3)$ and

$$\Sigma_x = \begin{bmatrix} 4 & 2 & 0 \\ 2 & 5 & -1 \\ 0 & -1 & 1 \end{bmatrix}$$

it can be observed that $\mu_3 = 3$, $\text{Var}(X_2) = \sigma_2^2 = 5$, and $\text{Cov}(X_1, X_3) = \sigma_{13} = 0$.   □

A useful property of Gaussian random variables is that their linear transformations and translations yield new Gaussian random variables. Consider the general linear transformation

$$\mathbf{Y} = \mathbf{AX} + \mathbf{B}$$

(in reality a linear transformation $\mathbf{AX}$ followed by a translation $\mathbf{B}$), where $\mathbf{X}$ is a Gaussian random vector. The characteristic function of $\mathbf{Y}$ is determined as

$$\phi_\mathbf{Y}(\boldsymbol{\omega}) = E[\exp(j\boldsymbol{\omega}^\mathrm{T}\mathbf{Y})] = E[\exp(j\boldsymbol{\omega}^\mathrm{T}(\mathbf{AX} + \mathbf{B}))]$$

$$= E[\exp(j\boldsymbol{\omega}^\mathrm{T}\mathbf{AX})\exp(j\boldsymbol{\omega}^\mathrm{T}\mathbf{B})] = \exp(j\boldsymbol{\omega}^\mathrm{T}\mathbf{B})E[\exp(j\boldsymbol{\omega}^\mathrm{T}\mathbf{AX})]$$

Letting $\boldsymbol{\omega}'^\mathrm{T} = \boldsymbol{\omega}^\mathrm{T}\mathbf{A}$ (or $\boldsymbol{\omega}' = \mathbf{A}^\mathrm{T}\boldsymbol{\omega}$)

$$E[\exp(j\boldsymbol{\omega}^\mathrm{T}\mathbf{AX})] = E[\exp(j\boldsymbol{\omega}'^\mathrm{T}\mathbf{X})] = \phi_\mathbf{X}(\boldsymbol{\omega}') = \exp(j\boldsymbol{\omega}'^\mathrm{T}\boldsymbol{\mu}_x - \boldsymbol{\omega}'^\mathrm{T}\Sigma_x\boldsymbol{\omega}'/2)$$

$$= \exp(j\boldsymbol{\omega}^\mathrm{T}\mathbf{A}\boldsymbol{\mu}_x - \boldsymbol{\omega}^\mathrm{T}\mathbf{A}\Sigma_x\mathbf{A}^\mathrm{T}\boldsymbol{\omega}/2)$$

Combining gives

$$\phi_\mathbf{Y}(\boldsymbol{\omega}) = \exp[j\boldsymbol{\omega}^\mathrm{T}(\mathbf{A}\boldsymbol{\mu}_x + \mathbf{B}) - \boldsymbol{\omega}^\mathrm{T}(\mathbf{A}\Sigma_x\mathbf{A}^\mathrm{T})\boldsymbol{\omega}/2]$$

which is a Gaussian characteristic function. Thus, $\mathbf{Y}$ is a Gaussian random variable with

$$\boldsymbol{\mu}_y = \mathbf{A}\boldsymbol{\mu}_x + \mathbf{B} \qquad \text{and} \qquad \Sigma_y = \mathbf{A}\Sigma_x\mathbf{A}^\mathrm{T} \tag{4.4.3}$$

or linear combinations of Gaussian random variables are Gaussian random variables. This is extremely useful in electrical engineering systems, since it implies that if Gaussian random variables are input to a linear system the output is also Gaussian. Then, only the mean vector and covariance matrix must be computed to completely characterize the statistics of the output.

Example 4.4.3.   Consider the case of a three-dimensional Gaussian random vector $\mathbf{X}$ with $\boldsymbol{\mu}^\mathrm{T} = (1, 2, 3)$ and

$$\Sigma_x = \begin{bmatrix} 4 & 2 & 0 \\ 2 & 5 & -1 \\ 0 & -1 & 1 \end{bmatrix}$$

with the linear transformation $\mathbf{Y} = \mathbf{A}\mathbf{X} + \mathbf{B}$, where $\mathbf{Y}^T = (Y_1, Y_2)$, and $Y_1 = X_1 - X_2 + X_3 + 4$ and $Y_2 = 2X_1 - X_3 + 6$. $\mathbf{Y}$ is a two-dimensional Gaussian random vector. Now $\mathbf{B}^T = (4, 6)$ and

$$\mathbf{A} = \begin{bmatrix} 1 & -1 & 1 \\ 2 & 0 & -1 \end{bmatrix}$$

which yields

$$\boldsymbol{\mu}_y = \begin{bmatrix} 1 & -1 & 1 \\ 2 & 0 & -1 \end{bmatrix} \begin{bmatrix} 1 \\ 2 \\ 3 \end{bmatrix} + \begin{bmatrix} 4 \\ 6 \end{bmatrix} = \begin{bmatrix} 2 \\ -1 \end{bmatrix} + \begin{bmatrix} 4 \\ 6 \end{bmatrix} = \begin{bmatrix} 6 \\ 5 \end{bmatrix}$$

and

$$\boldsymbol{\Sigma}_y = \begin{bmatrix} 1 & -1 & 1 \\ 2 & 0 & -1 \end{bmatrix} \begin{bmatrix} 4 & 2 & 0 \\ 2 & 5 & -1 \\ 0 & -1 & 1 \end{bmatrix} \begin{bmatrix} 1 & 2 \\ -1 & 0 \\ 1 & -1 \end{bmatrix}$$

$$= \begin{bmatrix} 2 & -4 & 2 \\ 8 & 5 & -1 \end{bmatrix} \begin{bmatrix} 1 & 2 \\ -1 & 0 \\ 1 & -1 \end{bmatrix} = \begin{bmatrix} 8 & 2 \\ 2 & 17 \end{bmatrix} \qquad \square$$

Example 4.4.3 illustrates that the linear transformation need not be a reversible transformation, nor even a transformation that preserves dimensionality (here $\mathbf{X}$ is three-dimensional and $\mathbf{Y}$ is two-dimensional).

Another property of Gaussian random variables is that any marginal density function formed from the N-dimensional Gaussian density function is also Gaussian. This can readily be seen by choosing $\mathbf{A}$, in the linear transformation given, to have 1's in the positions corresponding to variables to be retained in the marginal density function and 0's elsewhere (in the positions corresponding to variables to be eliminated), and $\mathbf{B} = \mathbf{0}$ (all entries 0).

Example 4.4.4. Let $\mathbf{Z} = \mathbf{C}\mathbf{X}$ where

$$\mathbf{C} = \begin{bmatrix} 1 & 0 & 0 \\ 0 & 1 & 0 \end{bmatrix}$$

and $\mathbf{X}$ is the three-dimensional Gaussian random variable of the previous example. Now, $\mathbf{Z}^T = (X_1, X_2)$, $\boldsymbol{\mu}_z = \mathbf{C}\boldsymbol{\mu}_x$ or $\boldsymbol{\mu}_z^T = (1, 2)$, and

$$\boldsymbol{\Sigma}_z = \mathbf{C}\boldsymbol{\Sigma}_x \mathbf{C}^T = \begin{bmatrix} 4 & 2 \\ 2 & 5 \end{bmatrix}$$

which is equivalent to picking the appropriate mean values from $\boldsymbol{\mu}_x$ and the appropriate variances and covariances from $\boldsymbol{\Sigma}_x$. $\qquad \square$

4.5 Binary Communication Scheme

Consider a binary communication scheme where either $s_1 = -a$ or $s_2 = a$ is transmitted during a signaling interval T, where a is a positive signal amplitude determined by the input power. A sequence of transmissions is shown in Fig. 4.5.1. Each transmitted signal (voltage) is assumed to be

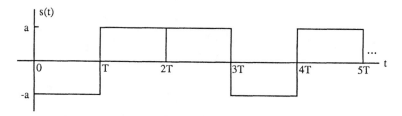

Fig. 4.5.1. Transmission sequence $s_1 s_2 s_2 s_1 s_2 \cdots$.

corrupted by the addition of a statistically independent signal (voltage), called additive noise, W. Thus each received signal, a corrupted version of S, is given as [X is one sample of $X(t) = S(t) + W(t)$]

$$X = S + W \qquad (4.5.1)$$

(normally N is used for the noise, but to avoid confusion with the number of samples N, W is used here). The signal random variable S takes on the two values s_1 and s_2, where $P(S = s_1)$ and $P(S = s_2)$ are assumed known. A common assumption for the noise, which will be used here, is that it is a Gaussian random variable with mean 0 and variance σ^2 (the 0 mean assumption is irrelevant to the outcome of the problem, but is a realistic assumption). The density function for the noise with this model is given as

$$f_W(w) = \frac{1}{\sqrt{2\pi\sigma^2}} \exp\left(\frac{-w^2}{2\sigma^2}\right) \qquad -\infty < w < \infty$$

The conditional density functions of the received signal X, given the transmitted signal S, are translations of the noise density function, since X given s_1 is $X = W - a$ and X given s_2 is $X = W + a$. Using Eq. (3.1.9) for a translation transformation, the conditional density function of X given s_1 is given as

$$f_{X|S}(x|s_1) = \frac{1}{\sqrt{2\pi\sigma^2}} \exp\left(\frac{-(x+a)^2}{2\sigma^2}\right) \qquad -\infty < x < \infty$$

which is Gaussian with mean $-a$ and variance σ^2, and the conditional density function of X given s_2 as

$$f_{X|S}(x|s_2) = \frac{1}{\sqrt{2\pi\sigma^2}} \exp\left(\frac{-(x-a)^2}{2\sigma^2}\right) \qquad -\infty < x < \infty$$

which is Gaussian with mean a and variance σ^2. These two conditional density functions are shown in Fig. 4.5.2 plotted on the same axis.

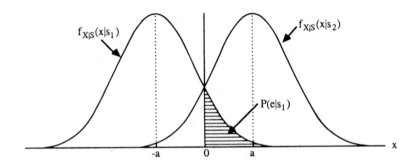

Fig. 4.5.2. Conditional density functions of received signal given the transmitted signal.

As seen in the figure, the received signal tends to be positive if s_2 is transmitted and negative if s_1 is transmitted, even though the conditional density functions overlap. The objective of the receiver is to decide which signal was transmitted for all possible received values of X ($-\infty < x < \infty$). A reasonable decision rule for the receiver would be to decide that s_1 was sent if the received signal is negative, $X < 0$, and that s_2 was sent if the received signal is nonnegative, $X \geq 0$. This decision rule is optimum and minimizes the probability of error, as for the binary channel model of Fig. 1.4.3 when $P(S=s_1) = P(S=s_2) = \frac{1}{2}$, i.e., s_1 and s_2 are equally likely.

The probability of error for this binary communication scheme, using Eq. (1.4.4) for the total probability, is expressed as

$$P(e) = P(e|s_1)P(S=s_1) + P(e|s_2)P(S=s_2)$$

The conditional probability of error given that s_1 was sent is the probability that $X \geq 0$ using $f_{X|S}(x|s_1)$ (X has mean $-a$ and variance σ^2) or

$$P(e|s_1) = P(X \geq 0|s_1) = P\left(\frac{X+a}{\sigma} \geq \frac{0+a}{\sigma}\right) = Q\left(\frac{a}{\sigma}\right)$$

where $Q(b)$, as defined in Section 2.2, is the probability that a Gaussian random variable with mean 0 and variance 1 exceeds b. Similarly, the conditional probability of error given that s_2 was sent is the probability that

$X < 0$ using $f_{X|S}(x|s_2)$ (X has mean a and variance σ^2) or

$$P(e|s_2) = P(X < 0|s_2) = 1 - P(X \geq 0) = 1 - P\left(\frac{X-a}{\sigma} \geq \frac{0-a}{\sigma}\right) = 1 - Q\left(-\frac{a}{\sigma}\right)$$

$$= Q\left(\frac{a}{\sigma}\right)$$

The two conditional probabilities of error are equal, which could have been observed from the symmetry of the conditional density functions. The probability of error is then

$$P(e) = Q\left(\frac{a}{\sigma}\right)P(S = s_1) + Q\left(\frac{a}{\sigma}\right)P(S = s_2) = Q\left(\frac{a}{\sigma}\right)[P(S = s_1) + P(S = s_2)]$$

or

$$P(e) = Q\left(\frac{a}{\sigma}\right) \qquad (4.5.2)$$

Thus for the decision rule of deciding s_1 was transmitted when $X < 0$ and deciding s_2 was transmitted when $X \geq 0$, the probability of error is independent of the probabilities of sending s_1 and s_2 [a different decision rule could reduce the probability of error if $P(S = s_1) \neq P(S = s_2)$].

Since the mean signal power is proportional to the mean square value of the signal, a^2, and the mean noise power is proportional to the mean square value of the noise, σ^2, a measure of performance, the signal-to-noise ratio is given as the ratio of a^2 to σ^2. The argument of the Q function for $P(e)$ is equal to the square root of the signal-to-noise ratio. Since the Q function [and $P(e)$] decreases as the argument increases (signal-to-noise ratio increases), the probability of error decreases as the signal power increases with the noise power held constant, and also decreases as the noise power is decreased with the signal power held constant. In addition, this illustrates that an amplification at the receiver amplifies not only the signal but also the noise, leaving the probability of error unchanged.

Example 4.5.1. If $(a/\sigma) = 1$ (signal-to-noise ratio of $10\log_{10}(a/\sigma)^2 = 0$ dB), $P(e) = Q(1) = 0.15866$. Also, if $(a/\sigma) = 3.16$ (signal-to-noise ratio of $10\log_{10}(a/\sigma)^2 = 10$ dB), $P(e) = Q(3.16) = 7.89 \times 10^{-4}$. $\square$

If $P(S = s_1) \neq P(S = s_2)$ the optimum receiver or decision rule, minimum probability of error, can be obtained in a manner similar to the discrete channel of Section 1.4 by using Bayes' rule. To minimize the probability of error it should be decided that s_1 was transmitted if the conditional probability of $S = s_1$ given $X = x$ (a *posterior* probability) is larger than the conditional probability of $S = s_2$ given $X = x$, and that s_2 was transmitted otherwise, for all values of x. That is, decide that s_1 was transmitted if and only if

$$P(S = s_1 | X = x) > P(S = s_2 | X = x) \qquad -\infty < x < \infty$$

and that s_2 was transmitted otherwise. Using Bayes' rule on both sides of the inequality gives: decide that s_1 was transmitted if and only if

$$\frac{f_{X|S}(x|s_1)P(S = s_1)}{f_X(x)} > \frac{f_{X|S}(x|s_2)P(S = s_2)}{f_X(x)} \qquad -\infty < x < \infty$$

and cancelling $f_X(x)$, which is common to both sides, yields: decide that s_1 was transmitted if and only if

$$f_{X|S}(x|s_1)P(S = s_1) > f_{X|S}(x|s_2)P(S = s_2) \qquad -\infty < x < \infty$$

These weighted conditional density functions are shown in Fig. 4.5.3 plotted on the same axis. From this figure it can be seen that choosing the value

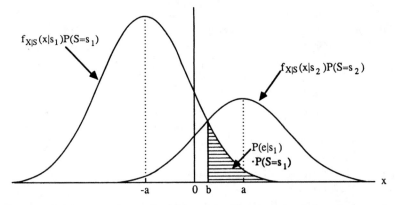

Fig. 4.5.3. Weighted conditional density functions of received signal given the transmitted signal $[P(S = s_1) > P(S = s_2)]$.

of S for which the weighted conditional density function is largest has shifted the decision boundary from 0. In fact, the decision boundary has been shifted away from the weighted conditional density function given s_1, which is the largest, or the one with the highest input probability. This should make sense, since if $P(S = s_1)$ is larger than $P(S = s_2)$, s_1 should be decided more than s_2, all other things being equal, which it will be, since now it has a bigger decision region. The probability of error can be expressed as

$$P(e) = P(S = s_1)P(e|s_1) + P(S = s_2)P(e|s_2)$$

$$= P(S = s_1)P(X \geq b | S = s_1) + P(S = s_2)P(X < b | S = s_2)$$

or

$$P(e) = P(S = s_1)Q\left(\frac{b+a}{\sigma}\right) + P(S = s_2)Q\left(\frac{a-b}{\sigma}\right) \quad (4.5.3)$$

Example 4.5.2. For $(a/\sigma) = 1$, $P(S = s_1) = \frac{3}{4}$, and $P(S = s_2) = \frac{1}{4}$, the value of b in Fig. 4.5.3 is determined as $0.549a$. Then the optimum receiver decides that s_1 was transmitted if $X < 0.549a$ and decides that s_2 was transmitted if $X \ge 0.549a$. The probability of error is calculated, using Eq. (4.5.3), as

$$P(e) = \tfrac{3}{4}Q(0.549 + 1) + \tfrac{1}{4}Q(1 - 0.549) = \tfrac{3}{4}Q(1.549) + \tfrac{1}{4}Q(0.451)$$

$$= \tfrac{3}{4}(0.06069) + \tfrac{1}{4}(0.32600) = 0.12702$$

Thus, if $P(S = s_1) \ne P(S = s_2)$, these values can be incorporated into the receiver, using Bayes' rule, to reduce the probability of error. □

If a/σ is fixed, the signal power cannot be increased, and the noise power cannot be reduced, it appears that $P(e)$ is fixed and cannot be reduced; e.g., for $(a/\sigma) = 1$ and $P(S = s_1) = P(S = s_2)$, $P(e) = 0.15866$. One way of reducing the probability of error, which is common in communication systems, is to sample the received signal a number of times in the signaling interval T and base a decision on the sum or average of these samples. The idea of sampling is that, even though they cannot be separated, the transmitted signal has the same value for all the samples (over T) and the noise varies over positive and negative values and tends to cancel out.

The samples here will be assumed to be statistically independent, which yields an expression that predicts better performance (lower probability of error) with an increased number of samples. All systems are bandlimited though, and this limits the maximum number of independent samples, which will limit this performance. The samples of the received signal are labeled $X_1, X_2, \ldots, X_N$ and the arithmetic average given as

$$Y = \frac{1}{N} \sum_{i=1}^{N} X_i$$

Since this is a linear combination of Gaussian random variables, regardless of whether s_1 or s_2 was sent, Y is Gaussian. The samples are identically distributed and therefore $E(X_i | S = s_1) = -a$, $E(X_i | S = s_2) = a$, and $\mathrm{Var}(X_i | S = s_1) = \mathrm{Var}(X_i | S = s_2) = \sigma^2$, $i = 1, 2, \ldots, N$. The mean of Y is obtained as

$$E(Y) = E\left[\frac{1}{N} \sum_{i=1}^{N} X_i\right] = \frac{1}{N} E\left[\sum_{i=1}^{N} X_i\right] = \frac{1}{N} \sum_{i=1}^{N} E(X_i) = E(X_i)$$

the last equality coming from the fact that there are N equal terms in the summation. Now $E(Y|S = s_1) = E(X_i|S = s_1) = -a$ and $E(Y|S = s_2) = E(X_i|S = s_2) = a$. Since the samples are statistically independent, the variance of Y is

$$\text{Var}(Y) = \text{Var}\left[\frac{1}{N}\sum_{i=1}^{N}X_i\right] = \frac{1}{N^2}\text{Var}\left[\sum_{i=1}^{N}X_i\right] = \frac{1}{N^2}\sum_{i=1}^{N}\text{Var}(X_i)$$

$$= \frac{1}{N^2}[N\,\text{Var}(X_i)] = \frac{1}{N}\text{Var}(X_i)$$

Now $\text{Var}(Y|S = s_1) = \text{Var}(Y|S = s_2) = \sigma^2/N$. The conditional density function of Y given s_1 is

$$f_{Y|S}(y|s_1) = \frac{1}{\sqrt{2\pi\sigma^2/N}}\exp\left[-\frac{(y+a)^2}{2\sigma^2/N}\right] \qquad -\infty < y < \infty$$

and the conditional density function of Y given s_2 is

$$f_{Y|S}(y|s_2) = \frac{1}{\sqrt{2\pi\sigma^2/N}}\exp\left[-\frac{(y-a)^2}{2\sigma^2/N}\right] \qquad -\infty < y < \infty$$

These two conditional density functions are shown in Fig. 4.5.4 plotted on the same axis. The same type of decision rule as before is assumed, i.e., s_1

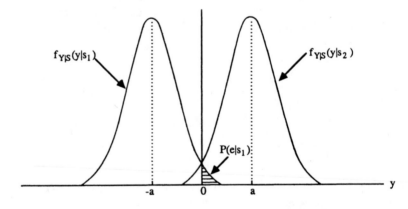

Fig. 4.5.4. Conditional density functions of the sampled received signal given the transmitted signal.

was sent if $Y < 0$ and s_2 was sent if $Y \ge 0$. Comparing Figs. 4.5.2 and 4.5.4 it can be seen that the probability of error for the samples has decreased since the means are the same but the variances of the conditional density functions have decreased. The probability of error is calculated in the same manner as before to yield

$$P(e) = P(e \mid s_1) = P(Y \geq 0 \mid S_1) = P\left(\frac{Y+a}{\sigma/\sqrt{N}} \geq \frac{0+a}{\sigma/\sqrt{N}}\right)$$

or

$$P(e) = Q\left(\frac{a}{\sigma}\sqrt{N}\right) \tag{4.5.4}$$

Example 4.5.3. For a 0-dB signal-to-noise ratio $(a/\sigma = 1)$ and $N = 3$ the probability of error is reduced from $Q(1) = 0.15866$ to $Q(1.732) = 0.04163$, and for a 10-dB signal-to-noise ratio $(a/\sigma = 3.16)$ it is reduced from $Q(3.16) = 7.89 \times 10^{-4}$ to $Q(5.47) = 2.26 \times 10^{-8}$. Thus, by sampling and averaging, the noise effects can be reduced. $\square$

An interesting question is, how accurate (number of bits) should the sample values X_i be? As given, they are analog values and require, theoretically, an infinite number of bits. What is a good engineering compromise, though, or how much degradation is encountered by using a finite number of bits to represent the X_i's? The simplest form is to use a single bit (a decision is made for each X_i as to whether an s_1 or an s_2 was transmitted, which is called a hard decision) to represent each X_i. This hard decision channel is the channel model given in Fig. 1.4.3, where there are two inputs and two outputs. Since a decision is made after the X_i's are summed, a reasonable rule in this case is to decide that s_1 was transmitted if for a majority of the X_i's it was decided that s_1 was transmitted. For $N = 3$ it would be decided that s_1 was transmitted if two or three or the X_i's were decided to be s_1. The probability of error can be determined here, using Eq. (2.3.6a), by summing the binomial probability that two or three errors are made in the X_i's. The hard decision probability of error for $N = 3$ and a 0-dB signal-to-noise ratio $(a/\sigma = 1)$ is obtained as

$$P_H(e) = \sum_{i=2}^{3} C_i^3 P_1^i(e)(1 - P_1(e))^{3-i} = 3P_1^2(e)(1 - P_1(e)) + P_1^3(e) = 0.06753$$

where $P_1(e)$ is the probability of error of each sample X_i. This value is still significantly better than the single-sample case but somewhat worse than using analog values for the X_i's.

Now if each X_i is represented by 2 bits (referred to as 2-bit soft decisions), the received signal is quantized into four levels, which yields a two-input, four-output channel. The received signal can be partitioned into four regions, as shown in Fig. 4.5.5 with the conditional density function for X (the same for each X_i) given the transmitted signals. The four regions shown in this figure can be described as follows: region 0, from $-\infty$ to $-a$, decide

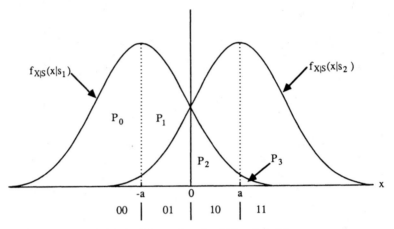

Fig. 4.5.5. Decision regions for 2-bit soft decisions.

with high reliability that an s_1 was transmitted; region 1, from $-a$ to 0, decide with low reliability that an s_1 was transmitted; region 2, from 0 to a, decide with low reliability that an s_2 was transmitted; and region 3, from a to ∞, decide with high reliability that an s_2 was transmitted. Thus, the 2-bit representation can be interpreted as the most significant bit being a hard decision bit and the least significant bit being a reliability bit. After the 2-bit quantization, let the quantized value be X'_i and take on the values 0, 1, 2, 3 corresponding to the region X_i is in. The probability of error will be determined by calculating the probability of error given s_1, and as such P_0, P_1, P_2, and P_3 are the probabilities of being in region 0, 1, 2, and 3, respectively, given that s_1 was transmitted. Figure 4.5.6 shows the conditional density function of X'_i given s_1, where $P(X'_i = i \mid S = s_1) = P_i$, $i = 0, 1, 2, 3$.

The sum of the quantized received values is given as

$$M = NY' = \sum_{i=1}^{3} X'_i$$

which takes on one of 10 discrete values, 0 (all three x'_i values 0) through

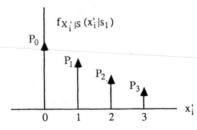

Fig. 4.5.6. Conditional density function of quantized received signal.

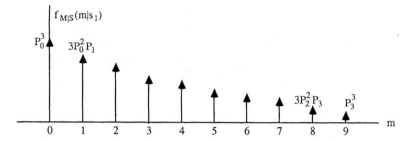

Fig. 4.5.7. Conditional density function of the sum of quantized received values.

9 (all three X_i' values 3), as shown in Fig. 4.5.7. The probabilities of the M values can be obtained by using a multinomial probability function, which is a generalization of the binomial probability function. A multinomial random variable can be viewed as a sum of N random variables, each of which has L discrete outcomes with identical probability ($L = 2$ corresponds to a binomial random variable). For $L = 4$, the probability of first obtaining n_0 0's, then n_1 1's, then n_2 2's, and then n_3 3's is $P_0^{n_0} P_1^{n_1} P_2^{n_2} P_3^{n_3}$, and the number of ways of obtaining n_0 0's, n_1 1's, n_2 2's, and n_3 3's is $N!/(n_0! n_1! n_2! n_3!)$. The multinomial probability function is then given as

$$P(n_0 \text{ 0's}, n_1 \text{ 1's}, n_2 \text{ 2's}, n_3 \text{ 3's}) = \frac{N! P_0^{n_0} P_1^{n_1} P_2^{n_2} P_3^{n_3}}{n_0! n_1! n_2! n_3!} \tag{4.5.5}$$

$$n_3 = N - n_0 - n_1 - n_2 \qquad P_3 = 1 - P_0 - P_1 - P_2$$

For the binomial probability function $n_0 = k$, $n_1 = N - k$, $P_0 = p$, and $P_1 = 1 - p$ in Eq. (4.5.5).

The decision rule corresponding to "decide s_1 was transmitted if $Y < 0$ and decide s_2 was transmitted if $Y \geq 0$" is "decide s_1 was transmitted if $M \leq 4$ and decide s_2 was transmitted if $M \geq 5$." The probability of error for four quantized outputs is obtained as

$$P_{S4}(e) = P_{S4}(e|s_1) = P(M = NY' \geq 5 | S = s_1)$$

which is evaluated in terms of the multinomial probability function. For the decision boundaries of $-a$, 0, and a with $a/\sigma = 1$, $P_0 = 0.50000$, $P_1 = 0.34134$, $P_2 = 0.13591$, and $P_3 = 0.02275$. Now,

$$P(M = 5) = 3 P_1 P_2^2 + 3 P_1^2 P_3 + 6 P_0 P_2 P_3$$

$$= 0.01892 + 0.00795 + 0.00928 = 0.03615$$

which indicates that there are three ways of obtaining one 1 and two 2's, three ways of obtaining two 1's and one 3, and six ways of obtaining one

0, one 2, and one 3, all yielding a quantized sum of 5. Also,

$$P(M=6) = P_2^3 + 6P_1P_2P_3 + 3P_0P_3^2 = 0.00251 + 0.00633 + 0.00078 = 0.00962$$

$$P(M=7) = 3P_2^2P_3 + 3P_1P_3^2 = 0.00126 + 0.00053 = 0.00179$$

$$P(M=8) = 3P_2P_3^2 = 0.00021$$

$$P(M=9) = P_3^3 = 0.00001$$

and finally

$$P_{S4}(e) = 0.04777$$

Thus, most of the degradation due to not using an infinite number of bits to represent the received signal is eliminated by using as few as 2-bit quantization. For 3-bit quantization, which yields eight output levels, this probability can be shown to decrease to $P_{S8}(e) = 0.04332$ for $a/\sigma = 1$. Normally 2- or 3-bit quantization is used.

4.6   Inequalities

A number of important inequalities will now be considered. The first one considered is called the Cauchy–Schwarz inequality. It is used in a variety of other applications, but only its relevance to probability will be considered here. The Cauchy–Schwarz inequality states that if X and Y are real random variables with finite second moments, then

$$[E(XY)]^2 \le E(X^2)E(Y^2) \tag{4.6.1}$$

This is proved by considering the function $H(\lambda) = E[(X - \lambda Y)^2]$, where λ is an arbitrary but real parameter. Since the term in [ ] is the square of a real number it cannot be negative and the average cannot be negative, so $H(\lambda) \ge 0$. Expanding the expression for $H(\lambda)$ yields

$$H(\lambda) = E[X^2 - 2\lambda XY + \lambda^2 Y^2] = E(X^2) - 2\lambda E(XY) + \lambda^2 E(Y^2) \ge 0$$

which is a nonnegative quadratic form in λ. If $H(\lambda)$ is plotted versus λ it is always in the upper half plane and never crosses the λ axis. Because it is a quadratic form, $H(\lambda)$ can remain nonnegative [setting $H(\lambda) = 0$] only if it does not have two unequal real roots [for two unequal real roots there would be a sign change on $H(\lambda)$ between the roots and $H(\lambda)$ would be negative for some values of λ]. The roots of the quadratic equation $H(\lambda)$ are obtained as

$$\text{roots} = \frac{E(XY) \pm \sqrt{[E(XY)]^2 - E(Y^2)E(X^2)]}}{E(Y^2)}$$

To ensure that the roots are not two unequal real roots (are complex or equal real roots), the argument of the square root in the quadratic equation must be ≤ 0. Thus,

$$[E(XY)]^2 - E(Y^2)E(X^2) \leq 0$$

or finally

$$[E(XY)]^2 \leq E(X^2)E(Y^2)$$

which is the desired inequality.

Since the Cauchy-Schwarz inequality applies to arbitrary real random variables, it also applies to $X - E(X)$ and $Y - E(Y)$, which yields

$$\{E[(X - E(X))(Y - E(Y))]\}^2 \leq E[(X - E(X))^2]E[(Y - E(Y))^2]$$

or

$$\text{Cov}^2(X, Y) \leq \text{Var}(X)\,\text{Var}(Y) \tag{4.6.2}$$

In addition, the correlation coefficient, from Eq. (4.3.12), is

$$\rho_{XY}^2 = \frac{\text{Cov}^2(X, Y)}{\text{Var}(X)\,\text{Var}(Y)} \leq 1$$

and is bounded as

$$-1 \leq \rho_{XY} \leq 1 \tag{4.6.3}$$

The Chebyshev inequality is one of the more important inequalities since it can be used to bound probabilities in a direct manner. It states that if X is a random variable with finite mean and variance, then

$$P[|X - E(X)| > \varepsilon] \leq \frac{\text{Var}(X)}{\varepsilon^2} \tag{4.6.4a}$$

for any $\varepsilon > 0$. An alternative form of Chebyshev's inequality is obtained by substituting $\varepsilon\sigma_x$ for ε in the inequality as

$$P[|X - E(X)| > \varepsilon\sigma_x] \leq \frac{1}{\varepsilon^2} \tag{4.6.4b}$$

Using the alternative form, the inequality says that for any random variable the probability of deviating from the mean by more than 2 standard deviations is $\leq \frac{1}{4}$ and the probability of deviating by more than 4 standard deviations is $\leq \frac{1}{16}$. When the form of the density function or probability function is known, in most cases much tighter bounds can be found; for example, the exact probabilities for Gaussian random variables deviating by more than 2 and 4 standard deviations from their means are 0.04550 and 6.34×10^{-5}, respectively.

To prove Chebyshev's inequality a general bound will be proved. This bound is stated as follows.

If X is a random variable with density function $f_X(x)$ and for an arbitrary $\delta > 0$, then

$$P[g(X) \geq \delta] \leq \frac{E[g(X)]}{\delta} \qquad (4.6.5)$$

if $E[g(X)]$ exists and $g(X) \geq 0$.

To prove this let $A = \{x : g(x) \geq \delta\}$. Then

$$E[g(X)] = \int_{-\infty}^{\infty} g(x) f_X(x) \, dx \geq \int_A g(x) f_X(x) \, dx$$

since A is a restriction on the range of x, i.e., not over the entire range (eliminating part of the range of an integral with a nonnegative integrand cannot increase the integral). Since $g(x) \geq \delta$ over the restricted range of integration, replacing $g(x)$ by δ in the integral yields

$$\int_A g(x) f_X(x) \, dx \geq \int_A \delta f_X(x) \, dx = \delta P[g(X) \geq \delta]$$

which strengthens the inequality. Combining gives

$$E[g(X)] \geq \delta P[g(X) \geq \delta]$$

and dividing by δ yields the desired result of Eq. (4.6.5).

Letting $g(X) = [X - E(X)]^2$ and $\varepsilon = \sqrt{\delta}$

$$P[\{X - E(X)\}^2 \geq \delta] \leq \frac{\mathrm{Var}(X)}{\delta}$$

or

$$P[|X - E(X)| \leq \varepsilon] \geq \frac{\mathrm{Var}(X)}{\varepsilon^2}$$

which is Chebyshev's inequality, Eq. (4.6.4a).

Let $\{X_i\}$ be a set of N statistically independent identically distributed random variables each with mean $E(X)$ and variance $\mathrm{Var}(X) < \infty$. This is exactly the same as the samples of the received signals of Section 4.5. For the arithmetic average of this set

$$Y = \frac{1}{N} \sum_{i=1}^{N} X_i$$

$E(Y) = E(X)$ and $\mathrm{Var}(Y) = \mathrm{Var}(X)/N$. Applying the Chebyshev inequality to Y or using Eq. (4.6.5) with $g(Y) = [Y - E(X)]^2$ and $\varepsilon = \sqrt{\delta}$ yields

$$P\left[\left|\frac{1}{N}\sum_{i=1}^{N} X_i - E(X)\right| \geq \varepsilon\right] \leq \frac{\text{Var}(X)}{N\varepsilon^2} \qquad (4.6.6)$$

From this it can be seen that for any number $\alpha > 0$, no matter how small, it is always possible to find a value of N, say N_0, such that

$$P\left[\left|\frac{1}{N}\sum_{i=1}^{N} X_i - E(X)\right| \geq \varepsilon\right] \leq \alpha$$

for $N \geq N_0$. This ensures that the arithmetic average can be obtained arbitrarily close to the true mean by taking a large enough sample. One form of the law of large numbers is obtained by taking the limit of Eq. (4.6.6) as

$$\lim_{N \to \infty} P\left[\left|\frac{1}{N}\sum_{i=1}^{N} X_i - E(X)\right| \geq \varepsilon\right] = 0$$

which states that the probability of the arithmetic average or sample mean differing from the true mean goes to 0 as N becomes arbitrarily large. An interpretation in terms of probability of an event can also be obtained. For an event A, with probability $P(A)$, define the Bernoulli random variables X_i, $i = 1, 2, \ldots, N$, which take on the value 1 if A occurs on the ith observation and 0 if A does not occur. Now $E(X_i) = 0(1 - P(A)) + 1P(A) = P(A)$, and the law of large numbers shows that the fraction of the times when A occurs converges to the probability of A. This indicates the convergence of the relative frequency of occurrence to the true probability. Chebyshev's inequality is a crude bound, but it does yield results when exact probabilities are difficult to evaluate and it was useful in developing the law of large numbers.

A much tighter bound on probabilities than the Chebyshev inequality, but more complex, is the Chernoff bound, given as

$$P[X \geq c] \leq e^{-\nu_0 c} M_X(\nu_0) \qquad c > E(X) \qquad (4.6.7a)$$

and

$$P[X \leq c] \leq e^{-\nu_0 c} M_X(\nu_0) \qquad c < E(X) \qquad (4.6.7b)$$

where c is any real number, $M_X(\nu)$ is the moment generating function given in Eq. (4.2.4), and ν_0 is obtained by solving

$$\left.\frac{dM_X(\nu)}{d\nu}\right|_{\nu = \nu_0} = cM_X(\nu_0) \qquad (4.6.7c)$$

This bound is the tightest exponential bound (no exponential bound can decrease more rapidly) on the probability statement.

To prove this bound let $g(X) = e^{\nu X}$ in Eq. (4.6.5) to obtain

$$P[e^{\nu X} \geq \delta] \leq \frac{E[e^{\nu X}]}{\delta}$$

and with $\delta = e^{\nu c}$

$$P[X \geq c] \leq e^{-\nu c} E[e^{\nu X}] = E[e^{\nu(X-c)}] \qquad \nu > 0 \qquad (4.6.8a)$$

$$P[X \leq c] \leq e^{-\nu c} E[e^{\nu X}] = E[e^{\nu(X-c)}] \qquad \nu < 0 \qquad (4.6.8b)$$

If ν is chosen to minimize the right side, the tightest exponential bound is obtained. Taking the derivative of the right side and setting to zero yields

$$\left. \frac{d\{E[e^{\nu(X-c)}]\}}{d\nu} \right|_{\nu=\nu_0} = E[(X-c)\,e^{\nu(X-c)}]\big|_{\nu=\nu_0} = 0$$

and

$$E[X\,e^{\nu_0 X}] = cE[e^{\nu_0 X}]$$

or equivalently Eq. (4.6.7c). Also,

$$\frac{d^2\{E[e^{\nu(X-c)}]\}}{d\nu^2} = E[(X-c)^2\,e^{\nu(X-c)}] > 0$$

which implies that $E[e^{\nu(X-c)}] = e^{-\nu c} M_X(\nu)$ is a function opening upward as shown in Fig. 4.6.1. Several points of interest from this figure are

$$E[e^{\nu(X-c)}]\big|_{\nu=0} = 1$$

and

$$\left. \frac{d\{E[e^{\nu(X-c)}]\}}{d\nu} \right|_{\nu=0} = E(X) - c$$

This means that the slope is positive at $\nu = 0$ for $c < E(X)$, Fig. 4.6.1a, and the slope is negative at $\nu = 0$ for $c > E(X)$, Fig. 4.6.1b. Now, for $c > E(X)$ the bound is >1 for all $\nu < 0$, which is useless for $\nu < 0$. Thus $c > E(X)$

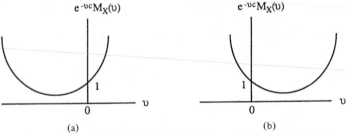

Fig. 4.6.1. Plot of $E[e^{\nu(X-c)}] = e^{-\nu c} M_x(\nu)$: (a) $c < E(X)$; (b) $c > E(X)$.

must correspond to $\nu > 0$. Likewise, for $c < E(X)$ the bound is > 1 for all $\nu > 0$, which is useless for $\nu > 0$, and thus $c < E(X)$ must correspond to $\nu < 0$. Combining this with Eqs. (4.6.8a) and (4.6.8b) and putting in the value of ν that minimizes the bound, ν_0, yields

$$P[X \geq c] \leq e^{-\nu_0 c} M_X(\nu_0) \qquad c > E(X)$$

$$P[X \leq c] \leq e^{-\nu_0 c} M_X(\nu_0) \qquad c < E(X)$$

which is the Chernoff bound, the tightest exponential bound.

This bound can be extended to the arithmetic average of a set of N statistically independent identically distributed random variables $\{X_i\}$ each with mean $E(X)$ and $\mathrm{Var}(X) < \infty$. If X is replaced by the arithmetic average in Eq. (4.6.7a)

$$P\left[\frac{1}{N}\sum_{i=1}^{N} X_i \geq c\right] \leq E\left[e^{-\nu_0 c}\exp\left(\nu_0 \sum_{i=1}^{N}\frac{X_i}{N}\right)\right] = e^{-\nu_0 c}\prod_{i=1}^{N} E[e^{\nu_0 X_i/N}]$$

$$= e^{-\nu_0 c}\{E[e^{\nu_0 X_i/N}]\}^N = \{e^{-\nu_0 c/N} E[e^{\nu_0 X_i/N}]\}^N$$

With $t_0 = \nu_0/N$ this becomes

$$P\left[\frac{1}{N}\sum_{i=1}^{N} X_i \geq c\right] \leq [e^{-t_0 c} M_{X_i}(t_0)]^N \qquad c > E(X) \qquad (4.6.9a)$$

Likewise

$$P\left[\frac{1}{N}\sum_{i=1}^{N} X_i \leq c\right] \leq [e^{-t_0 c} M_{X_i}(t_0)]^N \qquad c < E(X) \qquad (4.6.9b)$$

and t_0 is obtained from

$$\left.\frac{dM_{X_i}(t)}{dt}\right|_{t=t_0} = c M_{X_i}(t_0) \qquad (4.6.9c)$$

Now let X_i, $i = 1, 2, \ldots, N$, be Bernoulli random variables with $P(X_i = 1) = p$ and $P(X_i = 0) = 1 - p$. In this case

$$M_{X_i}(t) = p e^t + 1 - p \qquad \text{and} \qquad \frac{dM_{X_i}(t)}{dt} = p e^t$$

Solving Eq. (4.6.9c)

$$\left.\frac{dM_{X_i}(t_0)}{dt}\right|_{t=t_0} = p e^{t_0} = c[p e^{t_0} + 1 - p] = c M_{X_i}(t_0)$$

for e^{t_0} (in this case t_0 is not needed) yields

$$e^{t_0} = \frac{c(1-p)}{p(1-c)} .$$

Then

$$M_{X_i}(t_0) = p\frac{c(1-p)}{p(1-c)} + 1 - p = \frac{1-p}{1-c}$$

and

$$e^{-t_0 c} M_{X_i}(t_0) = \left[\frac{p(1-c)}{c(1-p)}\right]^c \frac{1-p}{1-c} = \left(\frac{p}{c}\right)^c \left[\frac{1-p}{1-c}\right]^{1-c}$$

Thus, the Chernoff bound becomes

$$P\left[\frac{1}{N}\sum_{i=1}^{N} X_i \geq c\right] \leq \left[\left(\frac{p}{c}\right)^c \left(\frac{1-p}{1-c}\right)^{1-c}\right]^N \qquad p < c \leq 1 \qquad (4.6.10a)$$

and

$$P\left[\frac{1}{N}\sum_{i=1}^{N} X_i \leq c\right] \leq \left[\left(\frac{p}{c}\right)^c \left(\frac{1-p}{1-c}\right)^{1-c}\right]^N \qquad 0 \leq c \leq p \qquad (4.6.10b)$$

Example 4.6.1.   Consider the case of Bernoulli random variables where $p = 0.5$ and $N = 2000$. The probability that the arithmetic average or sample mean differs from the true mean p by more than 10%, using the Chernoff bound of Eq. (4.6.10), is calculated as

$$P\left[\left|\frac{1}{N}\sum_{i=1}^{N} X_i - 0.5\right| \geq 0.05\right] = P\left[\frac{1}{N}\sum_{i=1}^{N} X_i \geq 0.55\right] + P\left[\frac{1}{N}\sum_{i=1}^{N} X_i \leq 0.45\right]$$

$$\leq a_1^N + a_2^N$$

Here c takes on two values, $c = p \pm 0.1p$, or let $d_1 = 0.55$ and $d_2 = 0.45$. Now

$$a_1 = \left(\frac{p}{d_1}\right)^{d_1} \left(\frac{1-p}{1-d_1}\right)^{1-d_1} = \left(\frac{0.5}{0.55}\right)^{0.55} \left(\frac{0.5}{0.45}\right)^{0.45} = 0.995$$

and

$$a_2 = \left(\frac{p}{d_2}\right)^{d_2} \left(\frac{1-p}{1-d_2}\right)^{1-d_2} = \left(\frac{0.5}{0.45}\right)^{0.45} \left(\frac{0.5}{0.55}\right)^{0.55} = 0.995$$

(normally a_1 and a_2 are not equal), which yields

$$P\left[\left|\frac{1}{N}\sum_{i=1}^{N} X_i - 0.5\right| \geq 0.05\right] \leq 2(4.46 \times 10^{-5}) = 8.92 \times 10^{-5}$$

Chebyshev's inequality for the sample mean of the Bernoulli random variables is, from Eq. (4.6.6), given as

$$P\left[\left|\frac{1}{N}\sum_{i=1}^{N} X_i - p\right| \geq \varepsilon\right] \leq \frac{p(1-p)}{N\varepsilon^2} \qquad (4.6.11)$$

Comparing this to the Chernoff bound, with the same parameters,

$$P\left[\left|\frac{1}{N}\sum_{i=1}^{N}X_i - 0.5\right| \ge 0.05\right] \le \frac{0.25}{2000(0.05)^2} = 0.05$$

which shows that the Chernoff bound is a much tighter bound. $\square$

Chernoff bounds are useful in determining confidence statements for simulation results, as will be shown in Chapter 5.

4.7 Central Limit Theorem

The last thing to be considered in this chapter is the central limit theorem. This does not yield an inequality or bound but can be used for approximate probability statements. Let $\{X_i\}$ be a set of N statistically independent identically distributed random variables each with mean μ and variance σ^2, and define

$$Y = \frac{\left(\dfrac{1}{N}\sum_{i=1}^{N}X_i\right) - \mu}{\sigma/\sqrt{N}} = \frac{\sum_{i=1}^{N}(X_i - \mu)}{\sigma\sqrt{N}}$$

which yields $E(Y) = 0$ and $\text{Var}(Y) = 1$. Then

$$\lim_{N\to\infty}\phi_Y(\omega) = e^{-\omega^2/2} \tag{4.7.1a}$$

or

$$\lim_{N\to\infty}F_Y(y) = \frac{1}{\sqrt{2\pi}}\int_{-\infty}^{y}e^{-t^2/2}\,dt \tag{4.7.1b}$$

which is called the central limit theorem. The central limit theorem then justifies the claim that the Gaussian random variable is one of the most important random variables. Strictly speaking, if $\{X_i\}$ are discrete random variables the limit of $f_Y(y)$ as N goes to infinity cannot equal the Gaussian density function since it is a continuous random variable, but the distribution function does converge to the Gaussian distribution function.

To prove the central limit theorem consider

$$\phi_Y(\omega) = E[e^{j\omega Y}] = E\left\{\exp\left[\frac{j\omega\sum_{i=1}^{N}(X_i - \mu)}{\sigma\sqrt{N}}\right]\right\}$$

$$= E\left\{\prod_{i=1}^{N}\exp\left[\frac{j\omega(X_i - \mu)}{\sigma\sqrt{N}}\right]\right\}$$

and since the X_i's are statistically independent and identically distributed

$$\phi_Y(\omega) = \left\{ E\left[\exp\left(\frac{j\omega(X_i - \mu)}{\sigma\sqrt{N}} \right) \right] \right\}^N$$

To simplify notation let

$$h\left(\frac{\omega}{\sigma\sqrt{N}} \right) = E\left\{ \exp\left[\frac{j\omega(X_i - \mu)}{\sigma\sqrt{N}} \right] \right\}$$

$$= \exp\left[-\frac{j\omega\mu}{\sigma\sqrt{N}} \right] \phi_X\left(\frac{\omega}{\sigma\sqrt{N}} \right)$$

Then with $\nu = \omega/(\sigma\sqrt{N})$

$$h(\nu) = e^{-j\mu\nu}\phi_X(\nu)$$

Since the first two derivatives exist, $h(\nu)$ can be expressed in a Maclaurin series as

$$h(\nu) = h(0) + h'(0)\nu + h''(\gamma)\frac{\nu^2}{2}$$

for some γ such that $-\nu < \gamma < \nu$, and a prime indicates a derivative with respect to ν. These terms are evaluated as

$$h(0) = 1$$
$$h'(\nu) = e^{-j\mu\nu}\phi_X'(\nu) - j\mu\, e^{-j\mu\nu}\phi_X(\nu)$$
$$h'(0) = 0$$
$$h''(\nu) = e^{-j\mu\nu}\phi_X''(\nu) - j2\mu\, e^{-j\mu\nu}\phi_X'(\nu) - \mu^2\, e^{-j\mu\nu}\phi_X(\nu)$$
$$h''(0) = -(\sigma^2 + \mu^2) + 2\mu^2 - \mu^2 = -\sigma^2$$

to yield

$$h(\nu) = 1 + h''(\gamma)\frac{\nu^2}{2} = 1 - \sigma^2\frac{\nu^2}{2} + [h''(\gamma) + \sigma^2]\frac{\nu^2}{2} \qquad -\nu < \gamma < \nu$$

and

$$h\left(\frac{\omega}{\sigma\sqrt{N}} \right) = 1 - \frac{\omega^2}{2N} + \left[\frac{h''(\gamma) + \sigma^2}{2\sigma^2 N} \right]\omega^2 \qquad \frac{-\omega}{\sigma\sqrt{N}} < \gamma < \frac{\omega}{\sigma\sqrt{N}}$$

Then

$$\phi_Y(\omega) = \{1 - \omega^2/(2N) + [(h''(\gamma) + \sigma^2)/(2\sigma^2 N)]\omega^2\}^N \qquad (4.7.2)$$

The useful property that for real b and c

$$\lim_{N\to\infty}\left[1+\frac{b}{N}+o\left(\frac{1}{N}\right)\right]^{cN}=e^{bc} \tag{4.7.3}$$

where $o(1/N)$ is

$$\lim_{N\to\infty}\left[\frac{o(1/N)}{1/N}\right]=0$$

$[o(1/N)$ drops off more rapidly than $1/N]$ will now be proved. Let

$$g(N)=\left[1+\frac{b}{N}+o\left(\frac{1}{N}\right)\right]^{cN}$$

and note that $\ln(1+x)=x+o(x)$ which can be shown using L'Hospital's rule as

$$\lim_{x\to0}\left[\frac{\ln(1+x)-x}{x}\right]=\lim_{x\to0}\left[\frac{1/(1+x)-1}{1}\right]=1$$

Then

$$\ln[g(N)]=cN\ln\left[1+\frac{b}{N}+o\left(\frac{1}{N}\right)\right]=cN\left[\frac{b}{N}+o\left(\frac{1}{N}\right)+o\left(\frac{b}{N}+o\left(\frac{1}{N}\right)\right)\right]$$

Thus

$$\lim_{N\to\infty}\{\ln[g(N)]\}=bc,\qquad \ln\{\lim_{N\to\infty}[g(N)]\}=bc$$

and finally

$$\lim_{N\to\infty}[g(N)]=e^{bc}$$

which is Eq. (4.7.3).

As $N\to\infty$, $\gamma\to0$ and $h''(\gamma)\to-\sigma^2$, which yields

$$\frac{[h''(\gamma)+\sigma^2]\omega^2}{2\sigma^2}\to0$$

and using Eq. (4.73)

$$\lim_{N\to\infty}\phi_Y(\omega)=e^{-\omega^2/2}$$

which is the central limit theorem, Eq. (4.7.1).

Example 4.7.1. For Example 4.6.1 where X_i, $i=1,2,\ldots,N$, are Bernoulli random variables with $P(X_i=1)=p=0.5$, $P(X_i=0)=1-p=0.5$, and $N=2000$, the probability statement that the sample mean differs from the true mean, using the central limit theorem, is

$$P\left[\left|\frac{1}{N}\sum_{i=1}^{N}X_i - 0.5\right| \geq 0.05\right] \simeq 2Q\left(\frac{0.05}{\sqrt{p(1-p)/N}}\right)$$

$$= 2Q(0.1\sqrt{N}) = 7.75 \times 10^{-6}$$

Although this is smaller than the Chernoff bound, the central limit theorem is just an approximation, while the Chernoff bound is an upper bound.

PROBLEMS

4.1.1. Determine $E(X)$, $E(X^2)$, and $\text{Var}(X)$ when $f_X(x) = [a^{n+1}x^n/n!]\,e^{-ax}$, $0 \leq x < \infty$, $a > 0$, and n an integer ≥ 0.

4.1.2. Determine $E(X)$, $E(X^2)$, and $\text{Var}(X)$ when $f_X(x) = [(a+b+1)!/a!\,b!]x^a(1-x)^b$, $0 \leq x \leq 1$ and a, b integers ≥ 0.

4.1.3. Determine $E(X)$, $E(X^2)$, and $\text{Var}(X)$ when $P(X=k) = e^{-a}a^k/k!$, $k = 0, 1, 2, \ldots$ and $a > 0$.

4.1.4. Determine $E(X)$, $E(X^2)$, and $\text{Var}(X)$ when $P(X=k) = p(1-p)^{k-1}$, $k = 1, 2, 3, \ldots$ and $0 < p < 1$.

4.1.5. In general, does $E(1/X) = 1/E(X)$? Justify your answer.

4.1.6. In general, if $E(X^2) = [E(X)]^2 = \mu^2$, determine $f_X(x)$.

4.1.7. Determine a and b for $Y = aX + b$ such that $E(Y) = 9$ and $\text{Var}(Y) = 16$ when $E(X) = 0$ and $\text{Var}(X) = 1$.

4.1.8. Determine a and b for $Y = aX + b$ such that $E(Y) = 9$ and $\text{Var}(Y) = 16$ when $E(X) = 1$ and $\text{Var}(X) = 4$.

4.1.9. Determine the value of c that minimizes $E[(X-c)^2]$.

4.1.10. Show that $E[(X-c)^2] \geq \text{Var}(X)$.

4.1.11. Determine the average value of a 100-Ω (uniformly distributed) 10% resistor and the average value of the conductance of this resistor.

4.1.12. Determine the probability that the conductance is between 0.0095 and 0.0105 for a 100-Ω (uniformly distributed) 10% resistor.

4.1.13. Determine the average value of the inductance and the average value of the impedance of a 1-mH (uniformly distributed) 10% inductor at an angular frequency of 10^4 rad/s.

4.1.14. Determine the probability that the impedance is between 9.5 and 10.5 Ω for a 1-mH (uniformly distributed) 10% inductor at an angular frequency of 10^4 rad/s.

4.1.15. Determine the average value of the capacitance and the average value of the impedance of a 0.1-μF (uniformly distributed) 10% capacitor at an angular frequency of 5×10^4 rad/s.

4.1.16. Determine the probability that the impedance is between 192 and 208 Ω for a $0.1\text{-}\mu F$ (uniformly distributed) 10% capacitor at an angular frequency of 5×10^4 rad/s.

4.2.1. Determine $\phi_X(\omega)$ when $f_X(x) = 1/(b-a)$, $a < x < b$ and $-\infty < a < b < \infty$.

4.2.2. Determine $\phi_X(\omega)$ when $f_X(x) = (1/b) e^{-x/b}$, $0 \le x < \infty$ and $b > 0$.

4.2.3. Determine $\phi_X(\omega)$ when $f_X(x) = (1/2b) e^{-|x-a|/b}$, $-\infty < x < \infty$, $-\infty < a < \infty$, and $b > 0$.

4.2.4. Determine $\phi_X(\omega)$ when $P(X = k) = e^{-a}a^k/k!$, $k = 0, 1, 2, ..$ and $a > 0$.

4.2.5. Determine $\phi_X(\omega)$ when $P(X = k) = C_k^N p^k(1-p)^{N-k}$, $k = 0, 1, \ldots, N$ and $0 < p < 1$.

4.2.6. Determine $\phi_X(\omega)$ when $P(X = k) = p(1-p)^{k-1}$, $k = 1, 2, 3, \ldots$ and $0 < p < 1$.

4.2.7. Determine $E(X)$, $E(X^2)$, and Var(X) when $\phi_X(\omega) = (1 - j\omega b)^{-n-1}$, $b > 0$.

4.2.8. Determine $E(X)$, $E(X^2)$, and Var(X) when $\phi_X(\omega) = e^{ja\omega}/(1 - b^2\omega^2)$, $-\infty < a < \infty$ and $b > 0$.

4.2.9. Determine $E(X)$, $E(X^2)$, and Var(X) when $\phi_X(\omega) = (1 - j\omega b)^{-1}$, $b > 0$.

4.2.10. Determine $E(X)$, $E(X^2)$, and Var(X) when $\phi_X(\omega) = p e^{j\omega}/[1 - (1-p) e^{j\omega}]$, $0 < p < 1$.

4.2.11. Determine $E(X)$, $E(X^2)$, and Var(X) when $\phi_X(\omega) = [p e^{j\omega} + 1 - p]^N$, $0 < p < 1$ and N an integer > 0.

4.2.12. Determine $E(X)$, $E(X^2)$, and Var(X) when $\phi_X(\omega) = \exp[a(e^{j\omega} - 1)]$, $a > 0$.

4.2.13. Determine $E(X)$, $E(X^2)$, and Var(X) when $\phi_X(\omega) = (e^{jb\omega} - e^{ja\omega})/[j(b-a)\omega]$, $-\infty < a < b < \infty$.

4.3.1. Determine Var(Y) when $Y = 3X_1 + 2X_2$ with Var$(X_1) = 1$, Var$(X_2) = 5$, Cov$(X_1, X_2) = 2$, and $E(X_1) = E(X_2) = 0$.

4.3.2. Determine $E(X^iY^j)$ when $f_{XY}(x, y) = 1/ab$, $0 \le x \le a$, $0 \le y \le b$, and i, j integers ≥ 0.

4.3.3. Determine $E[(X + Y)^i]$ when $f_{XY}(x, y) = 1/ab$, $0 \le x \le a$, $0 \le y \le b$, and i an integer ≥ 0.

4.3.4. Determine Cov(X, Y), ρ, and whether X and Y are uncorrelated when $f_{XY}(x, y) = (x + y)/3$, $0 \le x \le 1$ and $0 \le y \le 2$.

4.3.5. Determine Cov(X, Y), ρ, and whether X and Y are uncorrelated when $f_{XY}(x, y) = xy$, $0 \le x \le 1$ and $0 \le y \le 2$.

4.3.6. Determine Var(Y) when $Y = 3X_1 + 2X_2$ with Var$(X_1) = 1$, Var$(X_2) = 5$, Cov$(X_1, X_2) = 2$, $E(X_1) = 3$, and $E(X_2) = 4$.

4.3.7. Determine Cov(X, Y) and ρ when $Y = aX + b$, a and b real numbers.

4.3.8. Determine a that minimizes $E(W)$ and this minimum, in terms of moments of X and Y, where $W = (X + aY)^2$ and $E(X) = E(Y) = 0$.

4.3.9. Determine a and b for $Y_1 = X_1$ and $Y_2 = aX_1 + bX_2$ such that $E(X_1) = E(X_2) = E(Y_1) = E(Y_2) = 0$, $\text{Var}(X_1) = \text{Var}(X_2) = \text{Var}(Y_1) = \text{Var}(Y_2) = 1$, $\text{Cov}(X_1, X_2) = 0$, and $\text{Cov}(Y_1, Y_2) = 0.5$.

4.3.10. Determine a and b for $Y_1 = X_1$ and $Y_2 = aX_1 + bX_2$ such that $E(X_1) = E(X_2) = E(Y_1) = E(Y_2) = 0$, $\text{Var}(X_1) = \text{Var}(X_2) = \text{Var}(Y_1) = \text{Var}(Y_2) = 1$, $\text{Cov}(X_1, X_2) = 0.5$, and $\text{Cov}(Y_1, Y_2) = 0$.

4.3.11. Determine a and b for $Y_1 = X_1$ and $Y_2 = aX_1 + bX_2$ such that $E(X_1) = E(X_2) = E(Y_1) = E(Y_2) = 0$, $\text{Var}(X_1) = \text{Var}(Y_1) = 3$, $\text{Var}(X_2) = 13$, $\text{Var}(Y_2) = 9$, $\text{Cov}(X_1, X_2) = 6$, and $\text{Cov}(Y_1, Y_2) = 0$.

4.3.12. For $P(X_i = k) = C_k^{N_i} p^k (1-p)^{N_i - k}$, $k = 0, \ldots, N_i$, with $\phi_{X_i}(\omega) = [p e^{j\omega} + 1 - p]^{N_i}$, $i = 1, 2, 3$, determine $P(Y = k)$ for $Y = X_1 + X_2 + X_3$ with X_1, X_2, and X_3 statistically independent.

4.3.13. For $P(X_i = k) = e^{-a_i} a_i^k / k!$, $k = 0, 1, 2, \ldots$, with $\phi_{X_i}(\omega) = \exp[a_i(e^{j\omega} - 1)]$, $i = 1, 2, 3$, determine $P(Y = k)$ for $Y = X_1 + X_2 + X_3$ with X_1, X_2, and X_3 statistically independent.

4.3.14. For $P(X_i = k) = e^{-a_i} a_i^k / k!$, $k = 0, 1, 2, \ldots$, with $\phi_{X_i}(\omega) = \exp[a_i(e^{j\omega} - 1)]$, $i = 1, 2, \ldots, N$, determine $P(Y = k)$ for $Y = \sum_{i=1}^{N} X_i$ with the X_i's statistically independent.

4.3.15. Determine the probability that 7 photons are counted in the sum of three photomultiplier tubes where the number of photons counted in each tube is Poisson distributed with mean value 2.

4.3.16. Determine the probability that 7 photons are counted in the sum of three photomultiplier tubes where the number of photons counted in each tube is Poisson distributed with mean value 3.

4.4.1. Determine μ_y, Σ_y, μ_z, and Σ_z when $Y_1 = 2X_1 - 3X_2 + X_3 + 5$, $Y_2 = 4X_1 + X_2 - 2X_3 + 3$, and $Z^T = (X_1, X_3)$ where $\mu_x^T = (3, 4, 1)$ and

$$\Sigma_x = \begin{bmatrix} 3 & -1 & 2 \\ -1 & 5 & -2 \\ 2 & -2 & 4 \end{bmatrix}$$

4.4.2. Determine μ_y, Σ_y, μ_z, and Σ_z when $Y_1 = 3X_1 - X_2 + 2X_3 + 4$, $Y_2 = X_1 + 2X_2 - 4X_3 + 5$, and $Z^T = (X_2, X_3)$ where $\mu_x^T = (3, 4, 1)$ and

$$\Sigma_x = \begin{bmatrix} 3 & -1 & 2 \\ -1 & 5 & -2 \\ 2 & -2 & 4 \end{bmatrix}$$

4.4.3. Determine $f_{X_1 X_2}(x_1, x_2)$ in scalar form when $\mu_x^T = (0, 0)$ and

$$\Sigma_x = \begin{bmatrix} 5 & 3 \\ 3 & 2 \end{bmatrix}$$

4.4.4. Determine $f_{X_1 X_2}(x_1, x_2)$ in scalar form when $\mu_x^T = (3, -2)$ and

$$\Sigma_x = \begin{bmatrix} 1 & 2 \\ 2 & 5 \end{bmatrix}$$

4.4.5. Determine μ_x and Σ_x when $f_{X_1 X_2}(x_1, x_2) = [1/(2\pi\sqrt{5})]\exp[-(3x_1^2 - 8x_1 x_2 + 7x_2^2)/10]$, $-\infty < x_1 < \infty$, $-\infty < x_2 < \infty$.

4.4.6. Determine μ_x and Σ_x when $f_{X_1 X_2}(x_1, x_2) = [1/(4\pi)]\exp[-(5(x_1 + 1)^2 + 8(x_1 + 1)x_2 + 4x_2^2)/8]$, $-\infty < x_1 < \infty$, $-\infty < x_2 < \infty$.

4.4.7. Determine the probability that a Gaussian random variable with mean -1 and variance 1 is greater than a second Gaussian random variable with mean 1 and variance 1 that is statistically independent of the first.

4.4.8. Determine the probability that a Gaussian random variable with mean -1 and variance 1 is greater than a second Gaussian random variable with mean 2 and variance 2 that is statistically independent of the first.

4.4.9. Determine the probability that a Gaussian random variable with mean -1 and variance 1 is greater than a second Gaussian random variable with mean 1 and variance 1 where the covariance between the variables is 0.5.

4.5.1. Determine N to obtain $P(e) \leq 0.001$ for the communication scheme of Section 4.5 with no quantization and $a/\sigma = 1$.

4.5.2. Determine N to obtain $P(e) \leq 0.001$ for the communication scheme of Section 4.5 with no quantization and $a/\sigma = 2$.

4.5.3. Determine $P(e)$ for no quantization and $P_H(e)$ for hard decisions (1-bit quantization) for the communication scheme of Section 4.5 with $N = 3$ and $a/\sigma = 2$.

4.5.4. Determine $P(e)$ for no quantization and $P_H(e)$ for hard decisions (1-bit quantization) for the communication scheme of Section 4.5 with $N = 5$ and $a/\sigma = 1$.

4.6.1. Determine the bound on the probability that the sample mean, for the sum of Bernoulli random variables, differs from the true mean p by more than 20%, with $p = 0.5$ and $N = 500$, using the Chebyshev inequality and the Chernoff bound.

4.6.2. Determine the bound on the probability that the sample mean, for the sum of Bernoulli random variables, differs from the true mean p by more than 10%, with $p = 0.4$ and $N = 2000$, using the Chebyshev inequality and the Chernoff bound.

4.6.3. Determine the bound on the probability that the sample mean, for the sum of Bernoulli random variables, differs from the true mean p by more than 20%, with $p = 0.4$ and $N = 500$, using the Chebyshev inequality and the Chernoff bound.

4.7.1. Determine the Gaussian approximation for Problem 4.6.1.

4.7.2. Determine the Gaussian approximation for Problem 4.6.2.

4.7.3. Determine the Gaussian approximation for Problem 4.6.3.

Simulation 5

5.1 Theoretical Histogram

There are various situations in which solution of probabilistic models is impractical. However, simulation techniques can often be used to obtain information about the behavior of such systems. In many situations, as in reliability theory, the testing is destructive, in which case a simulation of the reliability may be warranted. This chapter deals with the basic ideas of simulation.

In a simulation, rather than mathematically analyzing a system, one causes another system to operate in an equivalent manner and measures appropriate parameters for the second system, which are then concluded to hold for the first system. Simulations of probabilistic systems involve generating random variables typical of those describing the operation of the real system, and then letting these random variables characterize the operation of the simulation model in an equivalent manner. For example, in a simulation of a communication system, random variables describing the transmitted signal and describing the noise would be generated, and the decision rule used by the receiver to determine the transmitted signal would be implemented on a computer. If the assumptions of the simulation model are valid, the law of large numbers states that the values obtained from the simulation will eventually converge to the correct quantities.

Since computers have finite word length, all numbers handled in a computer are discrete, and therefore a discrete approximation to density functions is needed. The most common approximation is a histogram. Techniques will be developed for generating random numbers, or numbers satisfying statistical tests for randomness, on computers, as well as tests to determine whether the numbers generated are realistic.

A histogram is a discrete approximation to a probability density function and, in fact, is a piecewise constant approximation. The density function is the derivative of the distribution function, with the limit form (interval width $\Delta x \to 0$) given in Eq. (2.1.3b). A theoretical histogram is obtained from this by letting Δx be nonzero, yielding the constant approximation

$$\hat{f}(x) = \frac{F_X(x + \Delta x) - F_X(x)}{\Delta x} = \frac{P(x < X \le x + \Delta x)}{\Delta x} \qquad (5.1.1)$$

This is similar to the probability $f_X(x) \, dx$ of being in the interval $(x, x + dx]$. The theoretical histogram is obtainable directly from the distribution function. If the range of $f_X(x)$, $a < x \le b$, is divided into K intervals such that $x_0 = a$, $x_K = b$, and $x_{i-1} < x_i$, $i = 1, 2, \ldots, K$, the ith interval width is given as $\Delta x_i = x_i - x_{i-1}$, $i = 1, 2, \ldots, K$. The theoretical histogram over all x is then given by

$$\hat{f}_i(x) = \frac{F_X(x_i) - F_X(x_{i-1})}{x_i - x_{i-1}} \qquad x_{i-1} < x \le x_i \quad i = 1, 2, \ldots, K \qquad (5.1.2)$$

which is the probability of being in the interval $(x_{i-1}, x_i]$ divided by the interval width, or a density function. For the uniform random variable with $f_X(x) = 1$, $0 < x \le 1$, $\hat{f}_i(x) = 1$ for all i.

There are two common ways of choosing the intervals for a histogram. The first and usually the simplest is to choose all of the intervals of equal length. Consider an example of a histogram with equally spaced intervals.

Example 5.1.1. A histogram for the linear random variable with density function

$$f_X(x) = 2x \qquad 0 < x \le 1$$

$$= 0 \qquad \text{otherwise}$$

and corresponding distribution function

$$F_X(x) = 0 \qquad x \le 0$$

$$= x^2 \qquad 0 < x \le 1$$

$$= 1 \qquad x > 1$$

will be determined. For $K = 5$ and equally spaced intervals, the nonzero range of the linear random variable produces the values $x_i = 0, 0.2, 0.4, 0.6, 0.8, 1.0$, $i = 0, 1, 2, 3, 4, 5$. The corresponding values of the distribution function are $F_X(x_i) = 0, 0.04, 0.16, 0.36, 0.64, 1.00$, $i = 0, 1, 2, 3, 4, 5$. Putting these into Eq. (5.1.2) gives the theoretical histogram values

$$\hat{f}_i(x) = 0.2 \quad i = 1$$
$$= 0.6 \quad i = 2$$
$$= 1.0 \quad i = 3$$
$$= 1.4 \quad i = 4$$
$$= 1.8 \quad i = 5$$

This theoretical histogram is shown in Fig. 5.1.1a along with the density function from which it was derived.   □

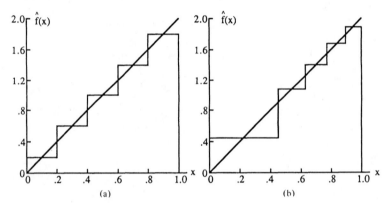

Fig. 5.1.1. Theoretical histogram for $f_X(x) = 2x$, $0 < x \le 1$: (a) equally spaced intervals; (b) equal-probability intervals.

As seen in Fig. 5.1.1a, the histogram is a piecewise constant approximation to the density function.

The other common method for choosing the intervals for a histogram is to choose them to have equal probability. This implies that the intervals are longer when $f_X(x)$ is smaller and shorter when $f_X(x)$ is larger.

Example 5.1.2. A histogram with equal probability intervals will be determined using the density function of Example 5.1.1. For $K = 5$ equal probability intervals, the distribution function values are $F_X(x_i) = 0, 0.2, 0.4, 0.6, 0.8, 1.0$, $i = 0, 1, 2, 3, 4, 5$. The interval boundaries are found by obtaining x in terms of $F_X(x)$ as $x = \sqrt{F_X(x)}$, which yields $x_i = 0, 0.447, 0.632, 0.775, 0.894, 1.000$, $i = 0, 1, 2, 3, 4, 5$. Putting these into Eq. (5.1.2) gives the theoretical histogram values for equal probability intervals as

$$\hat{f}_i(x) = 0.447 \qquad i = 1$$

$$= 1.081 \qquad i = 2$$

$$= 1.399 \qquad i = 3$$

$$= 1.681 \qquad i = 4$$

$$= 1.889 \qquad i = 5$$

This theoretical histogram is shown in Fig. 5.1.1b along with the linear density function. This is, again, a piecewise constant approximation to the density function. In this case, the area under each segment of the histogram is equal to $\frac{1}{5}$. □

When the range of the random variable is infinite, choosing equally spaced intervals results in infinite-length intervals and $\hat{f}_i(x) = 0$ for all i, as can be seen from Eq. (5.1.2). Equal-probability intervals result in either $\hat{f}_1(x) = 0$, $\hat{f}_K(x) = 0$, or both equal 0, since the end intervals would be infinite intervals. The normal procedure to compensate for an infinite range is to find an interval wide enough that the probability of being outside this interval is negligible, and determine the histogram as if the random variable were in this range.

Example 5.1.3. Consider the normalized Gaussian random variable with density function

$$f_X(x) = \frac{1}{\sqrt{2\pi}} e^{-x^2/2} \qquad -\infty < x < \infty$$

For $K = 7$ and equal-probability intervals (probability of each interval is $\frac{1}{7}$), the distribution function values are $F_X(x_i) = 0, 0.143, 0.286, 0.429, 0.571, 0.714, 0.857, 1.000$, $i = 0, 1, \ldots, 7$. The interval boundaries are obtained from Table A.1 as $x_i = -\infty, -1.068, -0.566, -0.180, 0.180, 0.566, 1.068, \infty$, $i = 0, 1, \ldots, 7$. Also from Table A.1, the probability of X being greater than 2.4 is 0.00820 and from symmetry the probability of X being less than -2.4 is 0.00820. Only a negligible part of the probability lies outside the range from -2.4 to 2.4, and thus picking $x_0 = -2.4$ and $x_7 = 2.4$ yields a histogram restricted to this range. Using Eq. (5.1.2), the theoretical histogram values for equal probability intervals are obtained as

$$\hat{f}_i(x) = 0.107 \quad i = 1$$
$$= 0.285 \quad i = 2$$
$$= 0.370 \quad i = 3$$
$$= 0.398 \quad i = 4$$
$$= 0.370 \quad i = 5$$
$$= 0.285 \quad i = 6$$
$$= 0.107 \quad i = 7$$

This theoretical histogram is shown in Fig. 5.1.2. In this case the piecewise constant approximation to the Gaussian density function has area $\frac{1}{7}$ under each segment of the histogram.   □

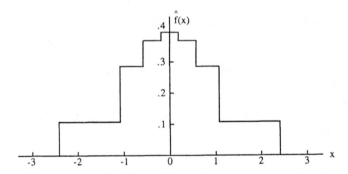

Fig. 5.1.2. Theoretical histogram for Gaussian density function.

Empirical histograms are defined in the same way as theoretical histograms except that measured values are used instead of known values of the interval probabilities. Empirical histograms will be considered in Section 5.3 after the generation of pseudorandom numbers is discussed.

5.2   Pseudorandom Numbers

Systematic algorithms for generating numbers on a computer which appear to be random are the most common way to obtain pseudorandom numbers. These numbers are not truly random, because if the algorithms are applied with the same starting conditions, the same sequence of numbers will be generated. They do pass many statistical tests for randomness, though, and hence are called pseudorandom numbers. However, almost all pseudorandom generators fail some high-dimensional test of randomness. Thus, multidimensional usage should be carefully analyzed. A few alternative approaches which are not necessarily easy to implement on a computer will be given first.

One approach to selecting random decimal digits is to use some of the less significant digits in tables of mathematical functions, such as tables of logarithms. Some tables of random numbers have been published, the largest being a table of 1 million random digits compiled by Rand Corporation. These digits are claimed to have passed all statistical tests for randomness that have been applied to them. Other procedures for generating random numbers use noise in electronic devices. The central limit theorem states that such noise has a Gaussian distribution. These generators also pass statistical tests for randomness. One systematic method for generating random numbers is to use successive digits in the expansion of irrational numbers such as π or e. A systematic technique for implementation on computers is to take an appropriately chosen large number as a starting value, square it, and extract the middle half of the digits in the squared value as the next number in the sequence, and so forth. This procedure has poor statistical properties.

The most common way to obtain pseudorandom numbers on a digital computer is to use a linear multiplicative congruential generator which generates a sequence of pseudorandom integers, R_1, R_2, R_3, ..., from

$$R_i = (AR_{i-1} + C) \bmod M \qquad i = 1, 2, 3, \ldots \qquad (5.2.1)$$

where R_0 is the seed or starting value, M the modulus, A a suitably chosen multiplier, and C an additive constant. The notation mod M or modulo M means that the arithmetic is done modulo M; that is, R_i is the remainder after dividing the sum $AR_{i-1} + C$ by M. The resulting sequence of pseudorandom numbers, for appropriately chosen seed R_0, modulus M, and multiplier A, will have good statistical properties and produce long sequences before repeating.

Numbers generated according to Eq. (5.2.1) appear to be statistically independent, identically distributed numbers, but are pseudorandom in the sense that given the same seed the same sequence will be produced. Also, if in the use of Eq. (5.2.1) the same pseudorandom number is obtained again at any point, the entire sequence must repeat from that point on. The modulus M is dependent on the word length of the computer and for signed numbers is normally chosen to be

$$M = 2^{\text{word length} - 1} \qquad (5.2.2)$$

where the word length -1 is used since 1 bit is required for the sign and this yields $2^{\text{word length}-1}$ numbers starting at 0. For a 32-bit computer $M = 2^{31} =$ 2147483648. Two's- or one's-complement arithmetic may play a part in selecting the modulus for a computer. The multiplier A is chosen to produce good statistical properties and long sequences before repeating. Several values of A that accomplish this and are in use on various computer systems are 65539, 16807, 630360016, and 764261123. The seed R_0 is normally chosen to be odd for better statistical properties.

If the congruential generator of Eq. (5.2.1) is used, the R_i's can be mapped into pseudouniform random numbers on the range 0 to 1 by dividing by M. For a 32-bit computer with a multiplier A of 764261123 and $C = 0$, pseudouniform random numbers can be generated with the Fortran code

$$IX = IX * 764261123$$

$$IF(IX.LT.O)IX = (IX + 2147483647) + 1 \qquad (5.2.3)$$

$$U = IX * .4656613E - 9$$

The RANDU generator in the IBM scientific subroutine package is equivalent to Eq. (5.2.3), with the multiplier 764261123 replaced by 65539. RANDU is known to be a poor generator and violates many of the statistical tests for randomness.

For the code of Eq. (5.2.3) to work, IX is an integer and U is a real (floating point) number. The multiplication in the first line overflows the integer register retaining the 32 least significant bits of the multiplication (this assumes that an overflow does not terminate the program). Retaining the 32 least significant bits allows the sign bit to be either 0 (positive number) or 1 (negative number). The IF statement leaves the positive numbers alone, but converts the negative numbers to positive ones by adding 2^{31}, or 1 in the sign position, to the negative number. Since 2^{31} cannot be represented as a signed integer on a 32-bit computer, the sum is accomplished by first adding $2^{31} - 1 = 2147483647$ and then adding 1 (this again produces an overflow). Thus, the first two lines accomplish the modulo M multiplication desired. The pseudouniform random numbers in the range 0 to 1 are obtained in line 3 by dividing the pseudorandom integers IX by the maximum range of IX, which is $1/(2^{31} - 1) = 0.4656613E - 9$.

Any integer greater than 0 and less than 2147483647 can be used as the starting value for IX, but an odd integer is preferred. This generator is used by specifying a starting value for IX and then looping through Eq. (5.2.3) as many times as desired. In excess of 10 million numbers can be generated, without repeating, by using this generator. Several good starting values are 1798563, 45791381, 45791383, 205372171, 1068749125, 65317391, 327148595, and 38371429.

When the modulus M of Eq. (5.2.1) is not a power of 2, the mod operation cannot be performed by discarding the high-order bits, as was done in Eq. (5.2.3). If the computer has DOUBLE PRECISION with at least as many bits as the product AR_{i-1} and if a mod operation is available, the realization is straightforward. For $M = 2^{31} - 1$ and $A = 16807$ the Fortran code for this generator is given as

$$IX = DMOD(16807DO * IX, 2147483647DO)$$
$$U = IX * .4656613E - 9 \tag{5.2.4}$$

A general generator for $M = 2^{31} - 1$ and $A = 16807$, which does not require a mod operation or DOUBLE PRECISION, is given as

$$IM = IX / 127773$$
$$IX = 16807 * (IX - IM * 127773) - IM * 2836$$
$$IF(IX.LT.O)IX = IX + 2147483647 \tag{5.2.5}$$
$$U = IX * .4656613E - 9$$

It can be seen that $(16807)(127773) = 2147483647 - 2836 = (2^{31} - 1) - 2836$. The term $(IX - IM * 127773)$ in the second line obtains IX mod 127773 and the term $16807 * (IX - IM * 127773)$ obtains $(16807 * IX) \bmod [(16807)(127773)]$. Thus, line 2 obtains $(16807 * IX) \bmod (2^{31} - 1)$. Line 3 converts negative numbers to positive numbers, and line 4 maps the numbers to the range 0 to 1. The starting value for IX can be any integer greater than 0 and less than 2147483647. Equation (5.2.5) is believed to be a good generator of pseudouniform random numbers.

Equation (5.2.3) with multiplier 764261123, or with a different multiplier A [or Eq. (5.2.5)], can be used to generate pseudouniform random numbers. The integral transform method of Eq. (3.1.11) can then be used to obtain many different pseudorandom numbers from the pseudouniform random numbers. In addition, the Box–Muller method of Eq. (3.2.7) can be used to obtain pairs of pseudo-Gaussian random numbers from pairs of pseudouniform random numbers. Generators other than linear multiplicative generators may yield better results, with regard to statistical independence of the pairs of pseudo-Gaussian random numbers, when used with the Box–Muller transformation.

Another systematic generator that is easily implemented on a computer, if bit manipulation is readily available, is a maximum length shift register. This method requires bit shifting and the Exclusive-OR operations and generates $2^N - 1$ pseudorandom numbers (all but 0) with an N-bit register. This can be accomplished in three lines of code, as was Eq. (5.2.3). Line 1 would be a 1-bit shift left (multiply by 2), line 2 an Exclusive-OR with a predetermined number if the pseudonumber was negative after the shift (a positive number is not changed), and line 3 the normalization to the range 0 to 1. The starting value can be any number except 0 and the Exclusive-OR value chosen to give a maximum length sequence. This type of generator has good statistical properties. For a 32-bit register (using a signed number) an Exclusive-OR value is the octal number 20000000011 and for a 16-bit register the octal number 100003.

5.3   Empirical Histogram

The law of large numbers implies that as the number of observations of a random variable approaches infinity, the probability of falling in the ith interval, $(x_{i-1}, x_i]$, which is $F_X(x_i) - F_X(x_{i-1})$, becomes equal to the relative frequency of the observations falling in this same interval, N_i/N; N_i is the number of observations falling in interval i and N the total number of observations. The empirical histogram, or histogram, replaces $F_X(x_i) - F_X(x_{i-1})$ in Eq. (5.1.2) by its estimate N_i/N, which yields the empirical histogram values

$$\hat{f}_i(x) = \frac{N_i}{N(x_i - x_{i-1})} \qquad x_{i-1} < x \leq x_i \quad i = 1, 2, \ldots, K \qquad (5.3.1)$$

The intervals used here are chosen in the same manner as for the theoretical histogram, i.e., as equal-length intervals or equal-probability intervals. If the probabilities of different intervals are not known beforehand, the intervals can be chosen so that the same number of observations fall in each interval.

The Fortran program of Table 5.3.1 uses a linear multiplicative congruential generator with multiplier 764261123 and starting value 45791381 along with the Box–Muller method to generate normalized pseudo-Gaussian random numbers. The starting value is given in line 4 and the multiplier in lines 7 and 10 for the two uniform numbers. Line 9 calculates the angle from one uniform number and line 12 the amplitude from a second uniform number [U_1 is used here instead of $1 - U_1$ as in Eq. (3.2.7), since both U_1 and $1 - U_1$ are uniformly distributed on the interval 0 to 1], which is used to calculate the two Gaussian numbers in lines 14 and 16. These statements are basically the only statements necessary for the execution of the program. Lines 5 and 6 are for the number of pseudo-Gaussian numbers desired and lines 17–26 for outputting the numbers. The subroutine ORDER puts the numbers in order from smallest to largest, which is convenient for counting the number in given intervals. Table 5.3.2a gives the 120 pseudo-Gaussian

Table 5.3.1

Pseudo-Gaussian Random Number Generator Using the Box–Muller Method with a 764261123
Multiplicative Congruential Generator

```
 1        DIMENSION G(240), H(240)
 2        WRITE(3,13)
 3        PI2=6.283185308
 4        IX=45791381
 5        DO 7 J1=1,2
 6        DO 8 J2=1,120,2
 7        IX=IX*764261123
 8        IF(IX.LT.0) IX=IX+2147483647+1
 9        ANG=PI2*IX*.4656613E-9
10        IX=IX*764261123
11        IF(IX.LT.0) IX=IX+2147483647+1
12        R=SQRT(-2.*ALOG(IX*.4656613E-9))
13        N=J2+120*(J1-1)
14        G(N)=R*COS(ANG)
15        N=N+1
16     8  G(N)=R*SIN(ANG)
17        WRITE(3,11) N
18        WRITE(3,10) (G(I), I=1,N)
19        CALL ORDER(N,G,H)
20        WRITE(3,12)
21     7  WRITE(3,10) (H(I), I=1,N)
22        STOP
23    13  FORMAT('1')
24    10  FORMAT(5X,10F7.3)
25    11  FORMAT(5X,I5,' GAUSSIAN PSEUDO RANDOM VARIABLES')
26    12  FORMAT(5X,' ORDERED GAUSSIAN)
27        END

28        SUBROUTINE ORDER(N,A,B)
29        DIMENSION A(240), B(240)
30        B(1)=A(1)
31        DO 2 J=2,N
32        J1=J-1
33        DO 5 I=1,J1
34        IF(A(J).LT.B(I)) GO TO 3
35     5  CONTINUE
36        B(J)=A(J)
37        GO TO 2
38     3  JI=J-I
39        DO 4 K=1,JI
40     4  B(J+1-K)=B(J-K)
41        B(I)=A(J)
42     2  CONTINUE
43        RETURN
44        END
```

Table 5.3.2a

120 Pseudo-Gaussian Random Numbers

120 GAUSSIAN PSEUDO RANDOM VARIABLES									
1.141	-0.907	-0.744	-0.742	0.132	0.143	-0.042	0.909	-0.195	0.229
-0.785	0.084	-1.130	-0.803	0.060	1.125	0.114	0.408	-1.726	-0.191
-0.585	-1.625	1.448	2.665	0.619	-0.303	-0.970	-1.066	1.426	1.875
0.247	-0.368	0.814	1.548	0.596	-1.409	0.598	0.965	0.134	0.226
-0.252	1.073	0.422	0.139	-0.217	-1.751	0.187	-0.445	-0.151	0.198
0.027	-0.555	-1.989	1.099	-0.497	0.276	-0.027	-1.855	-0.359	-1.038
-0.711	-1.322	0.132	1.156	0.522	1.072	-1.267	0.931	-0.544	-0.390
-0.310	1.093	0.106	1.176	1.840	1.098	-0.109	0.505	0.797	0.675
-1.670	0.638	0.259	0.167	-0.522	-0.255	0.232	-0.431	0.244	-0.877
0.238	-1.059	-0.450	0.459	1.395	-1.084	0.742	-1.904	1.004	-0.043
-2.118	0.627	0.072	1.396	0.776	0.423	0.941	-0.524	-0.173	-2.334
1.492	-0.461	-0.515	1.294	-0.394	-0.179	0.776	0.574	-1.119	0.503
ORDERED GAUSSIAN									
-2.334	-2.118	-1.989	-1.904	-1.855	-1.751	-1.726	-1.670	-1.625	-1.409
-1.322	-1.267	-1.130	-1.119	-1.084	-1.066	-1.059	-1.038	-0.970	-0.907
-0.877	-0.803	-0.785	-0.744	-0.742	-0.711	-0.585	-0.555	-0.544	-0.524
-0.522	-0.515	-0.497	-0.461	-0.450	-0.445	-0.431	-0.394	-0.390	-0.368
-0.359	-0.310	-0.303	-0.255	-0.252	-0.217	-0.195	-0.191	-0.179	-0.173
-0.151	-0.109	-0.043	-0.042	-0.027	0.027	0.060	0.072	0.084	0.106
0.114	0.132	0.132	0.134	0.139	0.143	0.167	0.187	0.198	0.226
0.229	0.232	0.238	0.244	0.247	0.259	0.276	0.408	0.422	0.423
0.459	0.503	0.505	0.522	0.574	0.596	0.598	0.619	0.627	0.638
0.675	0.742	0.776	0.776	0.797	0.814	0.909	0.931	0.941	0.965
1.004	1.072	1.073	1.093	1.098	1.099	1.125	1.141	1.156	1.176
1.294	1.395	1.396	1.426	1.448	1.492	1.548	1.840	1.875	2.665

numbers generated by the program of Table 5.3.1 and Table 5.3.2b gives 120 additional (240 total) numbers.

If the pseudo-Gaussian random numbers generated from the program of Table 5.3.1 are transformed as

$$F(N) = C * G(N) + D \qquad (5.3.2)$$

The $F(N)$'s would be pseudo-Gaussian random numbers with mean D and variance C^2.

Example 5.3.1.   A histogram for the pseudo-Gaussian numbers of Table 5.3.2b, $N = 240$, will now be obtained. For $K = 7$ equal-probability intervals, as done in Fig. 5.1.2, the interval boundaries are $x_i = -2.4, -1.068, -0.566, -0.180, 0.180, 0.566, 1.068, 2.4, i = 0, 1, \ldots, 7$. From the ordered portion of this table, the numbers in these intervals are obtained as $N_i = 40, 28, 38, 34, 35, 35, 30, i = 1, 2, \ldots, 7$. For completeness the point 2.665 was included in interval 7. The histogram values are then obtained from

Table 5.3.2b

240 Pseudo-Gaussian Random Numbers

240 GAUSSIAN PSEUDO RANDOM VARIABLES

1.141	-0.907	-0.744	-0.742	0.132	0.143	-0.042	0.909	-0.195	0.229
-0.785	0.084	-1.130	-0.803	0.060	1.125	0.114	0.408	-1.726	-0.191
-0.585	-1.625	1.448	2.665	0.619	-0.303	-0.970	-1.066	1.426	1.875
0.247	-0.368	0.814	1.548	0.596	-1.409	0.598	0.965	0.134	0.226
-0.252	1.073	0.422	0.139	-0.217	-1.751	0.187	-0.445	-0.151	0.198
0.027	-0.555	-1.989	1.099	-0.497	0.276	-0.027	-1.855	-0.359	-1.038
-0.711	-1.322	0.132	1.156	0.522	1.072	-1.267	0.931	-0.544	-0.390
-0.310	1.093	0.106	1.176	1.840	1.098	-0.109	0.505	0.797	0.675
-1.670	0.638	0.259	0.167	-0.522	-0.255	0.232	-0.431	0.244	-0.877
0.238	-1.059	-0.450	0.459	1.395	-1.084	0.742	-1.904	1.004	-0.043
-2.118	0.627	0.072	1.396	0.776	0.423	0.941	-0.524	-0.173	-2.334
1.492	-0.461	-0.515	1.294	-0.394	-0.179	0.776	0.574	-1.119	0.503
0.305	-0.319	-0.189	-0.322	-1.283	-2.296	2.394	1.426	0.473	-0.713
0.245	0.141	-1.186	-1.017	-1.815	0.230	-0.984	-0.412	0.087	-1.939
-2.066	0.699	1.413	0.226	-0.223	-0.423	0.575	0.487	0.947	-1.726
0.657	0.809	-0.887	-1.507	0.541	-0.063	1.254	-1.718	0.959	-0.437
1.224	-0.563	0.829	0.165	0.155	-0.259	-1.025	1.321	-0.559	1.505
-0.595	-1.278	-0.290	-0.363	0.648	-0.497	0.549	0.505	-2.002	-0.299
-0.750	0.212	-0.046	-0.630	-0.129	-1.151	-0.020	1.954	0.604	0.355
-1.869	0.781	-1.801	-1.310	0.625	0.319	0.093	-1.722	1.042	0.650
0.376	-1.041	-0.904	-1.178	-2.246	1.110	0.354	0.011	0.756	0.630
-1.508	0.213	-1.314	-0.457	0.987	-0.892	-1.470	-0.046	1.185	-1.269
-1.093	0.660	-1.054	0.141	-0.007	1.828	-0.315	0.601	0.379	-0.305
0.236	-1.337	-0.724	0.347	-0.699	0.072	0.153	-0.800	-0.857	-1.504

ORDERED GAUSSIAN

-2.334	-2.296	-2.246	-2.118	-2.066	-2.002	-1.989	-1.939	-1.904	-1.869
-1.855	-1.815	-1.801	-1.751	-1.726	-1.726	-1.722	-1.718	-1.670	-1.625
-1.508	-1.507	-1.504	-1.470	-1.409	-1.337	-1.322	-1.314	-1.310	-1.283
-1.278	-1.269	-1.267	-1.186	-1.178	-1.151	-1.130	-1.119	-1.093	-1.084
-1.066	-1.059	-1.054	-1.041	-1.038	-1.025	-1.017	-0.984	-0.970	-0.907
-0.904	-0.892	-0.887	-0.877	-0.857	-0.803	-0.800	-0.785	-0.750	-0.744
-0.742	-0.724	-0.713	-0.711	-0.699	-0.630	-0.595	-0.585	-0.563	-0.559
-0.555	-0.544	-0.524	-0.522	-0.515	-0.497	-0.497	-0.461	-0.457	-0.450
-0.445	-0.437	-0.431	-0.423	-0.412	-0.394	-0.390	-0.368	-0.363	-0.359
-0.322	-0.319	-0.315	-0.310	-0.305	-0.303	-0.299	-0.290	-0.259	-0.255
-0.252	-0.223	-0.217	-0.195	-0.191	-0.189	-0.179	-0.173	-0.151	-0.129
-0.109	-0.063	-0.046	-0.046	-0.043	-0.042	-0.027	-0.020	-0.007	0.011
0.027	0.060	0.072	0.072	0.084	0.087	0.093	0.106	0.114	0.132
0.132	0.134	0.139	0.141	0.141	0.143	0.153	0.155	0.165	0.167
0.187	0.198	0.212	0.213	0.226	0.226	0.229	0.230	0.232	0.236
0.238	0.244	0.245	0.247	0.259	0.276	0.305	0.319	0.347	0.354
0.355	0.376	0.379	0.408	0.422	0.423	0.459	0.473	0.487	0.503
0.505	0.505	0.522	0.541	0.549	0.574	0.575	0.596	0.598	0.601
0.604	0.619	0.625	0.627	0.630	0.638	0.648	0.650	0.657	0.660
0.675	0.699	0.742	0.756	0.776	0.776	0.781	0.797	0.809	0.814
0.829	0.909	0.931	0.941	0.947	0.959	0.965	0.987	1.004	1.042
1.072	1.073	1.093	1.098	1.099	1.110	1.125	1.141	1.156	1.176
1.185	1.224	1.254	1.294	1.321	1.395	1.396	1.413	1.426	1.426
1.448	1.492	1.505	1.548	1.828	1.840	1.875	1.954	2.394	2.665

Eq. (5.3.1) as

$$\hat{f}_i(x) = 0.125 \qquad i = 1$$
$$= 0.232 \qquad i = 2$$
$$= 0.410 \qquad i = 3$$
$$= 0.394 \qquad i = 4$$
$$= 0.378 \qquad i = 5$$
$$= 0.291 \qquad i = 6$$
$$= 0.094 \qquad i = 7$$

This histogram is shown in Fig. 5.3.1. It is not symmetric but it does look very similar to the theoretical histogram for the Gaussian density function given in Fig. 5.1.2, and both do seem to look like the bell curve of the Gaussian density function.   □

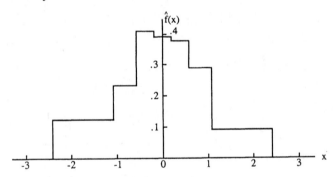

Fig. 5.3.1. Histogram for 240 pseudo-Gaussian random numbers.

A question that might be asked is, even if Fig. 5.3.1 looks like the Gaussian density function, is it reasonable to conclude that this histogram is Gaussian, and can it be concluded that these pseudorandom numbers are Gaussian? Looking at the histogram gives a subjective measure, but a quantitative measure would be more meaningful. A quantitative measure of the pseudorandom numbers with regard to their being Gaussian is considered next.

5.4   Goodness of Fit

In the situation just considered, pseudorandom numbers were generated that were supposed to be Gaussian random variables. There should be a quantitative measure to check whether it is reasonable to assume that these numbers are Gaussian. A variety of statistical goodness-of-fit tests have been developed for such situations. One of the most common, the chi-square test, will be considered here.

The chi-square test is widely used in statistics since a variety of situations can be shown to be described, at least approximately, by a chi-square density function. If X_i is a Gaussian random variable with $\mu = 0$ and $\sigma^2 = 1$, the density function of $Y_i = X_i^2$ can be determined as

$$f_{Y_i}(y_i) = \frac{1}{\sqrt{2\pi y_i}} e^{-y_i/2} \qquad y_i \geq 0$$

and the characteristic function, from Table C.2, given as

$$\phi_{Y_i}(\omega) = (1 - j2\omega)^{-1/2}$$

where this is a special case of the gamma density function with $a = \frac{1}{2}$, $b = -\frac{1}{2}$, and $\Gamma(\frac{1}{2}) = \sqrt{\pi}$. If $Z = Y_1 + Y_2 + \cdots + Y_r$, and the Y_i's are statistically independent (X_i's statistically independent), the characteristic function of Z is obtained as

$$\phi_Z(\omega) = [\phi_{Y_i}(\omega)]^r = (1 - j2\omega)^{-r/2}$$

and, from Table C.2 again, the density function of Z is given as

$$f_Z(z) = \frac{z^{(r-2)/2}}{2^{r/2}\Gamma(r/2)} e^{-z/2} \qquad z \geq 0 \tag{5.4.1}$$

where this is a special case of the gamma density function, with $a = \frac{1}{2}$ and $b = (r-2)/2$. This special case is called a chi-square random variable with r degrees of freedom (its only parameter), and the chi-square density function is described by Eq. (5.4.1). Thus, the sum of the squares of statistically independent normalized Gaussian random variables is a chi-square random vairable. The chi-square test is related to the chi-square random variable.

The chi-square test, which is a measure of the goodness of data fitting a particular model, is based on the chi-square statistic, which is given as

$$C_N(K) = \sum_{i=1}^{K} \frac{(N_i - Np_i)^2}{Np_i} \tag{5.4.2}$$

where N is the total number of observations, K the number of intervals, p_i the theoretical probability (assumed known) of being in interval i, and N_i the number of observations in interval i. This test statistic is a measure of how well the empirical histogram values fit the theoretical histogram values. It can be shown that $(N_i - Np_i)/\sqrt{Np_i}$ is approximately Gaussian, which makes $C_N(K)$ approximately a chi-square random variable with $r = K - 1$ degrees of freedom. Since $p_K = 1 - p_1 - p_2 - \cdots - p_{K-1}$ and $N_K = N - N_1 - N_2 - \cdots - N_{K-1}$, there are only $K - 1$ independent terms in Eq. (5.4.2) and thus $K - 1$ degrees of freedom. Replacing r by $K - 1$ in Eq. (5.4.1) gives the density function for the chi-square statistic $C_N(K)$.

Example 5.4.1.   Consider Example 5.3.1 where $N = 240$ (the pseudo-Gaussian numbers given in Table 5.3.2b), $K = 7$, which for equal probability intervals yields $p_i = \frac{1}{7}$, $i = 1, 2, \ldots, 7$. The N_i's are obtained for these equal-probability intervals, from Table 5.3.2b, as $N_i = 40, 28, 38, 34, 35, 35, 30$,

$$c_{240}(7) = [(40 - \tfrac{240}{7})^2 + (28 - \tfrac{240}{7})^2 + (38 - \tfrac{240}{7})^2 + (34 - \tfrac{240}{7})^2$$
$$+ (35 - \tfrac{240}{7})^2 + (35 - \tfrac{240}{7})^2 + (30 - \tfrac{240}{7})^2] / (\tfrac{240}{7}) = 3.075$$

where $c_{240}(7)$ indicates the value taken on by the random variable $C_{240}(7)$.   □

A small value of $c_{240}(7)$ indicates that the observed frequencies are close to those expected, since Np_i is the theoretical fraction of the observations that should fall in the ith interval. Thus, a smaller value of $c_N(K)$ indicates a better fit. Even though small is good, the question of how good a fit is given by a particular value of $c_N(K)$ has not yet been answered. Also, how can two chi-square statistics be compared if they result from different numbers of intervals; i.e., how can $c_N(K_1)$ be compared to $c_N(K_2)$ when $K_1 \neq K_2$? These questions are answered by using the calculated chi-square value and the chi-square density function of Eq. (5.4.1). Letting $T = c_N(K)$, the calculated chi-square value, the probability that the chi-square random variable exceeds T can be obtained, from Eq. (5.4.1) with $r = K - 1$, as

$$P[C_N(K) \geq T] = \int_T^\infty f_Z(z)\,dz = \int_T^\infty \frac{z^{(K-3)/2}}{2^{(K-1)/2}\Gamma((K-1)/2)}\,e^{-z/2}\,dz \quad (5.4.3)$$

For K odd, which makes the power of z an integer, this expression reduces to the finite series

$$P[C_N(K) \geq T] = e^{-T/2} \sum_{i=0}^{(K-3)/2} \frac{(T/2)^i}{i!} \quad (5.4.4)$$

In addition, the value of T is tabulated, for given percentage points of the chi-square distribution, in Table 5.4.1 for both even and odd values of r (or $K - 1$).

For the Gaussian histogram of Fig. 5.3.1 where $T = c_{240}(7) = 3.075$, the probability that the chi-square random variable, with 6 degrees of freedom ($K = 7$), exceeds 3.075 can be obtained from Eq. (5.4.4) as

$$P[C_{240}(7) \geq 3.075] = 0.799$$

Table 5.4.1

Percentage Points of the Chi-Square Distribution

r\P	.99	.975	.95	.9	.75	.5	.25	.1	.05	.025	.01
1	.0002	.0010	.0039	.0158	.1015	.4549	1.323	2.706	3.841	5.024	6.635
2	.0201	.0506	.1026	.2107	.5754	1.386	2.773	4.605	5.991	7.378	9.210
3	.1148	.2158	.3518	.5844	1.213	2.366	4.108	6.251	7.815	9.348	11.34
4	.2971	.4844	.7107	1.064	1.923	3.357	5.385	7.779	9.488	11.14	13.28
5	.5543	.8312	1.145	1.610	2.675	4.351	6.626	9.236	11.07	12.83	15.09
6	.8721	1.237	1.635	2.204	3.455	5.384	7.841	10.64	12.59	14.45	16.81
7	1.239	1.690	2.167	2.833	4.255	6.346	9.037	12.02	14.07	16.01	18.48
8	1.646	2.180	2.733	3.490	5.071	7.344	10.22	13.36	15.51	17.53	20.09
9	2.088	2.700	3.325	4.168	5.899	8.343	11.39	14.68	16.92	19.02	21.67
10	2.558	3.247	3.940	4.865	6.737	9.342	12.55	15.99	18.31	20.48	23.21
11	3.053	3.816	4.575	5.578	7.584	10.34	13.70	17.28	19.68	21.92	24.73
12	3.571	4.404	5.226	6.304	8.438	11.34	14.85	18.55	21.03	23.34	26.22
13	4.107	5.009	5.892	7.042	9.299	12.34	15.98	19.81	22.36	24.74	27.69
14	4.660	5.629	6.571	7.790	10.17	13.34	17.12	21.06	23.68	26.12	29.14
15	5.229	6.262	7.261	8.547	11.04	14.34	18.25	22.31	25.00	27.49	30.58
16	5.812	6.908	7.962	9.312	11.91	15.34	19.37	23.54	26.30	28.85	32.00
17	6.408	7.564	8.672	10.09	12.79	16.34	20.49	24.77	27.59	30.19	33.41
18	7.015	8.231	9.390	10.86	13.68	17.34	21.60	25.99	28.87	31.53	34.81
19	7.633	8.907	10.12	11.65	14.56	18.34	22.72	27.20	30.14	32.85	36.19
20	8.260	9.591	10.85	12.44	15.45	19.34	23.83	28.41	31.41	34.17	37.57
21	8.897	10.28	11.59	13.24	16.34	20.34	24.93	29.62	32.67	35.48	38.93
22	9.542	10.98	12.34	14.04	17.24	21.34	26.04	30.81	33.92	36.78	40.29
23	10.20	11.69	13.09	14.85	18.14	22.34	27.14	32.01	35.17	38.08	41.64
24	10.86	12.40	13.85	15.66	19.04	23.34	28.24	33.20	36.42	39.36	42.98
25	11.52	13.12	14.61	16.47	19.94	24.34	29.34	34.38	37.65	40.65	44.31
26	12.20	13.84	15.38	17.29	20.84	25.34	30.43	35.56	38.89	41.92	45.64
27	12.88	14.57	16.15	18.11	21.75	26.34	31.53	36.74	40.11	43.19	46.96
28	13.56	15.31	16.93	18.94	22.66	27.34	32.62	37.92	41.34	44.46	48.28
29	14.26	16.05	17.71	19.77	23.57	28.34	33.71	39.09	42.56	45.72	49.59
30	14.95	16.79	18.49	20.60	24.48	29.34	34.80	40.26	43.77	49.98	50.89

This probability means that, if the data were Gaussian and many different $c_{240}(7)$'s were calculated for different sets of the data, approximately 80% of these $c_{240}(7)$ values would be greater than 3.075. This is then a good indication that the observed data are Gaussian as modeled. The precise statement is that a chi-square test would be passed at the 80% level. This does not imply that no other assumed density function could pass the same test, but it means that the evidence favors the normalized Gaussian density function.

If $T = c_{240}(7) = 14$ had been calculated, $P[C_{240}(7) \geq 14] = 0.0296$ from Eq. (5.4.4), which means that, if the data were Gaussian, only 3% of the $c_{240}(7)$ values would be greater than 14. In this case it is a good indication that the observed data are not normalized Gaussian as modeled. These probabilities can also be obtained from Table 5.4.1, which would be necessary if K were even. For $P[C_{240}(7) \geq 3.075]$, this probability is found in the row with $r = 6$ ($K = 7$) between 0.75 for $T = 3.455$ and 0.9 for $T = 2.204$. This value can be obtained by linear interpolation as $0.75 + ([3.455 - 3.075]/[3.455 - 2.204])(0.9 - 0.75) = 0.796$, which is close to the value obtained from Eq. (5.4.4).

Even if the numbers of intervals are different, chi-square test values can be compared by using the chi-square probabilities.

Example 5.4.2.   For $c_N(5) = 3$ and $c_N(7) = 4$, the chi-square probabilities for these test values can be calculated, using Eq. (5.4.4), as

$$P[C_N(5) \geq 3] = e^{-1.5}[1 + 1.5] = 0.558$$

and

$$P[C_N(7) \geq 4] = e^{-2}[1 + 2 + 2] = 0.677$$

Thus, $c_N(7)$ would be a better fit to the data [even though $c_N[7] > c_N(5)$]. This should not be too unexpected since as the number of intervals increases, the number of terms in Eq. (5.4.2) increases and the chi-square value increases for the same fit of the data.   □

5.5   Simulation Confidence Statements

In simulations of communication systems or other systems, the most important consideration is how many samples are required to achieve some level of confidence for a desired accuracy of the simulated quantity. If the probability of error of a communication system is to be simulated, the samples, which indicate whether an error was made by the system or the system did not make an error, can be considered to be Bernoulli random variables with parameter p equal to the theoretical probability of error of the system. The probability of error of the system would then be approximated by the number of samples obtained in error, which is a binomial random variable since it is the sum of the Bernoulli random variables divided by the total number of samples.

The Chernoff bound for the sample mean of Bernoulli random variables (the sum divided by the number of samples), given in Eq. (4.6.10), can be used to develop a confidence statement on the simulation results. Letting the estimate of the probability of error be $\hat{p}$,

$$\hat{p} = \frac{1}{N} \sum_{i=1}^{N} Y_i = \frac{1}{N} \sum_{i=1}^{N} u(X_i - T)$$

where $Y_i = 1$ indicates an error, $u(\ )$ is the unit step, X_i the sample value,

T a threshold, and N the number of samples. Then

$$P(|\hat{p} - p| < \varepsilon p) \geq \text{confidence}$$

or

$$P(|\hat{p} - p| \geq \varepsilon p) \leq 1 - \text{confidence}$$

which states that the probability of the estimate of the probability of error differing from the true probability of error, by a small fractional amount of the true probability of error, provides a bound on the confidence of the samples. In terms of the Chernoff bound of Eq. (4.6.10), this can be written as

$$P(|\hat{p} - p| \geq \varepsilon p) = P(\hat{p} \geq d_1) + P(\hat{p} \leq d_2) \leq a_1^N + a_2^N = 1 - \text{confidence} \quad (5.5.1)$$

where

$$a_i = \left(\frac{p}{d_i}\right)^{d_i} \left(\frac{1-p}{1-d_i}\right)^{1-d_i} \qquad i = 1, 2$$

and

$$d_1 = (1 + \varepsilon)p \qquad d_2 = (1 - \varepsilon)p$$

Example 5.5.1. Let the theoretical probability of error in a simulation be $p = 10^{-3}$, the deviation from the theoretical error be $\varepsilon = 0.1$, and the number of samples be $N = 10^6$. Then $d_1 = 1.1 \times 10^{-3}$, $d_2 = 0.9 \times 10^{-3}$, $a_1 = 0.999995154$, and $a_2 = 0.999994819$, which yields

$$P(|\hat{p} - p| \geq \varepsilon p) = P(\hat{p} \geq d_1) + P(\hat{p} \leq d_2) \leq 0.007858159 + 0.005624964$$

$$= 0.013483123$$

or

$$P(|\hat{p} - p| < \varepsilon p) \geq 0.986516877$$

and confidence $= 0.986516877$. This means that more than 98.7% of the time when a simulation with these parameters is performed, there is less than 10% error in the estimated value of the probability of error. $\quad \square$

A rule of thumb that has been used is to have at least 100 errors occur in a simulation. Using this value for $p = 10^{-3}$ would require $N = 10^5$ samples, and with 90% confidence $\varepsilon \approx 0.25$. Thus, in this case, more than 90% of the time there is less than 25% error in the estimated value of p. This confidence and error in the estimated value is approximately true for 100 errors in the simulation for $p < 10^{-2}$ (it is better than this for $10^{-2} < p < 0.5$). To increase the confidence or reduce the error in the estimated value would require increasing the number of errors in the simulation (which increases N).

Example 5.5.2.   Consider the simulation of the probability that a normalized Gaussian random variable is greater than 2 [the theoretical value is $Q(2) = 0.02275$]. This simulation is accomplished by taking N Gaussian random samples X_i, $i = 1, 2, \ldots, N$, and letting $Y_i = u(X_i - 2)$ ($Y_i = 1$ if the sample is greater than 2 and $Y_i = 0$ if the sample is less than or equal to 2). The estimate for this probability $\hat{p}$ is the sum of the Y_i's divided by N. For the data of Table 5.3.2a $\hat{p} = \frac{1}{120} = 0.00833$, and for the data of Table 5.3.2b $\hat{p} = \frac{2}{240} = 0.00833$. Obviously, this is not a sufficient number of samples to obtain a good estimate.   □

Related to simulation is Monte Carlo integration or integration by random techniques. If a function to be integrated cannot be evaluated in closed form and a series approximation is too involved or too complicated, the integral can be evaluated by numerical integration or by Monte Carlo integration. In numerical integration techniques, the number of points or samples in the integration is directly proportional to the frequency of the function to be integrated (how much the function changes) and the desired accuracy of the approximation to the integral. In Monte Carlo integration, the number of points or samples depends only on the accuracy of the approximation to the integral. However, most of the time a properly chosen numerical technique can be found to yield greater accuracy, for a given number of samples, than a Monte Carlo technique. For the integral

$$A = \int_a^b g(x) \, dx$$

Monte Carlo integration is performed by obtaining pairs of statistically independent uniform random numbers, putting them in a two-dimensional plot, and counting the number that are below the line $g(x)$. Specifically, generate a set of u_1's and u_2's and let the variable of integration $x = (b-a)u_1 + a$ and the second variable $y = g_{max}u_2$, where g_{max} is the maximum value of $g(x)$ [assume $g(x) \geq 0$] over the interval from a to b, which is a rectangle containing the function $g(x)$ as shown in Fig. 5.5.1. The shaded area in this figure is the value of the integral, which consists of the values for which $y \leq g(x)$. Now, for each u_1, u_2 pair the number of times that $y = g_{max}u_2 \leq g(x) = g[(b-a)u_1 + a]$, N_{less}, is recorded (this is the number that fall in the shaded area). The ratio N_{less}/N, where N is the total number of sample pairs, then approximates the fraction of the area of the rectangle that belongs to A. Finally, A is this ratio times the area of the rectangle, or

$$A = \frac{N_{less}}{N} [(b-a)g_{max}] \tag{5.5.2}$$

The number of samples is determined, as in the simulation case, by using the Chernoff bound of Eq. (5.5.1) for the desired confidence and accuracy.

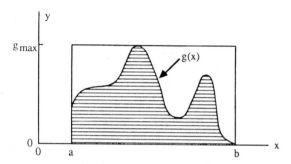

Fig. 5.5.1. Area for Monte Carlo integration.

Example 5.5.3. Consider the case where

$$A = \int_0^\pi \exp[\cos(\theta)] \, d\theta$$

Now $g(x) = \exp[\cos(\theta)]$, $x = \pi u_1$, $g_{max} = e = 2.7183$, $y = 2.7183 u_2$, and a sample lies in the area if $2.7183 u_2 \le \exp[\cos(\pi u_1)]$ or $u_2 \le 0.3679 \exp[\cos(\pi u_1)]$. For $u_1 = 0.4$ and $u_2 = 0.3$, $0.3679 \exp[\cos(0.4\pi)] = 0.5011$, u_2 is smaller, and this point is included in the area, whereas for $u_1 = 0.9$ and $u_2 = 0.6$, $0.3679 \exp[\cos(0.9\pi)] = 0.1421$, u_2 is not smaller, and this point is not included in the area. $\quad\square$

Importance sampling is a technique that can be applied in the simulation of events with low probability without the large number of samples necessary in regular sampling. This is accomplished by modifying the density function of the random quantity that is being simulated such that the low-probability events occur more frequently. The simulated probability is then obtained by weighting each error in the modified system with a factor that involves the original density function and the modified density function.

For X the random variable being sampled (the samples are $X = X_i$, $i = 1, 2, \ldots, N$) and $Y = u(X - T)$ the indicator of an error in X, in importance sampling X is transformed into Z (which has the same functional form) such that the low-probability events occur more frequently. The indicator of an error in z is given as $V = u(Z - T)w(Z)$, where $w(Z)$ is the weight of the error. The expected value of the error in the original system should equal the expected value of the error in the transformed system, and setting $E(Y) = E(V)$ yields

$$\int_{-\infty}^{\infty} u(x - T)f_X(x) \, dx = \int_{-\infty}^{\infty} u(z - T)w(z)f_Z(z) \, dz$$

$$= \int_T^{\infty} f_X(x) \, dx = \int_T^{\infty} w(z)f_Z(z) \, dz$$

A sufficient condition for equality is for the weight to be

$$w(z) = \frac{f_X(z)}{f_Z(z)} \tag{5.5.3}$$

Thus, for each sample Z_i that is greater than T, $w(Z_i)$ is added to the sum instead of 1, and the estimate $\hat{p}$ is the sum of these $w(Z_i)$'s divided by N or

$$\hat{p} = \frac{1}{N} \sum_{i=1}^{N} V_i = \frac{1}{N} \sum_{i=1}^{N} w(Z_i) u(Z_i - T) \tag{5.5.4}$$

Example 5.5.4. Consider the random variable X and its samples X_i, $i = 1, 2, \ldots, N$ to be Gaussian with $\mu_x = -2$ and $\sigma_x^2 = 1$, which are used to simulate the probability $P(X \geq 0) = Q(2)$. If X is transformed to the Gaussian random variable Z with $\mu_z = 0$ and $\sigma_z^2 = 1$ (Z_i, $i = 1, 2, \ldots, N$, are also Gaussian with $\mu_z = 0$ and $\sigma_z^2 = 1$), the simulation for $P(Z \geq 0)$ will have a significantly larger number of errors. The weight is obtained from Eq. (5.5.3) as

$$w(z) = \frac{\dfrac{1}{\sqrt{2\pi}} e^{-(z+2)^2/2}}{\dfrac{1}{\sqrt{2\pi}} e^{-z^2/2}} = e^{-2(z+1)}$$

Using this on the first 10 entries in Table 5.3.2a yields

$$\hat{p} = \tfrac{1}{10}\{\exp[-2(1.141+1)] + 0 + 0 + 0 + \exp[-2(0.132+1)]$$
$$+ \exp[-2(0.143+1)] + 0 + \exp[-2(0.909+1)]$$
$$+ 0 + \exp[-2(0.229+1)]\} = 0.03270$$

and for the entire table $\hat{p} = 0.02670$ [which is within 18% of the theoretical value of $Q(2) = 0.02275$]. Even though there are no values in Table 5.3.2a greater than 3, $Q(3)$ can be estimated by using importance sampling.   □

Importance sampling can also be applied to Monte Carlo integration.

5.6   Correlated Random Variables

In some simulations it is desirable to use correlated random variables instead of statistically independent random variables. It is possible to obtain correlated random variables from statistically independent ones by a linear transformation. For $\mathbf{X}$ an $N \times 1$ Gaussian random vector with $\boldsymbol{\mu}_x^T = (0, 0, \ldots, 0)$ and $\boldsymbol{\Sigma}_x = \mathbf{I}$ as could be obtained from the program of Table

5.3.1, Box–Muller method, an $N \times 1$ Gaussian random vector $\mathbf{Y}$ with $\boldsymbol{\mu}_y^T = (\mu_1, \mu_2, \ldots, \mu_N)$ and

$$\boldsymbol{\Sigma}_y = \begin{bmatrix} \sigma_{11} & \sigma_{12} \cdots & \sigma_{1N} \\ \sigma_{12} & \sigma_{22} \cdots & \sigma_{2N} \\ \vdots & \vdots & \vdots \\ \sigma_{1N} & \sigma_{2N} \cdots & \sigma_{NN} \end{bmatrix}$$

can be obtained by the linear transformation

$$\mathbf{Y} = \mathbf{TX} + \boldsymbol{\mu}_y \qquad (5.6.1)$$

where $\mathbf{T}$ is a lower triangular matrix given as

$$\mathbf{T} = \begin{bmatrix} t_{11} & 0 & \cdots & 0 \\ t_{21} & t_{22} & \cdots & 0 \\ \vdots & \vdots & & \vdots \\ t_{N1} & t_{N2} & \cdots & t_{NN} \end{bmatrix}$$

Equation (5.6.1) is valid only if $\boldsymbol{\Sigma}_y$ is a positive definite matrix (see Appendix D), but a modified $\mathbf{T}$ can be obtained if $\boldsymbol{\Sigma}_y$ is only positive semidefinite.

The elements of $\mathbf{T}$ are obtained by using Eq. (4.4.3) to yield

$$\boldsymbol{\Sigma}_y = \mathbf{T}\boldsymbol{\Sigma}_x\mathbf{T}^T = \mathbf{TIT}^T = \mathbf{TT}^T$$

Going across the first row of $\mathbf{T}$ and the first column of $\mathbf{T}^T$ yields the element

$$t_{11}^2 = \sigma_{11} \qquad \text{or} \qquad t_{11} = \sqrt{\sigma_{11}}$$

and across the first row of $\mathbf{T}$ and the ith column of $\mathbf{T}^T$ gives the element

$$t_{11}t_{i1} = \sigma_{i1} \qquad \text{or} \qquad t_{i1} = \frac{\sigma_{i1}}{\sqrt{\sigma_{11}}}$$

Going across the second row of $\mathbf{T}$ and the second column of $\mathbf{T}^T$ yields

$$t_{21}^2 + t_{22}^2 = \sigma_{22} \qquad \text{or} \qquad t_{22} = \sqrt{\sigma_{22} - t_{21}^2}$$

and across the second row of $\mathbf{T}$ and the ith column of $\mathbf{T}^T$ gives

$$t_{21}t_{i1} + t_{22}t_{i2} = \sigma_{i2} \qquad \text{or} \qquad t_{i2} = \frac{\sigma_{i2} - t_{21}t_{i1}}{t_{22}}$$

This is continued for the third row, fourth row, ..., Nth row. Combining these results, the t_{ij}'s are obtained as

$$t_{i1} = \frac{\sigma_{i1}}{\sqrt{\sigma_{11}}} \qquad i = 1, \ldots, N \qquad (5.6.2a)$$

$$t_{jj} = \sqrt{\sigma_{jj} - \sum_{k=1}^{j-1} t_{jk}^2} \qquad\qquad\qquad\qquad\qquad (5.6.2b)$$

$$\left. \begin{array}{ll} t_{ij} = 0 & i = 1,\ldots,j-1 \\[2ex] t_{ij} = \dfrac{\sigma_{ij} - \sum_{k=1}^{j-1} t_{jk} t_{ik}}{t_{jj}} & i = j+1,\ldots,N \end{array} \right\} \quad j = 2,\ldots,N$$

$$(5.6.2c)$$

$$(5.6.2d)$$

This method of obtaining correlated random variables from statistically independent random variables is called the square root method or Cholesky's method. This method is not limited to Gaussian random variables, but can be used for any variables with the given mean vector and covariance matrix.

Example 5.6.1. Let $\mathbf{X}$ be a 4×1 Gaussian random vector with $\boldsymbol{\mu}_x^T = (0,0,0,0)$ and $\boldsymbol{\Sigma}_x = \mathbf{I}$ and $\mathbf{Y}$ be a 4×1 Gaussian random vector with $\boldsymbol{\mu}_y^T = (0,0,0,0)$ and

$$\boldsymbol{\Sigma}_y = \begin{bmatrix} 16 & -4 & 4 & -12 \\ -4 & 10 & -7 & 3 \\ 4 & -7 & 9 & -1 \\ -12 & 3 & -1 & 35 \end{bmatrix}$$

The t_{ij}'s are calculated as

$$t_{11} = \frac{\sigma_{11}}{\sqrt{\sigma_{11}}} = \frac{16}{4} = 4$$

$$t_{21} = \frac{\sigma_{21}}{\sqrt{\sigma_{11}}} = \frac{-4}{4} = -1$$

$$t_{31} = \frac{\sigma_{31}}{\sqrt{\sigma_{11}}} = \frac{4}{4} = 1$$

$$t_{41} = \frac{\sigma_{41}}{\sqrt{\sigma_{11}}} = \frac{-12}{4} = -3$$

$$t_{22} = \sqrt{\sigma_{22} - t_{21}^2} = \sqrt{10 - (-1)^2} = 3$$

$$t_{32} = \frac{\sigma_{32} - t_{21} t_{31}}{t_{22}} = \frac{-7 - (-1)(1)}{3} = -2$$

$$t_{42} = \frac{\sigma_{42} - t_{21} t_{41}}{t_{22}} = \frac{3 - (-1)(-3)}{3} = 0$$

$$t_{33} = \sqrt{\sigma_{33} - t_{31}^2 - t_{32}^2} = \sqrt{9 - (1)^2 - (-2)^2} = 2$$

$$t_{43} = \frac{\sigma_{43} - t_{31} t_{41} - t_{32} t_{42}}{t_{33}} = \frac{-1 - (1)(-3) - (-2)(0)}{2} = 1$$

$$t_{44} = \sqrt{\sigma_{44} - t_{41}^2 - t_{42}^2 - t_{43}^2} = \sqrt{35 - (-3)^2 - (0)^2 - (1)^2} = 5$$

to yield

$$T = \begin{bmatrix} 4 & 0 & 0 & 0 \\ -1 & 3 & 0 & 0 \\ 1 & -2 & 2 & 0 \\ -3 & 0 & 1 & 5 \end{bmatrix}$$

Using Eq. (5.6.1), the scalar equations for the transformation are

$$Y_1 = 4X_1$$

$$Y_2 = -X_1 + 3X_2$$

$$Y_3 = X_1 - 2X_2 + 2X_3$$

$$Y_4 = -3X_1 + X_3 + 5X_4 \qquad \square$$

Uncorrelated random variables can be obtained from correlated random variables by solving Eq. (5.6.1) for X in terms of Y as

$$X = A(Y - \mu_y) \qquad (5.6.3)$$

where $A = T^{-1}$ is also a lower triangular matrix and given as

$$A = \begin{bmatrix} a_{11} & 0 & \cdots & 0 \\ a_{21} & a_{22} & \cdots & 0 \\ \vdots & \vdots & & \vdots \\ a_{N1} & a_{N2} & \cdots & a_{NN} \end{bmatrix}$$

Solving $AT = I$, the a_{ij}'s are obtained in terms of the t_{ij}'s as

$$a_{jj} = \frac{1}{t_{jj}} \qquad\qquad j = 1, \ldots, N \qquad (5.6.4a)$$

$$\left. \begin{array}{ll} a_{ij} = -a_{ii} \displaystyle\sum_{k=j}^{i-1} t_{ik} a_{kj} & j = 1, \ldots, i-1 \\[2mm] a_{ij} = 0 & j = i+1, \ldots, N \end{array} \right\} i = 2, \ldots, N \qquad \begin{array}{l}(5.6.4b) \\[4mm] (5.6.4c)\end{array}$$

Example 5.6.2. Determine the transformation A for Example 5.6.1. Using T of Example 5.6.1 and Eq. (5.6.4), the a_{ij}'s are calculated as

$$a_{11} = 1/t_{11} = \tfrac{1}{4}$$

$$a_{22} = 1/t_{22} = \tfrac{1}{3}$$

$$a_{33} = 1/t_{33} = \tfrac{1}{2}$$

$$a_{44} = 1/t_{44} = \tfrac{1}{5}$$

$$a_{21} = -a_{22}(t_{21}a_{11}) = -(\tfrac{1}{3})(-1)(\tfrac{1}{4}) = \tfrac{1}{12}$$

$$a_{31} = -a_{33}(t_{31}a_{11} + t_{32}a_{21}) = -(\tfrac{1}{2})[(1)(\tfrac{1}{4}) + (-2)(\tfrac{1}{12})] = -\tfrac{1}{24}$$

$$a_{32} = -a_{33}(t_{32}a_{22}) = -(\tfrac{1}{2})(-2)(\tfrac{1}{3}) = \tfrac{1}{3}$$

$$a_{41} = -a_{44}(t_{41}a_{11} + t_{42}a_{21} + t_{43}a_{31}) = -(\tfrac{1}{5})[(-3)(\tfrac{1}{4}) + (0)(\tfrac{1}{12})$$
$$+ (1)(-\tfrac{1}{24})] = \tfrac{19}{120}$$

$$a_{42} = -a_{44}(t_{42}a_{22} + t_{43}a_{32}) = -(\tfrac{1}{5})[(0)(\tfrac{1}{3}) + (1)(\tfrac{1}{3})] = -\tfrac{1}{15}$$

$$a_{43} = -a_{44}(t_{43}a_{33}) = -(\tfrac{1}{5})(1)(\tfrac{1}{2}) = -\tfrac{1}{10}$$

to yield

$$\mathbf{A} = \begin{bmatrix} \tfrac{1}{4} & 0 & 0 & 0 \\ \tfrac{1}{12} & \tfrac{1}{3} & 0 & 0 \\ -\tfrac{1}{24} & \tfrac{1}{3} & \tfrac{1}{2} & 0 \\ \tfrac{19}{120} & -\tfrac{1}{15} & -\tfrac{1}{10} & \tfrac{1}{5} \end{bmatrix}$$

Using Eq. (5.6.3), the scalar equations for the transformation are

$$X_1 = \tfrac{1}{4}(Y_1 - \mu_1)$$

$$X_2 = \tfrac{1}{12}(Y_1 - \mu_1) + \tfrac{1}{3}(Y_2 - \mu_2)$$

$$X_3 = -\tfrac{1}{24}(Y_1 - \mu_1) + \tfrac{1}{3}(Y_2 - \mu_2) + \tfrac{1}{2}(Y_3 - \mu_3)$$

$$X_4 = \tfrac{19}{120}(Y_1 - \mu_1) - \tfrac{1}{15}(Y_2 - \mu_2) - \tfrac{1}{10}(Y_3 - \mu_3) + \tfrac{1}{5}(Y_4 - \mu_4) \qquad \square$$

PROBLEMS

5.1.1. Determine a theoretical histogram for $f_X(x) = e^{-x}$, $x \geq 0$, with $K = 5$ and equally spaced intervals $x_i = 0, 1, 2, 3, 4, 5$, $i = 0, 1, \ldots, 5$.

5.1.2. Determine a theoretical histogram for $f_X(x) = e^{-x}$, $x \geq 0$, for equal probability intervals with $K = 5$ and $x_5 = 5$.

5.1.3. Determine a theoretical histogram for $f_X(x) = e^{-x}$, $x \geq 0$, with $K = 7$ and equally spaced intervals $x_i = 0, 0.6, 1.2, 1.8, 2.4, 3.0, 3.6, 4.2$, $i = 0, 1, \ldots, 7$.

5.1.4. Determine a theoretical histogram for $f_X(x) = e^{-x}$, $x \geq 0$, for equal probability intervals with $K = 7$ and $x_7 = 4.2$.

5.2.1. Develop the congruential generator for a 16-bit computer (with signed numbers) with multiplier 277 similar to Eq. (5.2.3).

5.2.2. For a 32-bit computer (with signed numbers), why will the code for a multiplier $A = 65539$ [equivalent to Eq. (5.2.5) for $A = 16807$] given below not work?

```
IM = IX/32766
IX = 65539 * (IX − IM * 32766) − IM * 32773
IF(IX.LT.O) IX = IX + 2147483647
U = IX * .4656613E − 9
```

5.2.3. Develop the general generator for a 16 bit computer (with signed numbers) with multiplier 277 similar to Eq. (5.2.5).

5.3.1. From the data of Table 5.3.2a, determine a histogram with $K = 9$ and $N = 120$ for equal-probability intervals. Take $x_0 = -2.4$ and $x_9 = 2.4$.

5.3.2. From the data of Table 5.3.2b, determine a histogram with $K = 9$ and $N = 240$ for equal-probability intervals. Take $x_0 = -2.4$ and $x_9 = 2.4$.

5.3.3. From the data of Table 5.3.2a, determine a histogram with $K = 5$ and $N = 120$ for equal-probability intervals. Take $x_0 = -2.4$ and $x_5 = 2.4$.

5.3.4. From the data of Table 5.3.2b, determine a histogram with $K = 5$ and $N = 240$ for equal-probability intervals. Take $x_0 = -2.4$ and $x_5 = 2.4$.

5.3.5. From the data of Table 5.3.2a, determine a histogram with $K = 5$ and $N = 120$ for equally spaced intervals. Take $x_0 = -2.4$ and $x_5 = 2.4$.

5.3.6. From the data of Table 5.3.2b, determine a histogram with $K = 5$ and $N = 240$ for equally spaced intervals. Take $x_0 = -2.4$ and $x_5 = 2.4$.

5.4.1. Calculate $c_{120}(9) = T$ and $P[C_{120}(9) \geq T]$ for Problem 5.3.1.

5.4.2. Calculate $c_{240}(9) = T$ and $P[C_{240}(9) \geq T]$ for Problem 5.3.2.

5.4.3. Calculate $c_{120}(5) = T$ and $P[C_{120}(5) \geq T]$ for Problem 5.3.3.

5.4.4. Calculate $c_{240}(5) = T$ and $P[C_{240}(5) \geq T]$ for Problem 5.3.4.

5.4.5. Calculate $c_{120}(5) = T$ and $P[C_{120}(5) \geq T]$ for Problem 5.3.5.

5.4.6. Calculate $c_{240}(5) = T$ and $P[C_{240}(5) \geq T]$ for Problem 5.3.6.

5.5.1. Determine the confidence in a simulation where the theoretical probability of error $p = 10^{-3}$, the deviation from the theoretical error is $\varepsilon = 0.2$, and the number of samples is $N = 10^5$.

5.5.2. Determine the confidence in a simulation where the theoretical probability of error $p = 10^{-3}$, the deviation from the theoretical error is $\varepsilon = 0.15$, and the number of samples is $N = 2 \times 10^5$.

5.5.3. Determine the number of samples required in a simulation to achieve a confidence of 0.9 where the theoretical probability of error is $p = 10^{-3}$ and the deviation from the theoretical error is $\varepsilon = 0.2$.

5.5.4. Determine the estimate of $Q(1)$ using the data of Table 5.3.2a. Repeat using the data of Table 5.3.2b.

5.5.5. Determine the estimate of $Q(1.5)$ using the data of Table 5.3.2a. Repeat using the data of Table 5.3.2b.

5.5.6. Determine the estimate of $Q(1.5)$ using importance sampling and the first 10 entries of Table 5.3.2a.

5.5.7. Determine the estimate of $Q(3)$ using importance sampling and the first 10 entries of Table 5.3.2a.

5.5.8. Determine the estimate of $Q(2.5)$ using importance sampling and the first 10 entries of Table 5.3.2a.

5.6.1. Determine the transformation to obtain a 3×1 Gaussian random vector **Y** with $\boldsymbol{\mu}_y^T = (0, 0, 0)$ and

$$\Sigma_y = \begin{bmatrix} 9 & -6 & -3 \\ -6 & 5 & 4 \\ -3 & 4 & 6 \end{bmatrix}$$

from a 3×1 Gaussian random vector **X** with $\boldsymbol{\mu}_x^T = (0, 0, 0)$ and $\Sigma_x = \mathbf{I}$.

5.6.2. Determine the transformation to obtain a 3×1 Gaussian random vector **Y** with $\boldsymbol{\mu}_y^T = (0, 0, 0)$ and

$$\Sigma_y = \begin{bmatrix} 16 & 8 & 20 \\ 8 & 13 & 16 \\ 20 & 16 & 30 \end{bmatrix}$$

from a 3×1 Gaussian random vector **X** with $\boldsymbol{\mu}_x^T = (0, 0, 0)$ and $\Sigma_x = \mathbf{I}$.

5.6.3. Determine the transformation to obtain a 3×1 Gaussian random vector **Y** with $\boldsymbol{\mu}_y^T = (8, 7, 6)$ and

$$\Sigma_y = \begin{bmatrix} 16 & 8 & 20 \\ 8 & 13 & 16 \\ 20 & 16 & 30 \end{bmatrix}$$

from a 3×1 Gaussian random vector **X** with $\boldsymbol{\mu}_x^T = (0, 0, 0)$ and $\Sigma_x = \mathbf{I}$.

5.6.4. Determine the transformation to obtain a 3×1 Gaussian random vector **X** with $\boldsymbol{\mu}_x^T = (0, 0, 0)$ and $\Sigma_x = \mathbf{I}$ from a 3×1 Gaussian random vector **Y** with $\boldsymbol{\mu}_y^T = (0, 0, 0)$ and

$$\Sigma_y = \begin{bmatrix} 4 & 12 & -8 \\ 12 & 37 & -22 \\ -8 & -22 & 36 \end{bmatrix}$$

5.6.5. Determine the transformation to obtain a 3×1 Gaussian random vector **X** with $\boldsymbol{\mu}_x^T = (0, 0, 0)$ and $\Sigma_x = \mathbf{I}$ from a 3×1 Gaussian random vector **Y** with $\boldsymbol{\mu}_y^T = (0, 0, 0)$ and

$$\Sigma_y = \begin{bmatrix} 1 & 4 & 3 \\ 4 & 20 & 24 \\ 3 & 24 & 54 \end{bmatrix}$$

Statistical Inference

6

6.1 Sampling and Estimation

Statistical tests for goodness of fit are examples of statistical inference, which is using observations of randomly generated data to infer something about the probability density functions or the parameters of the density functions of the random variables generating the data. In many situations it may be known that observations obey a Gaussian distribution, from the central limit theorem or from previous results that indicate this is a good model, but it is much less likely for the mean and variance of the Gaussian distribution to be known. Likewise, it might be known that some discrete random variable produces or is appropriately modeled by a binomial distribution or a Poisson distribution, but the parameters of the distribution are unknown.

In these and many other similar situations, it is often necessary to draw conclusions about a large group of individuals or objects (or a population). The population is assumed to be the source of the random variables, with each random variable generated considered to be a sample from this population. In order to draw such conclusions, a sample from the population is taken and certain facts are inferred about the population based on the sample. This is referred to as statistical inference.

Techniques will be developed for estimating parameters that describe distributions or unknown quantities. Both random and nonrandom parameter estimation will be considered, but the emphasis will be on nonrandom parameter estimation. For example, μ, the mean, and σ^2, the variance, are parameters for the Gaussian density function. It may be desired to estimate μ, σ^2, or both μ and σ^2 of a distribution that is known (or assumed) to be Gaussian. Alternatively, for discrete random variables it may be desired to

207

estimate the parameter p of a binomial distribution, the parameter a of a Poisson random variable, or parameters for essentially any probability distribution. Estimating the values of these nonrandom or random parameters is referred to as point estimation and is based on a sample from the population.

A sample of N observations of a random variable, $X_1, X_2, \ldots, X_N$, will be used to estimate one or more parameters of the density function describing these random variables. The joint density function of the sample is given as

$$f_{\mathbf{X}}(\mathbf{x}; \theta) = f_{X_1 X_2 \cdots X_N}(x_1, x_2, \ldots, x_N; \theta) \qquad (6.1.1a)$$

where θ is the general symbol for the parameter to be estimated. This joint density function is the same as the density functions previously discussed, but is augmented with the notation of θ to emphasize the parameter to be estimated. Similarly, for discrete random variables the joint probability function is

$$P(\mathbf{X} = \mathbf{x}; \theta) = P(X_1 = x_1, X_2 = x_2, \ldots, X_N = x_N; \theta) \qquad (6.1.1b)$$

The joint density function of Eq. (6.1.1a) and the joint probability function of Eq. (6.1.1b) are called the likelihood functions. If the samples are mutually independent (the usual assumption for tractability) the likelihood functions become

$$f_{\mathbf{X}}(\mathbf{x}; \theta) = \prod_{i=1}^{N} f_{X_i}(x_i; \theta) \qquad (6.1.2a)$$

for continuous random variables and

$$P(\mathbf{X} = \mathbf{x}; \theta) = \prod_{i=1}^{N} P(X_i = x_i; \theta) \qquad (6.1.2b)$$

for discrete random variables. If the samples are not statistically independent the likelihood function (joint density function of the N samples) cannot be obtained from the marginal density functions.

A variety of procedures for estimating θ from the sample are available, with the most common ones computed from the likelihood function in some manner. The first estimate that will be discussed is a Bayes estimate, which is more intuitive than the other types of estimates. A Bayes estimate treats θ as a random variable (the random variable is then written as Θ). The density function of $\Theta, f_\Theta(\theta)$ [or probability function $P(\Theta = \theta)$] is called the *a priori* density function of Θ (as in the communication example of Section 1.4). The likelihood function in this case is considered to be a conditional density function of $\mathbf{X}$ given that $\Theta = \theta$, or $f_{\mathbf{X}|\Theta}(\mathbf{x}|\theta)$, since the likelihood function evaluated at a particular value of θ is the density function for $\mathbf{X}$ that would be applicable if Θ had the value θ. Either Θ or $\mathbf{X}$ can be discrete, but here, for brevity, Θ and $\mathbf{X}$ will be considered continuous random variables.

Using a vector version of Eq. (2.5.4), the *a posteriori* density function of Θ is given as

$$f_{\Theta|\mathbf{X}}(\theta\,|\,\mathbf{x}) = \frac{f_{\Theta\mathbf{X}}(\theta,\mathbf{x})}{f_{\mathbf{X}}(\mathbf{x})}$$

Representing the numerator in terms of the alternative form of the conditional density function yields

$$f_{\Theta|\mathbf{X}}(\theta\,|\,\mathbf{x}) = \frac{f_{\mathbf{X}|\Theta}(\mathbf{x}\,|\,\theta)f_{\Theta}(\theta)}{f_{\mathbf{X}}(\mathbf{x})}$$

The numerator is a product of the *a priori* density function and the likelihood function, while the denominator is the marginal density function of $\mathbf{X}$, which is obtained by integrating the numerator over all values of θ. Thus,

$$f_{\Theta|\mathbf{X}}(\theta\,|\,\mathbf{x}) = \frac{f_{\Theta}(\theta)f_{\mathbf{X}|\Theta}(\mathbf{x}\,|\,\theta)}{\int_{-\infty}^{\infty} f_{\Theta}(\theta)f_{\mathbf{X}|\Theta}(\mathbf{x}\,|\,\theta)\,d\theta} \tag{6.1.3}$$

which is the continuous form of Bayes' rule. An appropriate function of this *a posteriori* density function is used as the estimate of Θ. The function most commonly used is the mean, $E(\Theta\,|\,\mathbf{X})$.

Example 6.1.1. Let θ be the unknown parameter p of a Bernoulli probability function. For N statistically independent samples from the Bernoulli distribution, the likelihood function of Eq. (6.1.2b) is given as

$$P(\mathbf{X} = \mathbf{x}\,|\,P = p) = p^k(1-p)^{N-k}$$

where $P(X_i = 1) = p$, $i = 1, 2, \ldots, N$, and k of these samples are 1. Also given is the *a priori* density function of p, which is uniformly distributed over the interval from 0 to 1, or

$$f_p(p) = 1 \qquad 0 \le p \le 1$$

$$= 0 \qquad \text{otherwise}$$

The *a posteriori* density function then becomes

$$f_{P|\mathbf{X}}(p\,|\,\mathbf{x}) = \frac{p^k(1-p)^{N-k}}{\int_0^1 p^k(1-p)^{N-k}\,dp}$$

The integral in the denominator is called a beta function and is defined as

$$\int_0^1 z^a(1-z)^b\,dz = \frac{\Gamma(a+1)\Gamma(b+1)}{\Gamma(a+b+2)}$$

For the case here $a = k$, with $\Gamma(k+1) = k!$, and $b = N - k$, with $\Gamma(N - k + 1) = (N - k)!$ and $\Gamma(k + N - k + 2) = (N + 1)!$, the denominator of the *a posteriori* density function reduces to $[k!(N - k)!]/(N + 1)!$ Finally, the *a posteriori* density function P is obtained as

$$f_{P|X}(p\,|x) = \left[\frac{(N+1)!}{k!(N-k)!}\right]p^k(1-p)^{N-k} \qquad 0 \le p \le 1$$

which is known as a beta density function. The mean of this beta random variable is given, from Table C.2, as

$$E(P|X) = \frac{k+1}{N+2}$$

which is the Bayes' estimate of P for a uniform *a priori* density function on P. The estimate of θ will be denoted as $\hat{\theta}$, and the Bayes estimate of P is written as

$$\hat{p} = \frac{k+1}{N+2}$$

For large N and k, this estimate converges to k/N, which from the law of large numbers is the true value of p as N approaches infinity.   □

In many situations the parameters being estimated are not random variables but rather unknown constants or nonrandom quantities. Bayes estimates can still be used, by assuming *a priori* density functions and going through the same procedures, but estimates based on the likelihood function alone appear more appropriate.

6.2   Maximum Likelihood Estimation

The estimate that is considered now is the most common form of estimate and is based on the likelihood function alone. This is the value of the parameter that maximizes the likelihood function $f_X(x; \theta)$, and it is appropriately called the maximum likelihood estimate. Justification for using maximum likelihood estimates will be given after several examples and some properties of estimators are considered. If the maximum of the likelihood function is interior to the range of θ and has a continuous first derivative, then a necessary condition on the maximum likelihood estimate is obtained by solving

$$\left.\frac{\partial f_X(x; \theta)}{\partial \theta}\right|_{\theta = \hat{\theta}} = 0 \qquad (6.2.1a)$$

The solution of Eq. (6.2.1a) is usable in many cases of interest, but not in all maximum likelihood cases. Since

$$\frac{\partial f_{\mathbf{X}}(\mathbf{x}; \theta)}{\partial \theta} = [f_{\mathbf{X}}(\mathbf{x}; \theta)] \frac{\partial \ln [f_{\mathbf{X}}(\mathbf{x}; \theta)]}{\partial \theta}$$

and since $f_{\mathbf{X}}(\mathbf{x}; \theta) = 0$ does not maximize the function, the estimate is equivalently obtained by solving

$$\frac{\partial \ln[f_{\mathbf{X}}(\mathbf{x}; \theta)]}{\partial \theta}\bigg|_{\theta = \hat{\theta}} = 0 \qquad (6.2.1b)$$

(maximizing the likelihood function is equivalent to maximizing a monotonic function of the likelihood function). Using Eq. (6.2.1b) is simpler in many cases because of the exponentials in many density functions and because the logarithm of a product is the sum of the logarithms of the terms in the product, which yields a derivative of a sum rather than a derivative of a product.

Example 6.2.1.   For Example 6.1.1

$$\ln[P(\mathbf{X} = \mathbf{x}; p)] = \ln[p^k(1-p)^{N-k}] = k \ln(p) + (N-k) \ln(1-p)$$

and

$$\frac{\partial \ln[P(\mathbf{X} = \mathbf{x}; p)]}{\partial p} = \frac{k}{p} - \frac{N-k}{1-p}$$

The maximum likelihood estimator (or estimate) is obtained as

$$\frac{k}{p} - \frac{N-k}{1-p}\bigg|_{p = \hat{p}} = 0$$

which yields

$$\hat{p} = \frac{k}{N} \qquad \square$$

The Bayes and maximum likelihood estimates of p in a Bernoulli distribution are quite similar and for large N are essentially indistinguishable.

Example 6.2.2.   Let $X_1, X_2, \ldots, X_N$ be a sample of mutually independent random variables from a Gaussian distribution with unknown mean θ ($\theta = \mu$) and known variance σ^2. The samples are identically distributed with density functions

$$f_{X_i}(x_i; \theta) = \frac{1}{\sqrt{2\pi\sigma^2}} \exp\left[\frac{-(x_i - \theta)^2}{2\sigma^2}\right] \qquad -\infty < x_i < \infty \quad i = 1, 2, \ldots, N$$

and the likelihood function is obtained as

$$f_{\mathbf{X}}(\mathbf{x}; \theta) = \prod_{i=1}^{N} \frac{1}{\sqrt{2\pi\sigma^2}} \exp\left[\frac{-(x_i - \theta)^2}{2\sigma^2}\right]$$

$$= \left[\frac{1}{\sqrt{2\pi\sigma^2}}\right]^N \exp\left[-\sum_{i=1}^{N} \frac{(x_i - \theta)^2}{2\sigma^2}\right]$$

Taking ln yields

$$\ln[f_{\mathbf{X}}(\mathbf{x}; \theta)] = -\frac{N}{2}\ln(2\pi\sigma^2) - \sum_{i=1}^{N} \frac{(x_i - \theta)^2}{2\sigma^2}$$

and the derivative is

$$\frac{\partial \ln[f_{\mathbf{X}}(\mathbf{x}; \theta)]}{\partial \theta} = \frac{1}{\sigma^2} \sum_{i=1}^{N} (x_i - \theta) \tag{6.2.2}$$

Setting this derivative equal to 0 yields the maximum likelihood estimator. This estimator is obtained from

$$\sum_{i=1}^{N} (x_i - \theta)\big|_{\theta = \hat{\theta}} = 0$$

or

$$\hat{\theta} = \hat{\mu} = \frac{1}{N} \sum_{i=1}^{N} X_i \tag{6.2.3}$$

where x_i (the value the random variable takes on) has been replaced by the random variable X_i, which illustrates that the maximum likelihood estimator is itself a random variable. □

The estimator in Example 6.2.2 is the sample mean, and thus the maximum likelihood estimator for the mean of a Gaussian distribution with known variance is given by the sample mean.

Example 6.2.3.   Consider the maximum likelihood estimator for $\theta = \sigma^2$ with μ known for a Gaussian distribution. The likelihood function for a sample of N mutually independent random variables is obtained as

$$f_{\mathbf{X}}(\mathbf{x}; \theta) = \prod_{i=1}^{N} \frac{1}{\sqrt{2\pi\theta}} \exp\left[\frac{-(x_i - \mu)^2}{2\theta}\right]$$

$$= \frac{1}{(2\pi\theta)^{N/2}} \exp\left[-\sum_{i=1}^{N} \frac{(x_i - \mu)^2}{2\theta}\right]$$

and

$$\ln[f_{\mathbf{X}}(\mathbf{x}; \theta)] = -\frac{N}{2}\ln(2\pi) - \frac{N}{2}\ln(\theta) - \sum_{i=1}^{N} \frac{(x_i - \mu)^2}{2\theta}$$

which has the derivative

$$\frac{\partial \ln[f_{\mathbf{X}}(\mathbf{x};\,\theta)]}{\partial \theta} = -\frac{N}{2\theta} + \sum_{i=1}^{N} \frac{(x_i - \mu)^2}{2\theta^2} \tag{6.2.4}$$

The maximum likelihood estimator is then obtained, by setting this derivative equal to 0, as

$$\hat{\theta} = \frac{1}{N} \sum_{i=1}^{N} (X_i - \mu)^2 \tag{6.2.5} \qquad \square$$

It is also possible to estimate multiple parameters. Before considering the estimation of both μ and σ^2 in a Gaussian distribution, several properties of estimators will be considered.

The most important property of an estimator is that it should be consistent. This means that, as the number of observations in the sample approaches infinity, the mean value of the estimator should approach the correct value and the variance of the estimator should approach 0.

Example 6.2.4. For the Bayes and maximum likelihood estimators of the probability p characterizing a Bernoulli distribution, Examples 6.1.1 and 6.2.1, the expected value of any single observation of a Bernoulli random variable is p and the expected value of the sum of N identically distributed observations (the sum equals k, the number of ones in the sample) is equal to the sum of the means or Np. For the Bayes estimator $E(\hat{p}) = (Np + 1)/(N + 2)$ and in the limit as N goes to infinity $E(\hat{p})$ goes to p, and for the maximum likelihood estimator $E(\hat{p}) = p$, which is always p. The variance of a Bernoulli random variable is $p(1 - p)$ and the variance of the sum of N statistically independent identically distributed samples is $Np(1 - p)$. For the Bayes estimator $\text{Var}(\hat{p}) = Np(1 - p)/(N + 2)^2$ [using Eq. (4.1.13)] and for the maximum likelihood estimator $\text{Var}(\hat{p}) = p(1 - p)/N$. Thus, as N approaches infinity, the variances of both estimators approach 0, and both estimators of the probability p characterizing a Bernoulli distribution are consistent. $\square$

Another estimator will be tested to see if it is consistent.

Example 6.2.5. For the maximum likelihood estimator of the mean of a Gaussian distribution with known variance σ^2, given in Eq. (6.2.3), the expected value is obtained as

$$E(\hat{\theta}) = E\left[\frac{1}{N} \sum_{i=1}^{N} X_i\right] = \frac{1}{N} \sum_{i=1}^{N} E(X_i) = \frac{1}{N} \sum_{i=1}^{N} \mu = \frac{1}{N} N\mu = \mu$$

and the variance as

$$\text{Var}(\hat{\theta}) = \text{Var}\left[\frac{1}{N}\sum_{i=1}^{N}X_i\right] = \frac{1}{N^2}\text{Var}\left(\sum_{i=1}^{N}X_i\right) = \frac{1}{N^2}\sum_{i=1}^{N}\text{Var}(X_i)$$

$$= \frac{1}{N^2}\sum_{i=1}^{N}\sigma^2 = \frac{1}{N^2}(N\sigma^2) = \frac{\sigma^2}{N}$$

which goes to 0 as N goes to infinity. Thus, the maximum likelihood estimator for the mean of a Gaussian distribution with known variance is a consistent estimator.   □

Also, the maximum likelihood estimator for the variance of a Gaussian distribution with known mean, Eq. (6.2.5), is a consistent estimator.

Another important property of estimators is unbiasedness. If

$$E(\hat{\theta}) = \theta \tag{6.2.6}$$

for all values of θ, $\hat{\theta}$ is said to be an unbiased estimator of θ. Being unbiased implies that the average value of the estimator equals the quantity that is being estimated, or on the average the true value is being estimated. As seen in the calculations of Example 6.2.4, the maximum likelihood estimator of the probability p characterizing the Bernoulii distribution is unbiased. Likewise, in the calculations of Example 6.2.5, the maximum likelihood estimator of the mean of a Gaussian distribution with known variance is unbiased.

Example 6.2.6.   Consider the estimator of the variance of a Gaussian distribution with known mean which is developed in Example 6.2.3. The expected value of this estimator is obtained, from Eq. (6.2.5), as

$$E(\hat{\theta}) = E\left[\frac{1}{N}\sum_{i=1}^{N}(X_i - \mu)^2\right] = \frac{1}{N}\sum_{i=1}^{N}E[(X_i - \mu)^2] = \frac{1}{N}\sum_{i=1}^{N}\sigma^2 = \sigma^2$$

and this estimator is also unbiased.   □

Figure 6.2.1 shows three estimators for the parameter θ. As shown, $\hat{\theta}_1$ and $\hat{\theta}_3$ are unbiased since their means are θ, while $\hat{\theta}_2$ is not unbiased or is a biased estimator. As shown in this figure, unbiased estimators are desirable since on the average an unbiased estimator is closer to the true value of θ, and as such $\hat{\theta}_1$ and $\hat{\theta}_3$ would be preferred over $\hat{\theta}_2$. Now, $\hat{\theta}_3$ would be preferred over $\hat{\theta}_1$, since, as can be seen for the density function of $\hat{\theta}_3$, the probability of $\hat{\theta}_3$ is more concentrated about θ, which is due to $\hat{\theta}_3$ having a smaller variance than $\hat{\theta}_1$. Thus, another desirable property of an estimator is to have a small variance or to have the minimum possible variance. If $\hat{\theta}_2$ has a smaller variance than $\hat{\theta}_1$, an interesting question arises.

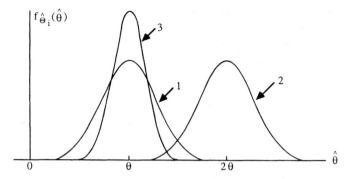

Fig. 6.2.1. Density functions of estimators.

Which is better, an estimator with a small bias and a small variance or one with no bias and a large variance? There is no general answer to this question. An example of this can be observed for the joint estimation of the mean and variance in a Gaussian distribution. This joint estimation will be considered after some discussion of the minimum variance of estimators.

An unbiased estimator that achieves the minimum possible variance is called an efficient or minimum variance estimator. If the variance of an estimator is determined, there remains the question whether it is the minimum possible variance or how close it is to the minimum variance. This question can be answered through the use of the Cramer–Rao bound.

The Cramer–Rao bound or minimum variance bound, which is a lower bound on the variance of an unbiased estimator, is given for the unbiased estimator $\hat{\theta}$ of θ as

$$\text{Var}(\hat{\theta}) \geq \left\{ E\left[\left(\frac{\partial \ln(f_{\mathbf{X}}(\mathbf{x};\,\theta))}{\partial \theta} \right)^2 \right] \right\}^{-1} = -\left\{ E\left[\frac{\partial^2 \ln(f_{\mathbf{X}}(\mathbf{x};\,\theta))}{\partial \theta^2} \right] \right\}^{-1} \quad (6.2.7a)$$

when $\partial f_{\mathbf{X}}(\mathbf{x};\,\theta)/\partial \theta$ and $\partial^2 f_{\mathbf{X}}(\mathbf{x};\,\theta)/\partial \theta^2$ exist and are absolutely integrable. Equality holds in Eq. (6.2.7a) if and only if

$$\frac{\partial \ln[f_{\mathbf{X}}(\mathbf{x};\,\theta)]}{\partial \theta} = (\hat{\theta} - \theta)c(\theta) \quad (6.2.7b)$$

where $c(\theta)$ is not a function of $\mathbf{x}$ but may be a function of θ. Thus, an estimator that achieves the bound of Eq. (6.2.7a) or satisfies Eq. (6.2.7b) is an efficient estimator (has minimum variance).

Before proving the Cramer–Rao bound, its application will be illustrated to help clarify its meaning.

Example 6.2.7. Consider Example 6.2.2. The maximum likelihood estimator for the mean of a Gaussian distribution with known variance is given in Eq. (6.2.3). That this estimator is an efficient estimator can be shown by rewriting Eq. (6.2.2) as

$$\frac{\partial \ln[f_{\mathbf{X}}(\mathbf{x};\,\theta)]}{\partial \theta} = \frac{1}{\sigma^2}\left[\sum_{i=1}^{N} X_i - N\theta\right] = \frac{N}{\sigma^2}(\hat{\theta}-\theta)$$

which is in the form of Eq. (6.2.7b) and indicates that the if and only if conditions for equality in the Cramer–Rao bound are satisfied.

It can also be shown directly that the variance of the maximum likelihood estimator satisfies the Cramer–Rao bound. The second form of the bound is normally easier to evaluate. Taking the second derivative of $\ln[f_{\mathbf{X}}(\mathbf{x};\,\theta)]$ with respect to θ, or differentiating Eq. (6.2.2) one additional time, yields

$$\frac{\partial^2 \ln[f_{\mathbf{X}}(\mathbf{x};\,\theta)]}{\partial \theta^2} = \frac{1}{\sigma^2}\sum_{i=1}^{N}(-1) = -\frac{N}{\sigma^2}$$

and

$$E\left[\frac{\partial^2 \ln(f_{\mathbf{X}}(\mathbf{x};\,\theta))}{\partial \theta^2}\right] = E\left[-\frac{N}{\sigma^2}\right] = -\frac{N}{\sigma^2}$$

which gives the Cramer–Rao bound as

$$\mathrm{Var}(\hat{\theta}) \ge \frac{\sigma^2}{N}$$

The actual variance of $\hat{\theta}$ was previously developed (in showing that $\hat{\theta}$ was consistent) as σ^2/N. Thus, the bound is satisfied and the maximum likelihood estimator $\hat{\theta}$ for the mean of a Gaussian distribution, with known variance, is efficient. $\square$

Another estimator will be considered to see if it is efficient.

Example 6.2.8.   Consider Example 6.2.3. The maximum likelihood estimator for the variance of a Gaussian distribution with known mean, given in Eq. (6.2.5), is also an efficient estimator. This can be shown by rewriting Eq. (6.2.4) as

$$\frac{\partial \ln(f_{\mathbf{X}}(\mathbf{x};\,\theta))}{\partial \theta} = -\frac{N}{2\theta} + \frac{1}{2\theta^2}(N\hat{\theta}) = \frac{N}{2\theta^2}(\hat{\theta}-\theta)$$

which is in the form of Eq. 6.2.7b and indicates that the if and only if conditions for equality in the bound are satisfied. $\square$

The Cramer–Rao bound will now be proved. The proof of the first part of the bound uses the fact that $E(\hat{\theta}-\theta)=0$, since the estimate $\hat{\theta}$ is assumed to be unbiased or $E(\hat{\theta})=\theta$. Then

$$\frac{d[E(\hat{\theta}-\theta)]}{d\theta} = \frac{d[0]}{d\theta} = 0$$

and writing the expectation in integral form

$$\frac{d}{d\theta}\int_{-\infty}^{\infty}(\hat{\theta}-\theta)f_{\mathbf{X}}(\mathbf{x};\theta)\,d\mathbf{x}=\int_{-\infty}^{\infty}\frac{\partial}{\partial\theta}[(\hat{\theta}-\theta)f_{\mathbf{X}}(\mathbf{x};\theta)]\,d\mathbf{x}=0$$

using Leibnitz's rule, Eq. (3.1.5), where the integration is multidimensional. Performing the partial derivative gives

$$-\int_{-\infty}^{\infty}f_{\mathbf{X}}(\mathbf{x};\theta)\,d\mathbf{x}+\int_{-\infty}^{\infty}\frac{\partial f_{\mathbf{X}}(\mathbf{x};\theta)}{\partial\theta}(\hat{\theta}-\theta)\,d\mathbf{x}=0$$

with the first integral, which is the integral of a density function, equal to 1. Since

$$\frac{\partial\ln[f_{\mathbf{X}}(\mathbf{x};\theta)]}{\partial\theta}=\frac{1}{f_{\mathbf{X}}(\mathbf{x};\theta)}\frac{\partial f_{\mathbf{X}}(\mathbf{x};\theta)}{\partial\theta}$$

$\partial f_{\mathbf{X}}(\mathbf{x};\theta)/\partial\theta$ can be replaced by

$$\frac{\partial f_{\mathbf{X}}(\mathbf{x};\theta)}{\partial\theta}=\frac{\partial\ln[f_{\mathbf{X}}(\mathbf{x};\theta)]}{\partial\theta}f_{\mathbf{X}}(\mathbf{x};\theta)$$

and using this substitution

$$-1+\int_{-\infty}^{\infty}\frac{\partial\ln[f_{\mathbf{X}}(\mathbf{x};\theta)]}{\partial\theta}f_{\mathbf{X}}(\mathbf{x};\theta)(\hat{\theta}-\theta)\,d\mathbf{x}=0$$

Grouping the integrand in a useful way results in

$$\int_{-\infty}^{\infty}\left\{\frac{\partial\ln(f_{\mathbf{X}}(\mathbf{x};\theta))}{\partial\theta}\sqrt{f_{\mathbf{X}}(\mathbf{x};\theta)}\right\}\{(\hat{\theta}-\theta)\sqrt{f_{\mathbf{X}}(\mathbf{x};\theta)}\}\,d\mathbf{x}=1 \qquad (6.2.8)$$

The Cauchy–Schwarz inequality, which can be used in many different situations, can now be used to finish the development of the Cramer–Rao bound.

The Cauchy–Schwarz inequality for integrals states that

$$\left[\int_{-\infty}^{\infty}a(t)b(t)\,dt\right]^{2}\le\left[\int_{-\infty}^{\infty}a^{2}(t)\,dt\right]\left[\int_{-\infty}^{\infty}b^{2}(t)\,dt\right] \qquad (6.2.9)$$

with equality if and only if $b(t)=ca(t)$. The proof of this is essentially the same as the proof of the Cauchy–Schwarz inequality for expectation, Eq. (4.6.1). Consider

$$\int_{-\infty}^{\infty}[b(t)-ca(t)]^{2}\,dt\ge 0$$

which has equality if and only if $b(t)=ca(t)$, where c is a constant.

Expanding yields the quadratic equation in c as

$$\int_{-\infty}^{\infty} b^2(t)\, dt - 2c \int_{-\infty}^{\infty} b(t)a(t)\, dt + c^2 \int_{-\infty}^{\infty} a^2(t)\, dt \geq 0$$

For any quadratic equation in c to be ≥ 0 for all c, the roots cannot be distinct real roots (imaginary roots for inequality or double root for equality). Thus,

$$[(\text{coefficient of } c)/2]^2 - (\text{coefficient of } c^2)(\text{coefficient of } c^0) \leq 0$$

which yields Eq. (6.2.9), the desired result.

Using the Cauchy–Schwarz inequality for integrals on Eq. (6.2.8) with $a(t)$ and $b(t)$ the factored terms or

$$b(x) = \frac{\partial \ln(f_{\mathbf{X}}(\mathbf{x}; \theta))}{\partial \theta} \sqrt{f_{\mathbf{X}}(\mathbf{x}; \theta)}$$

and

$$a(x) = (\hat{\theta} - \theta)\sqrt{f_{\mathbf{X}}(\mathbf{x}; \theta)}$$

yields

$$\left\{ \int_{-\infty}^{\infty} \left[\frac{\partial \ln(f_{\mathbf{X}}(\mathbf{x}; \theta))}{\partial \theta} \right]^2 f_{\mathbf{X}}(\mathbf{x}; \theta)\, d\mathbf{x} \right\} \left\{ \int_{-\infty}^{\infty} (\hat{\theta} - \theta)^2 f_{\mathbf{X}}(\mathbf{x}; \theta)\, d\mathbf{x} \right\} \geq 1$$

or in terms of expectations

$$E\left\{ \left[\frac{\partial \ln(f_{\mathbf{X}}(\mathbf{x}; \theta))}{\partial \theta} \right]^2 \right\} E[(\hat{\theta} - \theta)^2] \geq 1$$

which is the first part of the Cramer–Rao bound, where $E[(\hat{\theta} - \theta)^2] = \mathrm{Var}(\hat{\theta})$. Equality holds if and only if $b(x) = ca(x)$ or

$$\left[\frac{\partial \ln(f_{\mathbf{X}}(\mathbf{x}; \theta))}{\partial \theta} \right] \sqrt{f_{\mathbf{X}}(\mathbf{x}; \theta)} = c(\theta)(\hat{\theta} - \theta)\sqrt{f_{\mathbf{X}}(\mathbf{x}; \theta)}$$

which reduces to Eq. (6.2.7b), where $c(\theta)$ is not a function of the variable of integration $\mathbf{x}$ but may be a function of θ.

The proof of the second part of the bound involves showing that it is equal to the first form of the bound. For this, consider

$$\frac{d^2}{d\theta^2} \int_{-\infty}^{\infty} f_{\mathbf{X}}(\mathbf{x}; \theta)\, d\mathbf{x} = \frac{d^2[1]}{d\theta^2} = 0$$

or

$$\frac{d}{d\theta} \int_{-\infty}^{\infty} \frac{\partial f_X(\mathbf{x}; \theta)}{\partial \theta} \, d\mathbf{x} = \frac{d}{d\theta} \int_{-\infty}^{\infty} \frac{\partial \ln(f_X(\mathbf{x}; \theta))}{\partial \theta} f_X(\mathbf{x}; \theta) \, d\mathbf{x}$$

$$= \int_{-\infty}^{\infty} \left\{ \frac{\partial^2 \ln(f_X(\mathbf{x}; \theta))}{\partial \theta^2} + \left[\frac{\partial \ln(f_X(\mathbf{x}; \theta))}{\partial \theta} \right]^2 \right\} f_X(\mathbf{x}; \theta) \, d\mathbf{x}$$

$$= 0$$

where $\partial f_X(\mathbf{x}; \theta)/\partial \theta = \{\partial \ln[f_X(\mathbf{x}; \theta)]/\partial\theta\} f_X(\mathbf{x}; \theta)$ has been used twice. Writing the last expression in terms of expectations

$$E\left[\frac{\partial^2 \ln(f_X(\mathbf{x}; \theta))}{\partial \theta^2} \right] = -E\left\{ \left[\frac{\partial \ln(f_X(\mathbf{x}; \theta))}{\partial \theta} \right]^2 \right\}$$

which is the second form of Eq. (6.2.7a). In most cases the second form is easier to evaluate than the first.

An unbiased estimator that satisfies the Cramer–Rao bound, Eq. (6.2.7), with equality is called an efficient estimator and sometimes denoted as $\hat{\theta}_e$. One of the most important justifications for the use of maximum likelihood estimators is the fact that if an efficient estimator exists, it must be the maximum likelihood estimator. This can be proved by combining Eq. (6.2.1b), the definition of the maximum likelihood estimator, and Eq. (6.2.7b), the condition for an efficient estimator. With the maximum likelihood estimator denoted as $\hat{\theta}_{ml}$, this combination is given as

$$\left. \frac{\partial \ln(f_X(\mathbf{x}; \theta))}{\partial \theta} \right|_{\theta = \hat{\theta}_{ml}} = (\hat{\theta}_e - \theta) c(\theta) |_{\theta = \hat{\theta}_{ml}} = 0 \qquad (6.2.10)$$

This equation implies that either $c(\hat{\theta}_{ml}) = 0$ or $\hat{\theta}_e = \hat{\theta}_{ml}$. If $c(\hat{\theta}_{ml}) = 0$, the derivative can be made 0 independent of the data [$c(\theta)$ cannot depend on $\mathbf{x}$], and the maximum likelihood estimator does not depend on the data. This is meaningless for any reasonable estimation procedure, so $\hat{\theta}_e = \hat{\theta}_{ml}$ is the only valid solution. Thus, if an efficient estimator exists it is the maximum likelihood estimator.

Unfortunately, if an efficient estimator does not exist, it is not known how good the maximum likelihood estimator is and it is also not known how close the variances of other estimators are to the Cramer–Rao bound. Several other properties of maximum likelihood estimators will be given without proof. Maximum likelihood estimators are consistent, asymptotically efficient [$\text{Var}(\hat{\theta} - \theta)$ goes to the Cramer–Rao bound as N goes to infinity], and asymptotically Gaussian with mean θ.

Consider an example of a maximum likelihood estimator for a parameter of a discrete random variable.

Example 6.2.9.   Let $X_1, X_2, \ldots, X_N$ be a sample of mutually independent random variables from a binomial distribution with unknown parameter p and known parameter M. It is desired to obtain a maximum likelihood estimator of p, $\hat{p}$, whether $\hat{p}$ is unbiased, the variance of $\hat{p}$, and whether $\hat{p}$ is efficient. The samples are identically distributed with probability functions

$$P(X_i = x_i; \theta) = C_{x_i}^M \theta^{x_i}(1-\theta)^{M-x_i} \qquad x_i = 0, 1, \ldots, M \quad i = 1, 2, \ldots, N$$

where $\theta = p$, and the likelihood function, from Eq. (6.1.2b), is obtained as

$$P(X = x; \theta) = \prod_{i=1}^{N} P(X_i = x_i; \theta) = \prod_{i=1}^{N} C_{x_i}^M \theta^{x_i}(1-\theta)^{M-x_i}$$

$$= \left[\prod_{i=1}^{N} C_{x_i}^M \right] \theta^z (1-\theta)^{MN-z}$$

where $z = \sum_{i=1}^{N} x_i$. Taking the natural logarithm yields

$$\ln[P(X = x; \theta)] = \sum_{i=1}^{N} \ln(C_{x_i}^M) + \ln(\theta) \sum_{i=1}^{N} x_i + \ln(1-\theta)\left(MN - \sum_{i=1}^{N} x_i \right)$$

and the derivative is

$$\frac{\partial \ln[P(X = x; \theta)]}{\partial \theta} = \frac{1}{\theta}\left(\sum_{i=1}^{N} x_i \right) - \frac{1}{1-\theta}\left(MN - \sum_{i=1}^{N} x_i \right)$$

Setting this derivative equal to 0 yields the maximum likelihood estimator, which is obtained as

$$(1-\theta) \sum_{i=1}^{N} x_i - \theta\left(MN - \sum_{i=1}^{N} x_i \right) \Bigg|_{\theta = \hat{\theta}} = 0$$

or

$$\hat{\theta} = \hat{p} = \frac{1}{MN}\left(\sum_{i=1}^{N} X_i \right)$$

The expected value of $\hat{\theta}$ can be obtained as

$$E(\hat{\theta}) = E\left[\frac{1}{MN} \sum_{i=1}^{N} X_i \right] = \frac{1}{MN} \sum_{i=1}^{N} E(X_i) = \frac{1}{MN} \sum_{i=1}^{N} (M\theta) = \theta = p$$

where $E(X_i) = M\theta$ from Table C.1, which shows that $\hat{\theta} = \hat{p}$ is an unbiased estimator. The variance of $\hat{\theta}$ is then obtained as

$$\text{Var}(\hat{\theta}) = \text{Var}\left[\frac{1}{MN} \sum_{i=1}^{N} X_i \right] = \frac{1}{M^2 N^2} \sum_{i=1}^{N} \text{Var}(X_i)$$

$$= \frac{NM\theta(1-\theta)}{M^2 N^2} = \frac{\theta(1-\theta)}{MN} = \frac{p(1-p)}{MN}$$

where $\text{Var}(X_i) = M\theta(1-\theta)$.

To obtain the Cramer-Rao bound, the second derivative of the log likelihood function is given as

$$\frac{\partial^2 \ln[P(\mathbf{X}=\mathbf{x};\,\theta)]}{\partial\theta^2} = -\frac{1}{\theta^2}\sum_{i=1}^{N} x_i - \frac{1}{(1-\theta)^2}\left(MN - \sum_{i=1}^{N} x_i\right)$$

and the expected value as

$$E\left\{\frac{\partial^2 \ln[P(\mathbf{X}=\mathbf{x};\,\theta)]}{\partial\theta^2}\right\} = -\frac{1}{\theta^2}\sum_{i=1}^{N} E(X_i) - \frac{1}{(1-\theta)^2}\left[MN - \sum_{i=1}^{N} E(X_i)\right]$$

$$= -\frac{MN\theta}{\theta^2} - \frac{MN - NM\theta}{(1-\theta)^2}$$

$$= -\left(\frac{MN}{\theta} + \frac{MN}{1-\theta}\right) = -\frac{MN}{\theta(1-\theta)}$$

The Cramer-Rao bound is obtained from Eq. (6.2.7a) as

$$\mathrm{Var}(\hat{\theta}) \ge \frac{\theta(1-\theta)}{MN}$$

which is equal to the variance of $\hat{\theta}$, and thus $\hat{\theta} = \hat{p}$ is an efficient estimator for the parameter p for the binomial distribution. $\hat{\theta}$ is also a consistent estimator.   □

Now consider maximum likelihood estimators for the simultaneous estimation of the mean and the variance of a Gaussian distribution. In this case, the derivatives of the log likelihood function with respect to both the mean and the variance are set equal to zero, with the resulting equations solved simultaneously for the two estimators.

Let $X_1, X_2, \ldots, X_N$ be a sample of mutually independent random variables from a Gaussian distribution with mean $\mu = \theta_1$ and variance $\sigma^2 = \theta_2$. The density function of the samples is given as

$$f_{X_i}(x_i;\,\theta_1,\,\theta_2) = \frac{1}{\sqrt{2\pi\theta_2}}\exp\left[\frac{-(x_i-\theta_1)^2}{2\theta_2}\right] \qquad -\infty < x_i < \infty \quad i = 1, 2, \ldots, N$$

and the likelihood function obtained as

$$f_{\mathbf{X}}(\mathbf{x};\,\theta_1,\,\theta_2) = \prod_{i=1}^{N} \frac{1}{\sqrt{2\pi\theta_2}}\exp\left[\frac{-(x_i-\theta_1)^2}{2\theta_2}\right]$$

$$= \frac{1}{(2\pi\theta_2)^{N/2}}\exp\left[-\frac{1}{2\theta_2}\sum_{i=1}^{N}(x_i-\theta_1)^2\right]$$

The log likelihood function is then

$$\ln[f_{\mathbf{X}}(\mathbf{x}; \theta_1, \theta_2)] = -\frac{N}{2}\ln(2\pi) - \frac{N}{2}\ln(\theta_2) - \frac{1}{2\theta_2}\sum_{i=1}^{N}(x_i - \theta_1)^2$$

where the derivative with respect to θ_1 is

$$\frac{\partial \ln[f_{\mathbf{X}}(\mathbf{x}; \theta_1, \theta_2)]}{\partial \theta_1} = \frac{1}{\theta_2}\sum_{i=1}^{N}(x_i - \theta_1) \tag{6.2.11}$$

and the derivative with respect to θ_2 is

$$\frac{\partial \ln[f_{\mathbf{X}}(\mathbf{x}; \theta_1, \theta_2)]}{\partial \theta_2} = -\frac{N}{2\theta_2} + \frac{1}{2\theta_2^2}\sum_{i=1}^{N}(x_i - \theta_1)^2 \tag{6.2.12}$$

The maximum likelihood estimators are obtained by setting the two derivatives equal to 0 and letting $\theta_1 = \hat{\theta}_1$ and $\theta_2 = \hat{\theta}_2$. In this case, $\hat{\theta}_1$ is obtained directly from Eq. (6.2.11) as

$$\hat{\theta}_1 = \frac{1}{N}\sum_{i=1}^{N} X_i \tag{6.2.13}$$

Putting this into Eq. (6.2.12), $\hat{\theta}_2$ can be determined as

$$\hat{\theta}_2 = \frac{1}{N}\sum_{i=1}^{N}(X_i - \hat{\theta}_1)^2 \tag{6.2.14}$$

These are the simultaneous maximum likelihood estimators for the mean and variance of a Gaussian distribution. The estimator for the mean is identical to the previous result where the variance was known, Eq. (6.2.3), and the estimator for the variance differs from the previous result where the mean was known, Eq. (6.2.5), only in that the true mean is replaced by the estimator of the mean.

As shown in Examples 6.2.5 and 6.2.7, $\hat{\theta}_1$ is an unbiased and efficient estimator of the mean μ. It turns out, however, the $\hat{\theta}_2$ is not an unbiased estimator of the variance. Now $E(\hat{\theta}_2)$ can be obtained as

$$E(\hat{\theta}_2) = E\left[\frac{1}{N}\sum_{i=1}^{N}(X_i - \hat{\theta}_1)^2\right]$$

where the summed term can be expressed as

$$(X_i - \hat{\theta}_1)^2 = (X_i - \mu + \mu - \hat{\theta}_1)^2 = (X_i - \mu)^2 - 2(X_i - \mu)(\hat{\theta}_1 - \mu) + (\hat{\theta}_1 - \mu)^2$$

The sum of $(X_i - \mu)$ yields

$$\sum_{i=1}^{N}(X_i - \mu) = \sum_{i=1}^{N} X_i - N\mu = N\hat{\theta}_1 - N\mu = N(\hat{\theta}_1 - \mu)$$

and the sum of $(\hat{\theta}_1 - \mu)^2$ equals $N(\hat{\theta}_1 - \mu)^2$, which gives

$$\sum_{i=1}^{N}(X_i - \hat{\theta}_1)^2 = \sum_{i=1}^{N}(X_i - \mu)^2 - 2N(\hat{\theta}_1 - \mu)^2 + N(\hat{\theta}_1 - \mu)^2$$

$$= \sum_{i=1}^{N}(X_i - \mu)^2 - N(\hat{\theta}_1 - \mu)^2$$

Then

$$E(\hat{\theta}_2) = \frac{1}{N}\sum_{i=1}^{N}E[(X_i - \mu)^2] - E[(\hat{\theta}_1 - \mu)^2]$$

and since $E(\hat{\theta}_1) = \mu$

$$E[(\hat{\theta}_1 - \mu)^2] = \text{Var}(\hat{\theta}_1) = \frac{1}{N^2}\sum_{i=1}^{N}\text{Var}(X_i)$$

Finally,

$$E(\hat{\theta}_2) = \frac{1}{N}\sum_{i=1}^{N}\text{Var}(X_i) - \frac{1}{N^2}\sum_{i=1}^{N}\text{Var}(X_i) = \frac{\sigma^2 N}{N} - \frac{\sigma^2 N}{N^2}$$

or

$$E(\hat{\theta}_2) = \frac{N-1}{N}\sigma^2 \tag{6.2.15}$$

which shows that $\hat{\theta}_2$ is a biased estimator. But an unbiased estimate can be obtained simply as

$$\hat{\theta}_3 = \frac{N}{N-1}\hat{\theta}_2 = \frac{1}{N-1}\sum_{i=1}^{N}(X_i - \hat{\theta}_1)^2 \tag{6.2.16}$$

For large values of N, the difference between $\hat{\theta}_2$ and $\hat{\theta}_3$ is small, so it makes little difference which estimate is used. But for small values of N the difference is significant.

The most important property of an estimator is that it is consistent. As shown in Example 6.2.5, $\hat{\theta}_1$ is a consistent estimator with variance

$$\text{Var}(\hat{\theta}_1) = \frac{\sigma^2}{N} \tag{6.2.17}$$

Now for $\hat{\theta}_2$ and $\hat{\theta}_3$ the expected value of $\hat{\theta}_3$ is the true value and the expected value of $\hat{\theta}_2$ converges to the true value as N goes to infinity. To obtain the variance of $\hat{\theta}_2$ and $\hat{\theta}_3$ is a tedious but conceptually straightforward development. The variance of $\hat{\theta}_2$ can be obtained as

$$\text{Var}(\hat{\theta}_2) = E(\hat{\theta}_2^2) - [E(\hat{\theta}_2)]^2 = E(\hat{\theta}_2^2) - \frac{(N-1)^2}{N^2}\hat{\theta}_2^2$$

Expanding out Eq. (6.2.14) and substituting Eq. (6.2.13) for $\hat{\theta}_1$ yields

$$E(\hat{\theta}_2^2) = E\left\{\left[\frac{1}{N}\sum_{i=1}^{N}\left[X_i^2 - 2X_i\frac{1}{N}\sum_{j=1}^{N}X_j + \left(\frac{1}{N}\sum_{j=1}^{N}X_j\right)^2\right]\right]^2\right\}$$

and combining the second and third terms, which are similar, where a summation squared can be written as a double summation with different indices, gives

$$E(\hat{\theta}_2^2) = E\left\{\left[\frac{1}{N}\sum_{i=1}^{N}X_i^2 - \frac{1}{N^2}\sum_{i=1}^{N}\sum_{j=1}^{N}X_iX_j\right]^2\right\}$$

Now expanding this squared term

$$E(\hat{\theta}_2^2) = E\left\{\left[\frac{1}{N^2}\sum_{i=1}^{N}\sum_{j=1}^{N}X_i^2X_j^2 - \frac{2}{N^3}\sum_{i=1}^{N}\sum_{j=1}^{N}\sum_{k=1}^{N}X_i^2X_jX_k\right.\right.$$
$$\left.\left. + \frac{1}{N^4}\sum_{i=1}^{N}\sum_{j=1}^{N}\sum_{k=1}^{N}\sum_{m=1}^{N}X_iX_jX_kX_m\right]\right\}$$

and grouping equal terms [the double summation gives $E(X_i^4)$ and $E(X_i^2)E(X_j^2)$ terms, the triple summation gives $E(X_i^4)$, $E(X_i^3)E(X_j)$, $E(X_i^2)E(X_j^2)$, and $E(X_i^2)E(X_j)E(X_k)$ terms, and the quadruple summation gives $E(X_i^4)$, $E(X_i^3)E(X_j)$, $E(X_i^2)E(X_j^2)$, $E(X_i^2)E(X_j)E(X_k)$, and $E(X_i)E(X_j)E(X_k)E(X_m)$ terms]

$$E(\hat{\theta}_2^2) = \left(\frac{1}{N^2} - \frac{2}{N^3} + \frac{1}{N^4}\right)\sum_{i=1}^{N}E(X_i^4) + \left(-\frac{4}{N^3} + \frac{4}{N^4}\right)\sum_{i=1}^{N}\sum_{\substack{j=1\\j\neq i}}^{N}E(X_i^3)E(X_j)$$

$$+ \left(\frac{1}{N^2} - \frac{2}{N^3} + \frac{3}{N^4}\right)\sum_{i=1}^{N}\sum_{\substack{j=1\\j\neq i}}^{N}E(X_i^2)E(X_j^2)$$

$$+ \left(-\frac{2}{N^3} + \frac{6}{N^4}\right)\sum_{i=1}^{N}\sum_{\substack{j=1\\j\neq i}}^{N}\sum_{\substack{k=1\\k\neq i\\k\neq j}}^{N}E(X_i^2)E(X_j)E(X_k)$$

$$+ \frac{1}{N^4}\sum_{i=1}^{N}\sum_{\substack{j=1\\j\neq i}}^{N}\sum_{\substack{k=1\\k\neq i\\k\neq j}}^{N}\sum_{\substack{m=1\\m\neq i\\m\neq j\\m\neq k}}^{N}E(X_i)E(X_j)E(X_k)E(X_m)$$

All the terms in each summation are identical since the X's are samples from the same Gaussian distribution. There are N terms in the single summation, $N(N-1) = N^2 - N$ terms in the double summations $(i \neq j)$, $N(N-1)(N-2) = N^3 - 3N^2 + 2N$ terms in the triple summation $(i \neq j \neq k)$, and $N(N-1)(N-2)(N-3) = N^4 - 6N^3 + 11N^2 - 6N$ terms in the quadruple summation. Each mean value is given as $E(X_i) = \theta_1$ and each variance is given as $\mathrm{Var}(X_i) = \theta_2$, which gives each second moment as $E(X_i^2) = \theta_2 + \theta_1^2$.

For $Y = (X_i - \theta_1)/\sqrt{\theta_2}$, Y is a normalized Gaussian with $E(Y) = 0$ and $\mathrm{Var}(Y) = 1$. Then

$$E(Y^3) = \int_{-\infty}^{\infty} y^3 \frac{1}{\sqrt{2\pi}} e^{-y^2/2} \, dy = 0$$

due to symmetry or the integral of an odd function. From this

$$E[(X_i - \theta_1)^3] = 0 = E(X_i^3) - 3E(X_i^2)\theta_1 + 3E(X_i)\theta_1^2 - \theta_1^3$$

which yields

$$E(X_i^3) = 3\theta_2\theta_1 + \theta_1^3 \tag{6.2.18}$$

Also,

$$E(Y^4) = \int_{-\infty}^{\infty} y^4 \frac{1}{\sqrt{2\pi}} e^{-y^2/2} \, dy$$

which can be integrated by parts with $u = y^3$, $du = 3y^2 \, dy$, $dv = y \, e^{-y^2/2} \, dy$, and $v = -e^{-y^2/2}$ to yield

$$E(Y^4) = -\frac{y^3}{\sqrt{2\pi}} e^{-y^2/2} \Bigg|_{y=-\infty}^{y=\infty} + \int_{-\infty}^{\infty} 3y^2 \frac{1}{\sqrt{2\pi}} e^{-y^2/2} \, dy$$

$$= -0 + 0 + 3E(Y^2) = 3[\mathrm{Var}(Y) + (E(Y))^2] = 3[1 + 0] = 3$$

From this

$$E[(X_i - \theta_1)^4] = 3\theta_2^2 = E(X_i^4) - 4E(X_i^3)\theta_1 + 6E(X_i^2)\theta_1^2 - 4E(X_i)\theta_1^3 + \theta_1^4$$

which yields

$$E(X_i^4) = 3\theta_2^2 + 6\theta_2\theta_1^2 + \theta_1^4 \tag{6.2.19}$$

Combining, using Eqs. (6.2.18) and (6.2.19), $E(X_i)$ and $E(X_i^2)$, and the number of terms in each summation, yields

$$\mathrm{Var}(\hat{\theta}_2) = \left(\frac{N^2 - 2N + 1}{N^4} \right)(N)(3\theta_2^2 + 6\theta_2\theta_1^2 + \theta_1^4)$$

$$+ \left(\frac{-4N + 4}{N^4} \right)(N^2 - N)(3\theta_2\theta_1 + \theta_1^3)\theta_1$$

$$+ \left(\frac{N^2 - 2N + 3}{N^4} \right)(N^2 - N)(\theta_2 + \theta_1^2)^2$$

$$+ \left(\frac{-2N + 6}{N^4} \right)(N^3 - 3N^2 + 2N)(\theta_2 + \theta_1^2)\theta_1^2$$

$$+ \frac{1}{N^4}(N^4 - 6N^3 + 11N^2 - 6N)\theta_1^4 - \left[\frac{(N-1)^2}{N^2} \right]\theta_2^2$$

and finally

$$\text{Var}(\hat{\theta}_2) = \frac{2(N-1)}{N^2}\theta_2^2 = \frac{2(N-1)}{N^2}\sigma^4 \tag{6.2.20}$$

Equation (6.2.20) is surprisingly simple but does go to 0 as N approaches infinity, which, along with the mean converging to the true value, illustrates that $\hat{\theta}_2$ is a consistent estimator. Since $\hat{\theta}_3 = [N/(N-1)]\hat{\theta}_2$,

$$\text{Var}(\hat{\theta}_3) = \left(\frac{N}{N-1}\right)^2 \text{Var}(\hat{\theta}_2) = \frac{2}{N-1}\theta_2^2 = \frac{2}{N-1}\sigma^4 \tag{6.2.21}$$

which also approaches 0 as N approaches infinity. Thus $\hat{\theta}_3$ is also a consistent estimator. It can be noted that $N/(N-1) > 1$ and $[N/(N-1)]^2 > 1$, which gives $\text{Var}(\hat{\theta}_3) > \text{Var}(\hat{\theta}_2)$. An advantage of using $\hat{\theta}_3$ to estimate the variance is that it is unbiased, while an advantage of using $\hat{\theta}_2$ is that it has smaller variance than $\hat{\theta}_3$. A general statement as to which estimator of the variance is better cannot be made.

6.3 Sequential Estimation

In many applications it is useful to be able to calculate estimators sequentially, obtaining the estimator for the first N sample values from simple expressions involving the estimator for the first $N-1$ sample values and the Nth sample value. For example, in estimating the mean of a Gaussian distribution, for which the maximum likelihood estimator is the sample mean, it would be preferred not to have to add up all the sample values and divide by the new value of N each time a new sample is obtained. Sequential estimators simplify the amount of computation and greatly reduce the data storage requirements, since the Nth estimator is calculated from only the $(N-1)$th estimator and the Nth sample value.

It is convenient for sequential estimators to indicate the number of samples used for the estimate by a subscript. The estimator for the mean of a Gaussian distribution, given in Eq. (6.2.13), using N samples is given by

$$\hat{\mu}_N = \hat{\theta}_1 = \frac{1}{N}\sum_{i=1}^{N} X_i$$

A sequential estimator for this case can be developed as

$$\hat{\mu}_N = \frac{1}{N}\left(\sum_{i=1}^{N-1} X_i + X_N\right) = \frac{1}{N}[(N-1)\hat{\mu}_{N-1} + X_N]$$

since

$$\hat{\mu}_{N-1} = \frac{1}{N-1}\sum_{i=1}^{N-1} X_i$$

Rearranging gives the desired result

$$\hat{\mu}_N = \hat{\mu}_{N-1} + \frac{1}{N}(X_N - \hat{\mu}_{N-1}) \qquad N = 1, 2, 3, \ldots \quad \hat{\mu}_0 = 0 \qquad (6.3.1)$$

which is the sequential estimator for the mean of a Gaussian distribution, where $\hat{\mu}_0$ is the starting value. Equation (6.3.1) illustrates that the estimator is updated from the previous estimator by adding a weighted adjustment (which becomes small as N becomes large) of the difference between the new sample and the previous estimator.

The sequential form for the maximum likelihood (biased) estimator of the variance, $\hat{\theta}_2$, can be developed in the same manner but is somewhat more complicated. Using N samples, this estimator, from Eq. (6.2.14), is given as

$$\hat{V}_N = \hat{\theta}_2 = \frac{1}{N}\sum_{i=1}^{N}(X_i - \hat{\mu}_N)^2$$

Using Eq. (6.3.1), this can be written as

$$\hat{V}_N = \frac{1}{N}\left\{\sum_{i=1}^{N-1}\left[X_i - \hat{\mu}_{N-1} - \frac{1}{N}(X_N - \hat{\mu}_{N-1})\right]^2 + (X_N - \hat{\mu}_N)^2\right\}$$

Observing that

$$\sum_{i=1}^{N-1}(X_i - \hat{\mu}_{N-1}) = \sum_{i=1}^{N-1}X_i - (N-1)\hat{\mu}_{N-1} = 0$$

and expanding out the squared term in the summation gives

$$\hat{V}_N = \frac{1}{N}\left[\sum_{i=1}^{N-1}(X_i - \hat{\mu}_{N-1})^2 + \frac{N-1}{N^2}(X_N - \hat{\mu}_{N-1})^2 + (X_N - \hat{\mu}_N)^2\right]$$

where the sum of a constant is the number of terms in the summation times that constant. Also, from Eq. (6.3.1),

$$X_N - \hat{\mu}_N = X_N - \hat{\mu}_{N-1} - \frac{1}{N}(X_N - \hat{\mu}_{N-1}) = \left(1 - \frac{1}{N}\right)(X_N - \hat{\mu}_{N-1})$$

$$= \frac{N-1}{N}(X_N - \hat{\mu}_{N-1}) \qquad (6.3.2)$$

and using this in $\hat{V}_N$ yields

$$\hat{V}_N = \frac{1}{N}\left\{(N-1)\hat{V}_{N-1} + \left[\frac{N-1}{N^2} + \frac{(N-1)^2}{N^2}\right](X_N - \hat{\mu}_{N-1})^2\right\}$$

$$= \frac{1}{N}\left[(N-1)\hat{V}_{N-1} + \frac{N-1}{N}(X_N - \hat{\mu}_{N-1})^2\right]$$

Rearranging gives the desired result

$$\hat{V}_N = \hat{V}_{N-1} + \frac{1}{N} \left[\frac{N-1}{N} (X_N - \hat{\mu}_{N-1})^2 - \hat{V}_{N-1} \right]$$

$$N = 1, 2, 3, \dots \quad \hat{V}_0 = 0 \qquad (6.3.3a)$$

which is a sequential estimator for the variance of a Gaussian distribution, where $\hat{V}_0$ is the starting value. Equation (6.3.3a) illustrates that the estimator is updated from the previous estimator by adding a weighted adjustment (which becomes small as N becomes large) of the difference between a new squared term and the previous estimator. An alternative form for the sequential estimator for the variance, which is in terms of $\hat{\mu}_N$ as opposed to $\hat{\mu}_{N-1}$, can be obtained by using Eq. (6.3.2) in Eq. (6.3.3a) as

$$\hat{V}_N = \hat{V}_{N-1} + \frac{1}{N} \left[\frac{N}{N-1} (X_N - \hat{\mu}_N)^2 - \hat{V}_{N-1} \right]$$

$$N = 2, 3, 4, \dots \quad \hat{V}_0 = \hat{V}_1 = 0 \qquad (6.3.3b)$$

Example 6.3.1.   Determine the sequential estimators $\hat{\mu}_N$ and $\hat{V}_N$ for the first 10 entries in Table 5.3.2a. Using Eq. (6.3.1), $\hat{\mu}_N = 1.142, 0.117, -0.170, -0.313, -0.224, -0.163, -0.146, -0.014, -0.034, -0.008$, and using Eq. (6.3.3a), $\hat{V}_N = 0, 1.049, 0.864, 0.709, 0.599, 0.518, 0.446, 0.512, 0.458, 0.418.$ □

As mentioned previously, an advantage of sequential estimators is reduced data storage requirements, and Eqs. (6.3.1) and (6.3.3a) or (6.3.3b) would be implemented without subscripts. Using Eqs. (6.3.1) and (6.3.3a) without subscripts would result in the Fortran code

$$V = V + ((N-1) * (X - \mu) ** 2 / N - V) / N$$

$$\mu = \mu + (X - \mu) / N$$

where the right side of the equation is calculated and replaces the contents of the register on the left side of the equation, and X indicates the current data value. V should be calculated first since it uses the old value of μ. If Eqs. (6.3.1) and (6.3.3b) are used, the Fortran code is

$$\mu = \mu + (X - \mu) / N$$

$$V = V + (N * (X - \mu) ** 2 / (N-1) - V) / N$$

where μ should be calculated first since V uses the updated value of μ.

Example 6.3.2.   Determine the sequential form for the unbiased estimator of the variance, $\hat{\theta}_3$, of a Gaussian distribution. With the notation

$\hat{W}_N = \hat{\theta}_3$, $\hat{W}_N$ can be obtained from Eq. (6.2.16) as

$$\hat{W}_N = \frac{N}{N-1}\,\hat{V}_N$$

Putting this, along with $\hat{W}_{N-1} = (N-1)\hat{V}_{N-1}/(N-2)$, into the equation immediately preceding Eq. (6.3.3a) results in

$$\frac{N-1}{N}\,\hat{W}_N = \frac{1}{N}\left[(N-2)\hat{W}_{N-1} + \frac{N-1}{N}(X_N - \hat{\mu}_{N-1})^2\right]$$

and rearranging yields

$$\hat{W}_N = \hat{W}_{N-1} + \frac{1}{N-1}\left[\frac{N-1}{N}(X_N - \hat{\mu}_{N-1})^2 - \hat{W}_{N-1}\right]$$

$$N = 2, 3, \ldots \quad \hat{W}_0 = \hat{W}_1 = 0 \qquad (6.3.4) \qquad \square$$

Sequential estimators for the mean and the variance, $\hat{\mu}_N$ and $\hat{V}_N$, obtained from a larger sample of Gaussian random numbers than that given in Table 5.3.2b (400 instead of 240 random numbers, where the first 240 are the same as those in Table 5.3.2b) are plotted in Fig. 6.3.1. For each estimator, dotted lines are included showing the most probable range of the estimators as a function of N. These bounding curves are obtained as the true parameter $\pm$ the standard deviation of the estimator, or $\mu \pm \sqrt{\mathrm{Var}(\hat{\mu})}$ for the mean and $V \pm \sqrt{\mathrm{Var}(\hat{V})}$ for the variance. From Eq. (6.2.17)

$$\mathrm{Var}(\hat{\mu}_N) = \frac{V}{N}$$

and from Eq. (6.2.20)

$$\mathrm{Var}(\hat{V}_N) = \frac{2(N-1)}{N^2}\,V^2$$

where, for the case here, the true parameters are $\mu = 0$ and $V = 1$. Since $\hat{\mu}_N$ is itself a Gaussian random variable, and the probability that a Gaussian random variable exceeds its mean by more than 1 standard deviation (mean ± 1 standard deviation) is 0.3173, most of the time the estimators should stay between the bounding curves.

6.4 Random Parameter Estimation

A bound similar to the Cramer-Rao bound is available when the parameter to be estimated is random rather than an unknown constant. The example considered in Section 6.1, using the *a posteriori* density function

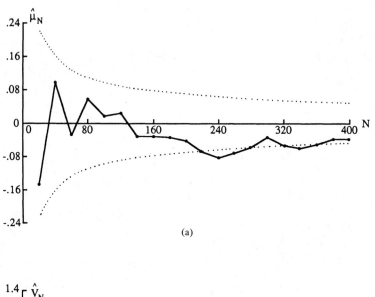

(a)

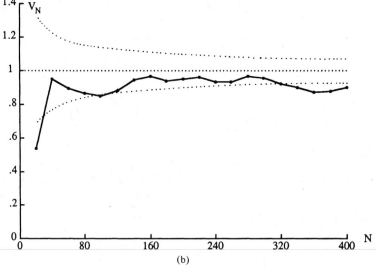

(b)

Fig. 6.3.1. Sequential estimators for a Gaussian distribution: (a) mean; (b) variance.

of the parameter given the sample, was a case of estimating a random parameter. For $X_1, X_2, \ldots, X_N$ a sample of mutually independent random variables and Θ a random parameter, the mean square error of any estimate, $\hat{\theta}$, satisfies the lower bound

$$E[(\hat{\theta} - \Theta)^2] \geq \left\{ E\left[\left\{\frac{\partial \ln(f_{X\Theta}(\mathbf{x}, \theta))}{\partial \theta}\right\}^2\right]\right\}^{-1}$$

$$= -\left\{ E\left[\frac{\partial^2 \ln(f_{X\Theta}(\mathbf{x}, \theta))}{\partial \theta^2}\right]\right\}^{-1} \qquad (6.4.1a)$$

with equality holding if and only if

$$\frac{\partial \ln[f_{X\Theta}(\mathbf{x}, \theta)]}{\partial \theta} = (\hat{\theta} - \theta)c \qquad (6.4.1b)$$

If equality holds, the estimator is again said to be efficient. This bound is similar to the Cramer-Rao bound of Eq. (6.2.7), with the variance of the estimator replaced by the mean square error, the density function of $\mathbf{X}$ replaced by the joint density function of $\mathbf{X}$ and Θ, the expectation over $\mathbf{X}$ replaced by the expectation over $\mathbf{X}$ and Θ, and c not a function of $\mathbf{X}$ or Θ. The proof of this bound is a slight modification of the proof of the Cramer-Rao bound and will not be given here. Solving the equation

$$\frac{\partial \ln[f_{X\Theta}(\mathbf{x}, \theta)]}{\partial \theta}\bigg|_{\theta = \hat{\theta}} = \frac{\partial \ln[f_{\Theta|X}(\theta|\mathbf{x})]}{\partial \theta}\bigg|_{\theta = \hat{\theta}} = 0 \qquad (6.4.2)$$

which is similar to Eq. (6.2.1b), yields the maximum *a posteriori* estimate of the random parameter θ, since

$$f_{X\Theta}(\mathbf{x}, \theta) = f_{\Theta|X}(\theta|\mathbf{x})f_X(\mathbf{x})$$

and $f_X(\mathbf{x})$ does not depend on θ. Combining Eqs. (6.4.1b) and (6.4.2), with the maximum *a posteriori* estimator denoted as $\hat{\theta}_{map}$ and an efficient estimator denoted as $\hat{\theta}_e$, yields

$$\frac{\partial \ln[f_{X\Theta}(\mathbf{x}, \theta)]}{\partial \theta}\bigg|_{\theta = \hat{\theta}_{map}} = (\hat{\theta}_e - \theta)c\big|_{\theta = \hat{\theta}_{map}} = 0 \qquad (6.4.3)$$

which is similar to Eq. (6.2.10). This implies that $\hat{\theta}_e = \hat{\theta}_{map}$, or if an efficient estimator exists it is the maximum *a posteriori* estimator. Also, if an efficient estimator exists it is a mean-square error estimator, which is the mean of the *a posteriori* density function. This is the estimator that was used in Section 6.1 for the random parameter of a Bernoulli distribution. As a matter of fact, the *a posteriori* density function must be Gaussian for an efficient estimate to exist.

Consider the maximum *a posteriori* estimator for the mean of a Gaussian random variable when the mean is another statistically independent Gaussian random variable. Let $X_1, X_2, \ldots, X_N$ be a sample of mutually independent random variables from a Gaussian distribution with mean θ. The samples are identically distributed with density functions

$$f_{X_i|\Theta}(x_i|\theta) = \frac{1}{\sqrt{2\pi\sigma_x^2}} \exp\left[\frac{-(x_i - \theta)^2}{2\sigma_x^2}\right] \qquad -\infty < x_i < \infty \quad i = 1, 2, \ldots, N$$

and the mean has density function

$$f_\Theta(\theta) = \frac{1}{\sqrt{2\pi\sigma_\theta^2}} \exp\left(\frac{-\theta^2}{2\sigma_\theta^2}\right) \qquad -\infty < \theta < \infty$$

The conditional density function of **X** given Θ is obtained as

$$f_{\mathbf{X}|\Theta}(\mathbf{x}|\theta) = \prod_{i=1}^{N}\left\{\frac{1}{\sqrt{2\pi\sigma_x^2}} \exp\left[\frac{-(x_i - \theta)^2}{2\sigma_x^2}\right]\right\}$$

$$= \frac{1}{(2\pi\sigma_x^2)^{N/2}} \exp\left[-\frac{1}{2\sigma_x^2}\sum_{i=1}^{N}(x_i - \theta)^2\right]$$

and the joint density function of **X** and Θ as

$$f_{\mathbf{X}\Theta}(\mathbf{x}, \theta) = K \exp\left[-\sum_{i=1}^{N}\frac{(x_i - \theta)^2}{2\sigma_x^2} - \frac{\theta^2}{2\sigma_\theta^2}\right]$$

where K is the constant

$$K = \frac{1}{\sqrt{2\pi\sigma_\theta^2}(2\pi\sigma_x^2)^{N/2}}$$

Taking the ln yields

$$\ln[f_{\mathbf{X}\Theta}(\mathbf{x}, \theta)] = \ln(K) - \sum_{i=1}^{N}\frac{(x_i - \theta)^2}{2\sigma_x^2} - \frac{\theta^2}{2\sigma_\theta^2}$$

and the derivative becomes

$$\frac{\partial \ln[f_{\mathbf{X}\Theta}(\mathbf{x}, \theta)]}{\partial \theta} = \sum_{i=1}^{N}\frac{(x_i - \theta)}{\sigma_x^2} - \frac{\theta}{\sigma_\theta^2} \tag{6.4.4}$$

Setting this derivative equal to 0, the maximum *a posteriori* estimator is obtained as

$$\hat{\theta} = \frac{\sigma_\theta^2}{N\sigma_\theta^2 + \sigma_x^2}\sum_{i=1}^{N}X_i = \frac{\sigma_N^2}{\sigma_x^2}\sum_{i=1}^{N}X_i \tag{6.4.5}$$

where

$$\sigma_N^2 = \frac{\sigma_\theta^2\sigma_x^2}{N\sigma_\theta^2 + \sigma_x^2} \tag{6.4.6}$$

Since the mean square value of $\hat{\theta}$ requires the expectation over both $\mathbf{X}$ and Θ, this will be represented as

$$E[(\hat{\theta}-\Theta)^2] = E_\Theta E_\mathbf{X}[(\hat{\theta}-\Theta)^2] \tag{6.4.7}$$

Now the variance of $\hat{\theta}$ over $\mathbf{X}$ is given as

$$\text{Var}_\mathbf{X}(\hat{\theta}) = \left(\frac{\sigma_N^2}{\sigma_x^2}\right)^2 \sum_{i=1}^N \text{Var}_\mathbf{X}(X_i) = \left(\frac{\sigma_N^2}{\sigma_x^2}\right)^2 (N\sigma_x^2)$$

and the expected value of $\hat{\theta}$ over $\mathbf{X}$ as

$$E_\mathbf{X}(\hat{\theta}) = \frac{\sigma_N^2}{\sigma_x^2}(N\Theta)$$

The mean square value over x is then

$$E_\mathbf{X}[(\hat{\theta}-\Theta)^2] = E_\mathbf{X}[\hat{\theta}^2 - 2\hat{\theta}\Theta + \Theta^2] = \text{Var}_\mathbf{X}(\hat{\theta}) + [E_\mathbf{X}(\hat{\theta})]^2 - 2\Theta E_\mathbf{X}(\hat{\theta}) + \Theta^2$$

$$= \left(\frac{\sigma_N^2}{\sigma_x^2}\right)^2 (N\sigma_x^2 + N^2\Theta^2) - 2\left(\frac{\sigma_N^2}{\sigma_x^2}\right)(N\Theta^2) + \Theta^2$$

With $E_\Theta(\Theta^2) = \text{Var}_\Theta(\Theta) = \sigma_\theta^2$, the expected value over Θ is

$$E_\Theta\{E_\mathbf{X}[(\hat{\theta}-\Theta)^2]\} = \left(\frac{\sigma_N^2}{\sigma_x^2}\right)^2 (N\sigma_x^2 + N^2\sigma_\theta^2) - 2\frac{\sigma_N^2}{\sigma_x^2}(N\sigma_\theta^2) + \sigma_\theta^2$$

which reduces to

$$E[(\hat{\theta}-\Theta)^2] = E_\Theta\{E_\mathbf{X}[(\hat{\theta}-\Theta)^2]\} = \sigma_N^2 \tag{6.4.8}$$

To determine the mean square error bound the second derivative of $\ln[f_{\mathbf{X}\Theta}(\mathbf{x}, \theta)]$ is obtained from Eq. (6.4.4) as

$$\frac{\partial^2 \ln[f_{\mathbf{X}\Theta}(\mathbf{x}, \theta)]}{\partial \theta^2} = -\frac{N}{\sigma_x^2} - \frac{1}{\sigma_\theta^2} = -\frac{1}{\sigma_N^2}$$

and the expected value as

$$E\left\{\frac{\partial^2 \ln[f_{\mathbf{X}\Theta}(\mathbf{x}, \theta)]}{\partial \theta^2}\right\} = -\frac{1}{\sigma_N^2}$$

Thus, from Eq. (6.4.1a), the mean square error bound is given as

$$E[(\hat{\theta}-\Theta)^2] \geq \sigma_N^2 \tag{6.4.9}$$

and $\hat{\theta}$ is an efficient estimator of the random mean Θ.

The *a posteriori* density function of Θ can be obtained as

$$f_{\Theta|\mathbf{X}}(\theta|\mathbf{x}) = \frac{1}{\sqrt{2\pi\sigma_N^2}} \exp\left[\frac{-(\theta-\hat{\theta})^2}{2\sigma_N^2}\right] \tag{6.4.10}$$

which shows that the mean of the *a posteriori* density function is, in this case, also the maximum *a posteriori* estimator.

A sequential form of the maximum *a posteriori* estimator can be obtained, letting $\hat{\theta}$ of Eq. (6.4.5) equal $\hat{\theta}_N$, as

$$\hat{\theta}_N = \frac{\sigma_N^2}{\sigma_x^2} \sum_{i=1}^{N} X_i = \frac{\sigma_N^2}{\sigma_x^2} \left[\sum_{i=1}^{N-1} X_i + X_N \right]$$

$$= \frac{\sigma_N^2}{\sigma_x^2} \left\{ \left[\frac{(N-1)\sigma_\theta^2 + \sigma_x^2}{\sigma_\theta^2} \right] \hat{\theta}_{N-1} + X_N \right\}$$

which reduces to

$$\hat{\theta}_N = \hat{\theta}_{N-1} + \frac{\sigma_N^2}{\sigma_x^2} (X_N - \hat{\theta}_{N-1}) \qquad N = 1, 2, 3, \ldots \quad \hat{\theta}_0 = 0 \quad (6.4.11)$$

A sequential form of σ_N^2 can also be obtained as

$$\frac{1}{\sigma_N^2} = \frac{N\sigma_\theta^2 + \sigma_x^2}{\sigma_\theta^2 \sigma_x^2} = \frac{(N-1)\sigma_\theta^2 + \sigma_x^2 + \sigma_\theta^2}{\sigma_\theta^2 \sigma_x^2}$$

or

$$\frac{1}{\sigma_N^2} = \frac{1}{\sigma_{N-1}^2} + \frac{1}{\sigma_x^2} \qquad N = 1, 2, 3, \ldots \quad \sigma_0^2 = \sigma_\theta^2 \quad (6.4.12)$$

This estimator is called a Kalman estimator or a discrete Kalman filter for a single variable. Equation (6.4.11) is similar to Eq. (6.3.1) for the estimation for a unknown constant (nonrandom) mean of a Gaussian distribution. Equation (6.3.1) can be obtained from Eq. (6.4.11) by letting $\sigma_\theta^2 = \infty$. The estimator $\hat{\theta}_N$ will converge to the mean of Θ more rapidly for smaller values of σ_θ^2.

Example 6.4.1. Determine the maximum *a posteriori* estimator for the random parameter θ of an exponential random variable. Let $X_1, X_2, \ldots, X_N$ be a sample of mutually independent random variables from an exponential distribution with parameter θ. The samples are identically distributed with density function

$$f_{X_i|\Theta}(x_i|\theta) = \theta e^{-\theta x_i} \qquad x_i \geq 0 \quad i = 1, 2, \ldots, N$$

and the parameter has density function

$$f_\Theta(\theta) = e^{-\theta} \qquad \theta \geq 0$$

The conditional density function of **X** given Θ is obtained as

$$f_{\mathbf{X}|\Theta}(\mathbf{x}|\theta) = \prod_{i=1}^{N} [\theta e^{-\theta x_i}] = \theta^N \exp\left(-\theta \sum_{i=1}^{N} x_i \right)$$

and the joint density function of $\mathbf{X}$ and Θ as

$$f_{\mathbf{X}\Theta}(\mathbf{x}, \theta) = \theta^N \exp\left[-\theta\left(1 + \sum_{i=1}^N x_i\right)\right]$$

Taking the ln yields

$$\ln[f_{\mathbf{X}\Theta}(\mathbf{x}, \theta)] = N \ln(\theta) - \theta\left(1 + \sum_{i=1}^N x_i\right)$$

and the derivative becomes

$$\frac{\partial \ln[f_{\mathbf{X}\Theta}(\mathbf{x}, \theta)]}{\partial \theta} = \frac{N}{\theta} - \left(1 + \sum_{i=1}^N x_i\right)$$

Setting this derivative equal to 0, the maximum *a posteriori* estimator is obtained as

$$\hat{\theta} = \frac{N}{1 + \sum_{i=1}^N X_i} \qquad \square$$

PROBLEMS

6.2.1. For the sample of mutually independent random variables $X_1, X_2, \ldots, X_N$ where $f_{X_i}(x_i; \theta) = (1/\theta) e^{-x_i/\theta}$, $x_i \geq 0$, $i = 1, 2, \ldots, N$, and $\theta > 0$, determine the maximum likelihood estimator $\hat{\theta}$ for θ and whether $\hat{\theta}$ is unbiased. If $\hat{\theta}$ is unbiased determine the Cramer-Rao bound for $\hat{\theta}$ and whether $\hat{\theta}$ is efficient. (A helpful integral is $\int_0^\infty y^m e^{-cy} \, dy = m!/c^{m+1}$.)

6.2.2. For the sample of mutually independent random variables $X_1, X_2, \ldots, X_N$ where $f_{X_i}(x_i; a) = a e^{-ax_i}$, $x_i \geq 0$, $i = 1, 2, \ldots, N$, and $a > 0$, determine the maximum likelihood estimator $\hat{a}$ for a and whether $\hat{a}$ is unbiased. If $\hat{a}$ is unbiased determine the Cramer-Rao bound for $\hat{a}$ and whether $\hat{a}$ is efficient.

6.2.3. For the sample of mutually independent random variables $X_1, X_2, \ldots, X_N$ where $f_{X_i}(x_i; b) = (1/\sqrt{b}) e^{-x_i/\sqrt{b}}$, $x_i \geq 0$, $i = 1, 2, \ldots, N$, and $b > 0$, determine the maximum likelihood estimator $\hat{b}$ for b and whether $\hat{b}$ is unbiased. If $\hat{b}$ is unbiased determine the Cramer-Rao bound for $\hat{b}$ and whether $\hat{b}$ is efficient.

6.2.4. For the sample of mutually independent random variables $X_1, X_2, \ldots, X_N$ where $f_{X_i}(x_i; \theta) = (x_i/\theta^2) e^{-x_i/\theta}$, $x_i \geq 0$, $i = 1, 2, \ldots, N$, and $\theta > 0$, determine the maximum likelihood estimator $\hat{\theta}$ for θ and whether $\hat{\theta}$ is unbiased. If $\hat{\theta}$ is unbiased determine the Cramer-Rao bound for $\hat{\theta}$ and whether $\hat{\theta}$ is efficient.

6.2.5. For the sample of mutually independent random variables $X_1, X_2, \ldots, X_N$ where $f_{X_i}(x_i; a) = (x_i/a) e^{-x_i/\sqrt{a}}$, $x_i \geq 0$, $i = 1, 2, \ldots, N$, and $a > 0$, determine the maximum likelihood estimator $\hat{a}$ for a and whether $\hat{a}$ is unbiased. If $\hat{a}$ is unbiased determine the Cramer-Rao bound for $\hat{a}$ and whether $\hat{a}$ is efficient.

6.2.6. For the sample of mutually independent random variables $X_1, X_2, \ldots, X_N$ where $f_{X_i}(x_i; \theta) = [x_i^m/(m! \theta^{m+1})] e^{-x_i/\theta}$, $x_i \geq 0$, $i = 1, 2, \ldots, N$, $\theta > 0$, and m an integer ≥ 0, determine the maximum likelihood estimator $\hat{\theta}$ for θ and whether $\hat{\theta}$ is unbiased. If $\hat{\theta}$ is unbiased determine the Cramer-Rao bound for $\hat{\theta}$ and whether $\hat{\theta}$ is efficient.

6.2.7. For the sample of mutually independent random variables $X_1, X_2, .., X_N$ where $f_{X_i}(x_i; \theta) = (x_i/\theta) e^{-x_i^2/(2\theta)}$, $x_i \geq 0$, $i = 1, 2, \ldots, N$, and $\theta > 0$, determine the maximum likelihood estimator $\hat{\theta}$ for θ and whether $\hat{\theta}$ is unbiased. If $\hat{\theta}$ is unbiased determine the Cramer-Rao bound for $\hat{\theta}$ and whether $\hat{\theta}$ is efficient.

6.2.8. For the sample of mutually independent random variables $X_1, X_2, \ldots, X_N$ where $P(X_i = x_i; \theta) = e^{-\theta}\theta^{x_i}/x_i!$, $x_i = 0, 1, 2, \ldots$, $i = 1, 2, \ldots, N$, and $\theta > 0$, determine the maximum likelihood estimator $\hat{\theta}$ for θ and whether $\hat{\theta}$ is unbiased. If $\hat{\theta}$ is unbiased determine the Cramer-Rao bound for $\hat{\theta}$ and whether $\hat{\theta}$ is efficient.

6.2.9. For the estimator $\hat{\theta}$ of Eq. (6.2.5), determine $\text{Var}(\hat{\theta})$, the Cramer-Rao bound for $\hat{\theta}$, and whether $\hat{\theta}$ is efficient.

6.2.10. Determine the estimator $\hat{\sigma}$ for Example 6.2.3 where $\theta = \sigma^2$ and $\hat{\theta}$ is given in Eq. (6.2.5), and whether $\hat{\sigma}$ is efficient.

6.2.11. For the sample of mutually independent random variables $X_1, X_2, \ldots, X_N$, where $P(X_i = x_i; p) = (1-p)^{x_i-1}p$, $x_i = 1, 2, \ldots$, $i = 1, 2, \ldots, N$, and $0 < p < 1$, determine the maximum likelihood estimator $\hat{p}$ for p and whether $\hat{p}$ is unbiased. If $\hat{p}$ is unbiased determine the Cramer-Rao bound for $\hat{p}$ and whether $\hat{p}$ is efficient.

6.2.12. For the sample of mutually independent random variables $X_1, X_2, \ldots, X_N$ where $P(X_i = x_i; \theta) = (1 - 1/\theta)^{x_i-1}(1/\theta)$, $x_i = 1, 2, \ldots$, $i = 1, 2, \ldots, N$, and $1 < \theta < \infty$, determine the maximum likelihood estimator $\hat{\theta}$ for θ and whether $\hat{\theta}$ is unbiased. If $\hat{\theta}$ is unbiased determine the Cramer-Rao bound for $\hat{\theta}$ and whether $\hat{\theta}$ is efficient.

6.2.13. For the sample of mutually independent random variables $Y_1, Y_2, \ldots, Y_N$ where $Y_i = \sum_{j=1}^{M} X_{ij}$ and X_{ij}, $i = 1, 2, \ldots, N$, $j = 1, 2, \ldots, M$, are statistically independent Gaussian random variables with mean 0 and variance σ_x^2, determine the maximum likelihood estimator $\hat{M}$ for M and whether $\hat{M}$ is unbiased (treat M as a continuous parameter). If $\hat{M}$ is unbiased determine the Cramer-Rao bound for $\hat{M}$ and whether $\hat{M}$ is efficient.

6.2.14. Show that

$$E[(\hat{\theta} - \theta)^2] \geq \frac{[1 + dB(\theta)/d\theta]^2}{E\{[\partial \ln f_X(x; \theta)/\partial \theta]^2\}}$$

where $\hat{\theta}$ is a biased estimate of θ and $E(\hat{\theta}) = \theta + B(\theta)$. This is the Cramer-Rao bound (on the mean-square error) for biased estimates.

6.2.15. Determine the Cramer-Rao bound for the biased estimator of Eq. (6.2.14).

6.2.16. Determine the Cramer-Rao bound for the biased estimator of Problem 6.2.3.

6.3.1. For the maximum likelihood estimator $\hat{\theta}_N = (\sum_{i=1}^{N} X_i)/(2N)$, determine the sequential form for $\hat{\theta}_N$.

6.3.2. For the maximum likelihood estimator $\hat{\theta}_N = (\sum_{i=1}^{N} X_i)/(3N)$, determine the sequential form for $\hat{\theta}_N$.

6.3.3. Express $\hat{W}_N$ from Eq. (6.3.4) in terms of $\hat{W}_{N-1}$ and $\hat{\mu}_N$, i.e., in the form $\hat{W}_N = \hat{W}_{N-1} + a[b(X_N - \hat{\mu}_N)^2 - c]$.

6.3.4. Determine the sequential estimators $\hat{\mu}_N$ and $\hat{V}_N$ for the last 10 entries in Table 5.3.2a (unordered) starting with 1.492.

6.3.5. Determine the sequential estimators $\hat{\mu}_N$ and $\hat{V}_N$ for the last 10 entries in Table 5.3.2b (unordered) starting with 0.236.

6.3.6. Determine the number of samples required such that the probability of the sequential estimator $\hat{V}$ of Eq. (6.3.3) being within 10% of the true value V is 0.6827 (within one standard deviation).

6.3.7. Determine the number of samples required such that the probability of the sequential estimator $\hat{V}$ of Eq. (6.3.3) being within 5% of the true value V is 0.6827 (within one standard deviation).

6.3.8. Determine the number of samples required such that the probability of the sequential estimator $\hat{V}$ of Eq. (6.3.3) being within 10% of the true value V is 0.9545 (within two standard deviations).

6.4.1. For the sample of mutually independent random variables $X_1, X_2, \ldots, X_N$ where $f_{X_i|\Theta}(x_i | \theta) = \theta e^{-\theta x_i}$, $x_i \geq 0$, $i = 1, 2, \ldots, N$, and $f_\Theta(\theta) = \theta e^{-\theta}$, $\theta \geq 0$, determine the maximum *a posterior* estimator $\hat{\theta}$ for θ.

6.4.2. For the sample of mutually independent random variables $X_1, X_2, \ldots, X_N$ where $P(X_i = x_i | \Theta = \theta) = e^{-\theta} \theta^{x_i} / x_i!$, $x_i = 0, 1, 2, \ldots$, $i = 1, 2, \ldots, N$, and $f_\Theta(\theta) = b e^{-b\theta}$, $\theta \geq 0$, determine the maximum *a posteriori* estimator $\hat{\theta}$ for θ.

6.4.3. For the sample of mutually independent random variables $X_1, X_2, \ldots, X_N$ where $P(X_i = x_i | \Theta = \theta) = C_{x_i}^m \theta^{x_i}(1 - \theta)^{m-x_i}$, $x_i = 0, 1, \ldots, m$, $i = 1, 2, \ldots, N$, and $f_\Theta(\theta) = [(a+b+1)!/a!b!]\theta^a(1-\theta)^b$, $0 < \theta < 1$, a and b integers ≥ 0, determine the maximum *a posteriori* estimator $\hat{\theta}$ for θ.

6.4.4. For the sample of mutually independent random variables $X_1, X_2, \ldots, X_N$ where $f_{X_i|\Theta}(x_i | \theta) = [\theta^{m+1} x_i^m / m!] e^{-\theta x_i}$, $x_i \geq 0$. $i = 1, 2, \ldots, N$, and $f_\Theta(\theta) = e^{-\theta}$, $\theta \geq 0$, determine the maximum *a posteriori* estimator $\hat{\theta}$ for θ.

Random Processes 7

7.1 Statistical Description

A random process or stochastic process is a function that maps all elements of a sample space into a collection or ensemble of time functions called sample functions. The term sample function is used for the time function corresponding to a particular realization of the random process, which is similar to the designation of outcome for a particular realization of a random variable. A random process is governed by probabilistic laws, so that different observations of the time function can differ because a single point in the sample space maps to a single sample function. The value of a random process at any given time t cannot be predicted in advance. If a process is not random it is called nonrandom or deterministic.

As in the treatment of random phenomena earlier, it is convenient to consider the particular realization, of an observed random process, to be determined by random selection of an element from a sample space S. This implies that a particular element $s \in S$ is selected according to some random choice, with the realization of the random process completely determined by this random choice. To represent the time dependence and the random dependence, a random process is written as a function of two variables as $X(t, s)$, with t representing the time dependence and s the randomly chosen element of S. As was the case for random variables, for which the notation indicating the dependence on s was often suppressed, i.e., X was used instead of $X(s)$, a random process will be written as $X(t)$ instead of $X(t, s)$ when it is not necessary to use the latter notation for clarity.

A precise definition of a random process is as follows:

(a) Let S be a nonempty set,
(b) Let $P(\ )$ be a probability measure defined over subsets of S, and
(c) To each $s \in S$ let there correspond a time function $X(t, s)$.

238

Then this probability system is called a random process. This definition is simply a more precise statement of the earlier comments that the actual realization of the random process is determined by a random selection of an element from S.

The collection of all possible realizations $\{X(t, s): s \in S\} = \{X(t, s_1), X(t, s_2), \ldots\}$ is called the ensemble of functions in the random process, where the elements in this set are the sample functions. (As given, S is countable, but S may be uncountable.) Sometimes it is useful to denote the possible values of t by indicating that they are elements of another set, T. The ensemble of functions in the random process would then be given as $\{X(t, s): t \in T, s \in S\}$.

To help clarify these ideas, several examples of random processes will now be considered. With the Bernoulli random variable $X(t_k) = X_k$, which takes on the values 0 and 1, and with t_k a time index, $\{X(t_k, s): k = \ldots, -2, -1, 0, 1, 2, \ldots, s = 0, 1\}$ or simply $\{X_k: k = \ldots, -2, -1, 0, 1, 2, \ldots\}$ (where the s variation is suppressed) is the ensemble of functions in a Bernoulli random process. There is an infinite number of sample functions in this ensemble. Also, if

$$Y_N = \sum_{k=1}^{N} X_k$$

Y_N is a binomial random variable, and for N a time index the binomial counting random process is expressed as $Y(t) = Y_N$, $NT \le t < (N+1)T$, $N = 1, 2, \ldots$, where T is the observation period. There is an infinite number of sample functions in the ensemble of the binomial random process. A typical sample function for the binomial random process $[(x_1, x_2, \ldots) = (1, 0, 0, 1, 1, 1, 0, 1, \ldots)$ and $(y_1, y_2, \ldots) = (1, 1, 1, 2, 3, 4, 4, 5, \ldots)]$ is shown in Fig. 7.1.1. As shown, the process may increment by 1 only at the discrete times $t_k = kT$, $k = 1, 2, \ldots$.

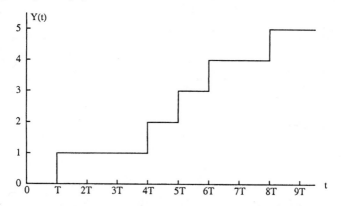

Fig. 7.1.1. Sample function for a binomial random process.

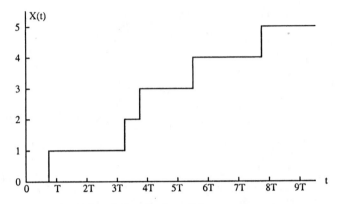

Fig. 7.1.2. Sample function for a Poisson random process.

Another counting process is the Poisson random process, which counts the number of events of some type (e.g., photons in a photomultiplier tube) that are obtained from some initial time (often $t = 0$) until time t. The number of events obtained in a fixed interval of time is described by a Poisson random variable. If N_t denotes the number of arrivals before time t, then this process is given as $X(t) = N_t$. A typical sample function for the Poisson random process is shown in Fig. 7.1.2. As can be seen in this figure, the Poisson random process differs from the binomial random process in that it can be incremented by 1 at any time and is not limited to the discrete times $t_k = kT$, $k = 1, 2, \ldots$.

A random process called a random telegraph signal can be obtained from the Poisson random process by taking the value at $t = 0$ to be either $+1$ or -1 with equal probability, and changing to the opposite value at the points where the Poisson process is incremented. A typical sample function of this random process is shown in Fig. 7.1.3. This telegraph signal can change values at any time.

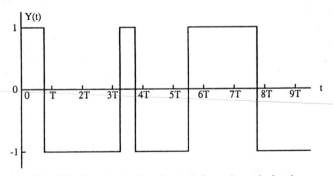

Fig. 7.1.3. Sample function for a random telegraph signal.

Another example of a random process is the sine wave random process given as

$$X(t) = V \sin(\Omega t + \Theta)$$

where the amplitude V may be random (which is the case for amplitude modulation), the frequency Ω may be random (which is the case for frequency modulation), the phase Θ may be random (which is the case for phase modulation), or any combination of these three parameters may be random. For the random process $X(t) = \cos(\omega_0 t + \Theta)$, where ω_0 is a constant and Θ is a uniform phase with $f_\Theta(\theta) = 1/(2\pi)$, $0 \le \theta \le 2\pi$, there is an infinite number of sample functions (all of the same frequency and maximum value, with different phase angles), since there is an infinite number of values in the interval from 0 to 2π. The random process for a simple binary communication scheme is $X(t) = \cos(\omega_0 t + \Theta)$, where Θ has the value $\theta = 0$ or $\theta = \pi$, and consists of the two sample functions $x(t, s_1) = \cos(\omega_0 t)$ and $x(t, s_2) = \cos(\omega_0 t + \pi)$. This binary phase modulation or, as it is commonly called, phase shift keying is the most efficient (yields the smallest probability of error) binary communication scheme.

The last example of a random process is a noise waveform which might distort the received waveform in a communication system. A typical sample function is shown in Fig. 7.1.4. The noise waveforms are greatly affected

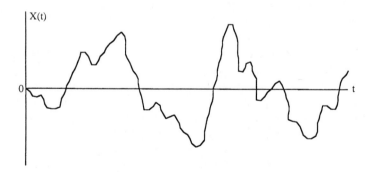

Fig. 7.1.4. Sample function for a noise random process.

by the filtering and other operations performed on the transmitted waveforms, so it is difficult to draw a general waveform. The most common assumption concerning the type of noise random process is that it is Gaussian.

Since a random process is a function of two variables, t and s, either or both of these may be chosen to be fixed. With the fixed values denoted by a subscript, these descriptions are

(a) $X(t, s) = X(t)$ is a random process.
(b) $X(t_i, s) = X(t_i) = X_{t_i}$ is a random variable.
(c) $X(t, s_j) = x(t, s_j)$ is a deterministic time function or sample function.
(d) $X(t_i, s_j) = x(t_i, s_j)$ is a real number.

For case (b) the time is fixed, so the possible values are the values that $X(t)$ can take on at this one instant in time, which is completely equivalent to the description of a one-dimensional random variable. Thus, $X(t_i)$ is a random variable and can be described by a probability density function. Similar interpretations hold for the other cases.

Both parameters, t and s, of a random process may be either discrete or continuous. If the possible values $X(t)$ can take on are a discrete set of values, $X(t)$ is said to be a discrete random process, whereas if the possible values are a continuum of values, $X(t)$ is said to be a continuous random process. The Bernoulli, binomial, Poisson, and telegraph random processes are discrete random processes, and the sine wave and noise random processes are continuous random processes. If only values at the time instants $t_1, t_2, \ldots, t_k, \ldots$ are of interest, the random process has a discrete parameter or is designated as a discrete time random process (unless a parameter such as time is explicitly stated, the terms continuous and discrete describe the range of the real numbers the random process can take on). Such random processes are common in sampled data systems. If time takes on a continuum of values, the random process has a continuous parameter or is a continuous time random process. The Bernoulli and binomial random processes are discrete time random processes, while the Poisson, telegraph, sine wave, and noise random processes are continuous time random processes.

The complete statistical description of a general random process can be infinitely complex. In general, the density function of $X(t_i)$ depends on the value of t_i. If $X(t)$ is sampled at N times, $\mathbf{X}^T = (X(t_1), X(t_2), \ldots, X(t_N))$ is a random vector with joint density function that depends on $t_1, t_2, \ldots, t_N$. A suitable description can in theory be given by describing the joint density function of $\mathbf{X}$ (or joint probability mass function) for all N and for all possible choices of $t_1, t_2, \ldots, t_N$. Such extremely general random process characterizations normally cannot be easily analyzed, so various simplifying assumptions are usually made. Fortunately, these simplifying assumptions are reasonable in many situations of practical interest. Random processes can be specified in several ways:

(a) Processes for which the rule for determining the density function is stated directly, e.g., the Gaussian random process
(b) Processes consisting of a deterministic time function with parameters that are random variables, e.g., the sine wave random process

(c) Operations on known random processes, e.g., filtering
(d) Specification of the probability of a finite number of sample functions

The most common simplifying assumption on random processes is that they satisfy some type of definition of stationarity. The concept of stationarity for a random process is similar to the idea of steady state in the analysis of the response of electrical circuits. It implies that the statistics of the random process are, in some sense, independent of the absolute value of time. This does not imply that the joint statistics of $X(t_1)$ and $X(t_2)$ are independent of the relative times t_1 and t_2, since for most random processes, as t_1 approaches t_2, $X(t_2)$ becomes more predictable from the value of $X(t_1)$. This type of behavior is readily satisfied, however, by allowing the dependence on time of these joint statistics to depend only on the difference between the two times, not on the precise value of either of the times.

The first type of stationarity considered is the strongest type. The statement that a random process is stationary if its statistical properties are invariant with respect to time translation is strict sense stationarity. Precisely stated, the random process $X(t, s)$ is strict sense stationary if and only if, for every value of N and for every set of time instants $\{t_i \in \mathbf{T}, i = 1, 2, \ldots, N\}$

$$F_{X(t_1), X(t_2), \ldots, X(t_N)}(x_1, x_2, \ldots, x_N) = F_{X(t_1+\tau), X(t_2+\tau), \ldots, X(t_N+\tau)}(x_1, x_2, \ldots, x_N)$$

(7.1.1)

holds true for all values of $x_1, x_2, \ldots, x_N$ and all τ such that $(t_i + \tau) \in T$ for all i. This definition is simply a mathematical statement of the property, which has already been stated, that the statistics depend only on time differences. Such differences are preserved if all time values are translated by the same amount τ.

The statistics of the Bernoulli random process do not change with time, so the Bernoulli random process is strict sense stationary, whereas the statistics of the binomial and the Poisson process do change with time and they are nonstationary.

Strict sense stationarity is sometimes unnecessarily restrictive, since most of the more important results for real-world applications of random processes are based on second-order terms, or terms involving only two time instants. A weaker definition of stationarity involving the first and second moments will be given shortly.

7.2 Statistical Averages

It is often difficult to prove that a process is strict sense stationary, but proof of nonstationarity can at times be easy. A random process is nonstationary if any of its density functions (or probability functions) or any of its moments depend on the precise value of time.

Example 7.2.1.   Consider the sine wave process with random amplitude given as

$$X(t) = Y \cos(\omega_0 t) \qquad -\infty < t < \infty$$

where ω_0 is a constant frequency and Y is a random variable uniformly distributed from 0 to 1, i.e.,

$$f_Y(y) = 1 \qquad 0 \le y \le 1$$

$$= 0 \qquad \text{otherwise}$$

The mean of the random process, where the expectation is over the random variation (in this case Y), is obtained as

$$E[X(t)] = E[Y \cos(\omega_0 t)] = \int_{-\infty}^{\infty} y \cos(\omega_0 t) f_Y(y) \, dy = \int_{0}^{1} y \cos(\omega_0 t)(1) \, dy$$

$$= \cos(\omega_0 t) \int_{0}^{1} y \, dy = \tfrac{1}{2} \cos(\omega_0 t)$$

where t is a constant with respect to the integration. Since the first moment is a function of time, the process is nonstationary.   □

Now consider the sine wave process with random phase.

Example 7.2.2.   Consider the sine wave process given as

$$X(t) = \cos(\omega_0 t + \Theta) \qquad -\infty < t < \infty$$

where again ω_0 is a constant and the density function of Θ is

$$f_\Theta(\theta) = \frac{1}{2\pi} \qquad 0 \le \theta < 2\pi$$

$$= 0 \qquad \text{otherwise}$$

The mean of $X(t)$ is obtained as

$$E[X(t)] = E[\cos(\omega_0 t + \Theta)] = \int_{-\infty}^{\infty} \cos(\omega_0 t + \theta) f_\Theta(\theta) \, d\theta$$

$$= \int_{0}^{2\pi} [\cos(\omega_0 t) \cos(\theta) - \sin(\omega_0 t) \sin(\theta)] \left(\frac{1}{2\pi} \right) d\theta$$

$$= \frac{1}{2\pi} \left[\cos(\omega_0 t) \sin(\theta) \Big|_{\theta=0}^{\theta=2\pi} + \sin(\omega_0 t) \cos(\theta) \Big|_{\theta=0}^{\theta=2\pi} \right]$$

$$= \frac{1}{2\pi} [\cos(\omega_0 t)(0-0) + \sin(\omega_0 t)(1-1)] = 0 \qquad □$$

Example 7.2.2 in itself does not prove or disprove that $X(t) = \cos(\omega_0 t + \Theta)$ is stationary. That this random process is stationary is shown in Example 7.2.3.

Example 7.2.3. The sine wave random process of Example 7.2.2 is shown to be strict sense stationary by first observing that

$$\Theta = \cos^{-1}[X(t_1)] - \omega_0 t_1 \quad \text{or} \quad \Theta = 2\pi - \cos^{-1}[X(t_1)] - \omega_0 t_1$$

From Example 3.3.2, the density function of $X(t_1)$ is obtained as

$$f_{X(t_1)}(x_1) = \frac{1}{\pi\sqrt{1 - x_1^2}} \quad -1 \le x_1 \le 1$$

$$= 0 \quad \text{otherwise}$$

Since neither this density function nor the density function for $X(t_1 + \tau)$ depends on t_1,

$$f_{X(t_1)}(x_1) = f_{X(t_1+\tau)}(x_1)$$

for all τ and t_1. Knowledge that $X(t_1) = x_1$ specifies the value of the random variable Θ and correspondingly the sample function of the random process $X(t)$. Given that $X(t_1) = x_1$, the value a_i that will be observed at time t_i is therefore not random, but depends only on x_1 and the time difference $(t_i - t_1)$, and is given as

$$a_i = \cos[\omega_0(t_i - t_1) + \cos^{-1}(x_1)] \quad \text{or} \quad a_i = \cos[\omega_0(t_i - t_1) + 2\pi - \cos^{-1}(x_1)]$$

The conditional density function of $X(t_i)$ given $X(t_1)$ is then

$$f_{X(t_i)|X(t_1)}(x_i | x_1) = \delta(x_i - a_i) \quad i = 2, 3, \ldots, N$$

and does not depend on the time origin. Also, the conditional density function of $X(t_i + \tau)$ given $X(t_1 + \tau)$,

$$f_{X(t_i+\tau)|X(t_1+\tau)}(x_i | x_1) = \delta(x_i - a_i) \quad \text{all } \tau \text{ and } t_i \quad i = 2, 3, \ldots, N$$

does not depend on the time origin. Thus for

$$\mathbf{X}^T(t) = (X(t_1), X(t_2), \ldots, X(t_N))$$

and

$$\mathbf{X}^T(t + \tau) = (X(t_1 + \tau), X(t_2 + \tau), \ldots, X(t_N + \tau))$$

it follows that

$$f_{\mathbf{X}(t)}(\mathbf{x}) = f_{X(t_1)}(x_1) \prod_{i=2}^{N} \delta(x_i - a_i) = f_{\mathbf{X}(t+\tau)}(\mathbf{x})$$

which shows that $X(t)$ is strict sense stationary. $\square$

The complete set of joint and marginal density (or probability) functions give a complete description of a random process, but they are not always available. Further, they contain more information than is often needed. Much of the study of random processes is based on a second-order theory, for which only the joint statistics applicable for two different instants of time are needed. These statistics are adequate for computing mean values of power (a second-order quantity, since it is based on the mean square value). The frequency spectra are also adequately described by these second-order statistics. An important random process that is completely described by second-order statistics is the Gaussian random process.

A situation where the second-order statistics are useful can be observed by evaluating the mean square value of the random output of the linear system shown in Fig. 7.2.1. The random output of the linear system is

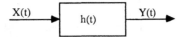

Fig. 7.2.1. Linear system with random input.

obtained in terms of the convolution integral of the random input and the impulse response of the system as

$$Y(t) = \int_{-\infty}^{\infty} X(u)h(t-u)\, du$$

The mean square value is then obtained as

$$E[Y^2(t)] = E\left\{\left[\int_{-\infty}^{\infty} X(u)h(t-u)\, du\right]^2\right\}$$

$$= E\left\{\int_{-\infty}^{\infty}\int_{-\infty}^{\infty} X(u)X(v)h(t-u)h(t-v)\, du\, dv\right\}$$

Taking the expectation inside the double integration and associating it with the random quantity yields

$$E[Y^2(t)] = \int_{-\infty}^{\infty}\int_{-\infty}^{\infty} E[X(u)X(v)]h(t-u)h(t-v)\, du\, dv$$

The term $E[X(u)X(v)]$ in this mean square value is a fundamental quantity in the consideration of random processes. It is called the autocorrelation function of the random process $X(t)$ and is defined, for the time instants t_1 and t_2, as

$$R_x(t_1, t_2) = E[X(t_1)X(t_2)] = \int_{-\infty}^{\infty}\int_{-\infty}^{\infty} x_1 x_2 f_{X(t_1)X(t_2)}(x_1, x_2)\, dx_1\, dx_2 \quad (7.2.1)$$

As can be seen, the autocorrelation function of the input to a linear system is needed to compute the mean square value of the output.

Closely related to the autocorrelation function is the covariance function, which is a direct generalization of the definition of covariance. The covariance function is defined as

$$K_x(t_1, t_2) = \text{Cov}[X(t_1), X(t_2)] = E\{[X(t_1) - E(X(t_1))][X(t_2) - E(X(t_2))]\}$$

$$= R_x(t_1, t_2) - E[X(t_1)]E[X(t_2)]$$

$$= R_x(t_1, t_2) - m_x(t_1)m_x(t_2) \tag{7.2.2}$$

where $m_x(t) = E[X(t)]$ is the mean function. The covariance function for a zero mean random process is identical to the autocorrelation function.

Example 7.2.4. Consider the sine wave process of Example 7.2.2 where $X(t) = \cos(\omega_0 t + \Theta)$ with $f_\Theta(\theta) = 1/(2\pi)$, $0 \le \theta < 2\pi$. The autocorrelation is given as

$$R_x(t_1, t_2) = E[X(t_1)X(t_2)] = E[\cos(\omega_0 t_1 + \Theta) \cos(\omega_0 t_2 + \Theta)]$$

which is expressed in terms of only one integral, since there is only the one random variable Θ, as

$$R_x(t_1, t_2) = \int_0^{2\pi} \cos(\omega_0 t_1 + \theta) \cos(\omega_0 t_2 + \theta) \left(\frac{1}{2\pi}\right) d\theta$$

$$= \frac{1}{4\pi} \int_0^{2\pi} [\cos(\omega_0 t_1 + \omega_0 t_2 + 2\theta) + \cos(\omega_0 t_2 - \omega_0 t_1)] d\theta$$

$$= \tfrac{1}{2} \cos[\omega_0(t_2 - t_1)]$$

where the trigonometric identity $\cos(A)\cos(B) = [\cos(A+B) + \cos(A-B)]/2$ was used to help evaluate the integral. (The first term in the integral becomes the integral of a cosine over two periods, which is zero, while the second term does not involve θ and yields 2π times the constant value.) ☐

In Example 7.2.4 $R_x(t_1, t_2)$ depends only on the difference between the two time instants, $t_2 - t_1$. Strict sense stationarity, which states that density or probability functions are invariant under translations of the time axis, implies that for a strict sense stationary random process the autocorrelation function depends only on the difference between t_2 and t_1. The converse of this is not necessarily true; i.e., the autocorrelation function depending only on time differences does not necessarily imply strict sense stationarity (for an important class of random processes, Gaussian random processes, the converse is true, however). An example in which the autocorrelation function depends only on the time difference and the process is not strict sense stationary is now given.

Example 7.2.5. Consider the random process $X(t)$ with the sample functions

$$x(t, s_1) = \cos(t) \qquad x(t, s_2) = -\cos(t)$$
$$x(t, s_3) = \sin(t) \qquad x(t, s_4) = -\sin(t)$$

which are equally likely. It can readily be determined that

$$m_x(t) = E[X(t)] = \frac{1}{4} \sum_{i=1}^{4} X(t, s_i) = 0$$

and

$$R_x(t_1, t_2) = E[X(t_1)X(t_2)] = \frac{1}{4} \sum_{i=1}^{4} X(t_1, s_i)X(t_2, s_i) = \frac{1}{2}\cos(t_2 - t_1)$$

which illustrates that the autocorrelation function depends only on $t_2 - t_1$. That $X(t)$ is not strict sense stationary can be shown by observing that at $t_1 = 0$

$$f_{X(t_1)}(x_1) = \tfrac{1}{4}\delta(x_1 + 1) + \tfrac{1}{2}\delta(x_1) + \tfrac{1}{4}\delta(x_1 - 1)$$

and at $t_2 = t_1 + \tau = \pi/4$

$$f_{X(t_1 + \tau)}(x_1) = \tfrac{1}{2}\delta\left(x_1 + \frac{1}{\sqrt{2}}\right) + \tfrac{1}{2}\delta\left(x_1 - \frac{1}{\sqrt{2}}\right)$$

or

$$f_{X(t_1)}(x_1) \neq f_{X(t_1 + \tau)}(x_1) \qquad \square$$

As stated previously, a large part of the study of random processes is built on the study of the autocorrelation function and related functions [the mean function $m_x(t)$ is also important in such studies]. For such analyses, only a form of stationarity which guarantees that the functions actually used depend on time differences is really needed. This form is considerably weaker than strict sense stationarity and leads to the definition of wide sense stationarity.

A random process $X(t)$ is wide sense stationary if the mean function $m_x(t) = E[X(t)]$ does not depend on t [$m_x(t)$ is a constant] and $R_x(t_1, t_2) = R_x(\tau)$ is a function only of $\tau = t_2 - t_1$. If $X(t)$ is wide sense stationary, $R_x(\tau) = E[X(t)X(t + \tau)]$ for all t.

The random process of Example 7.2.5, which has four sample functions, is wide sense stationary even though it is not strict sense stationary.

It was shown in Section 4.4 that a linear combination of Gaussian random variables is a Gaussian random variable. In a similar manner, the random variables $X_1, X_2, \ldots, X_N$ are jointly Gaussian if and only if

$$Y = \sum_{i=1}^{N} g_i X_i$$

is a Gaussian random variable for any set of g_i's. Now if $X(t)$ is a random process and

$$Y = \int_{-\infty}^{\infty} g(t)X(t)\,dt \tag{7.2.3}$$

where $g(t)$ is any function such that Y has finite second moment, then $X(t)$ is a Gaussian random process if and only if Y is a Gaussian random variable for every $g(t)$.

A direct consequence of this is that the output of a linear system is a Gaussian random process if the input is a Gaussian random process. To show that this is true, consider the output of a linear system with impulse response $h(t)$ and input $X(t)$ which is a Gaussian random process. The output is given as

$$Y(t) = \int_{-\infty}^{\infty} h(t-u)X(u)\,du$$

which is a Gaussian random process if

$$Z = \int_{-\infty}^{\infty} g(t)Y(t)\,dt$$

is a Gaussian random variable for all $g(t)$. Substituting for $Y(t)$ and interchanging the order of integration yields

$$Z = \int_{-\infty}^{\infty} g(t)\left[\int_{-\infty}^{\infty} h(t-u)X(u)\,du\right]dt$$

$$= \int_{-\infty}^{\infty}\left[\int_{-\infty}^{\infty} g(t)h(t-u)\,dt\right]X(u)\,du = \int_{-\infty}^{\infty} g'(u)X(u)\,du$$

where

$$g'(u) = \int_{-\infty}^{\infty} g(t)h(t-u)\,dt$$

Since $X(t)$ is a Gaussian random process Z is a Gaussian random variable for all $g'(t)$, and thus, since Z is a Gaussian random variable, $Y(t)$ is a Gaussian random process.

Another consequence of the definition of a Gaussian random process, given in Eq. (7.2.3), is that if $X(t)$ is a Gaussian random process the N random variables $X(t_1), X(t_2), \ldots, X(t_N)$ are jointly Gaussian random variables [have an N-dimensional Gaussian density function as given in Eq. (4.4.1)]. This is shown by using

$$g(t) = \sum_{i=1}^{N} g_i \delta(t - t_i)$$

in Eq. (7.2.3). Frequently this property is used as the definition of a Gaussian random process; i.e., a Gaussian random process is defined as a random process for which the N random variables $X(t_1), X(t_2), \ldots, X(t_N)$ are jointly Gaussian random variables for any N and any $t_1, t_2, \ldots, t_N$. Even though this statement is straightforward, it is easier to prove that the output of a linear system is a Gaussian random process if the input is a Gaussian random process by using the definition given here rather than using this last property.

The Gaussian random process is important for essentially the same reasons as Gaussian random variables; it is appropriate for many engineering models or, using the central limit theorem, if it is obtained from the contributions of many quantities, e.g., electron movement. In addition, analytical results are more feasible for the Gaussian random process than most other random processes. Just as a Gaussian random variable is specified by the mean and the variance, a Gaussian random process is specified by knowledge of the mean function $m_x(t)$ and the covariance function $K_x(t_1, t_2)$ [or equivalently by the mean function and the autocorrelation function $R_x(t_1, t_2)$].

If $X(t)$ is wide sense stationary, $m_x(t) = m_x$, a constant, and $R_x(\tau)$ is a function only of the time difference $\tau = t_2 - t_1$. From Eq. (7.2.2), $K_x(\tau)$ also depends only on the time difference. Since the two functions that specify a Gaussian random process do not depend on the time origin (only on time difference), strict sense stationarity is also satisfied. Thus, wide sense stationarity implies strict sense stationarity for a Gaussian random process.

In general, strict sense stationarity implies wide sense stationarity, since wide sense stationarity involves only the first two moments. The converse is not necessarily true; i.e., wide sense stationarity does not necessarily imply strict sense stationarity for a general random process, although the converse is true for the special case of a Gaussian random process.

Example 7.2.6. If $X(t)$ is a stationary Gaussian random process with $m_x(t) = 0$ and $R_x(\tau) = \sin(\pi\tau)/(\pi\tau)$, the covariance matrix of the Gaussian random vector $\mathbf{X}^T = (X(t_1), X(t_2), X(t_3))$, where $t_1 = 0$, $t_2 = \frac{2}{3}$, and $t_3 = \frac{3}{2}$, is given as

$$\Sigma_x = \begin{bmatrix} 1 & 0.413 & -0.212 \\ 0.413 & 1 & 0.191 \\ -0.212 & 0.191 & 1 \end{bmatrix} \qquad \square$$

The covariance matrix for a Gaussian random vector can be generated for any set of sample values using the autocorrelation function $R_x(\tau)$.

Another important concept in the study of random processes is that of ergodicity. A random process is said to be ergodic if ensemble (statistical) averages can be replaced by time averages in evaluating the mean function, autocorrelation function, or any function of interest. If the ensemble averages can be replaced by time averages, these averages cannot be a function of time, and the random process must be stationary. Thus, if a random process is ergodic it must be stationary. The converse of this is not necessarily true; i.e., a stationary random process does not necessarily have to be ergodic.

For an ergodic random process an alternative way to obtain the mean function of the random process $X(t)$ is by averaging $X(t)$ over an infinitely long time interval as

$$m_x = \lim_{T \to \infty} \frac{1}{2T} \int_{-T}^{T} X(t) \, dt \qquad (7.2.4)$$

and the autocorrelation function can be obtained by averaging the value of $X(t)X(t+\tau)$ over an infinitely long time interval as

$$R_x(\tau) = \lim_{T \to \infty} \frac{1}{2T} \int_{-T}^{T} X(t)X(t+\tau) \, dt \qquad (7.2.5)$$

Ergodicity is very useful mainly because it allows various quantities such as the autocorrelation function to be measured from actual sample functions. In fact, all real correlators are based on time averages, and as such most of the random processes in engineering are assumed to be ergodic.

An example of a random process that is stationary but not ergodic is now given.

Example 7.2.7. Consider the random process $X(t)$ with the sample functions

$$X(t, s_1) = +1 \qquad X(t, s_2) = -1$$

All the statistical properties of $X(t)$ are invariant with respect to time and $X(t)$ is strict sense stationary. With both sample functions equally likely $m_x(t) = 0$, while the time average of $X(t)$ is $+1$ for the first sample function and -1 for the second sample function, and $X(t)$ is not ergodic. $\qquad \square$

Now consider the calculation of the mean function and autocorrelation function of a more involved random process.

Example 7.2.8. Determine the mean function and the autocorrelation function for the random process (random telegraph signal) of Fig. 7.1.3, with the assumption that $P[X(0) = 1] = P[X(0) = -1] = \frac{1}{2}$. With the parameter of the Poisson random variable of Eq. (2.3.10) $a = \lambda t$, the probability function of the number of points in the interval of length T, $n(T)$, is given as

$$P[n(T) = i] = \frac{e^{-\lambda t}(\lambda t)^i}{i!}$$

which describes the number of times the random telegraph signal $X(t)$ changes sign in the interval of length T. Using this probability function,

$$P[X(t) = 1 \mid X(0) = 1] = P[n(T) = 0] + P[n(T) = 2] + \cdots$$

$$= e^{-\lambda t}\left[1 + \frac{(\lambda t)^2}{2!} + \cdots\right] = e^{-\lambda t}\cosh(\lambda t)$$

and

$$P[X(t) = 1 \mid X(0) = -1] = P[n(T) = 1] + P[n(T) = 3] + \cdots$$

$$= e^{-\lambda t}\left[\lambda t + \frac{(\lambda t)^3}{3!} + \cdots\right] = e^{-\lambda t}\sinh(\lambda t)$$

Then

$$P[X(t) = 1] = P[X(t) = 1 \mid X(0) = 1]P[X(0) = 1]$$

$$+ P[X(t) = 1 \mid X(0) = -1]P[X(0) = -1]$$

$$= e^{-\lambda t}\cosh(\lambda t)(\tfrac{1}{2}) + e^{-\lambda t}\sinh(\lambda t)(\tfrac{1}{2}) = \tfrac{1}{2}$$

and $P[X(t) = -1] = 1 - P[X(t) = 1] = \frac{1}{2}$. Finally, the mean function is obtained as

$$m_x(t) = E[X(t)] = (1)P[X(t) = 1] + (-1)P[X(t) = -1] = 0$$

With $\tau = t_2 - t_1$ and $s = |\tau|$

$$P[X(t_2) = 1 \mid X(t_1) = 1] = e^{-\lambda s}\cosh(\lambda s)$$

and

$$P[X(t_2) = 1, X(t_1) = 1] = \tfrac{1}{2} e^{-\lambda s}\cosh(\lambda s)$$

Similarly,

$$P[X(t_2) = 1, X(t_1) = -1] = \tfrac{1}{2} e^{-\lambda s}\sinh(\lambda s)$$

$$P[X(t_2) = -1, X(t_1) = 1] = \tfrac{1}{2} e^{-\lambda s}\sinh(\lambda s)$$

$$P[X(t_2) = -1, X(t_1) = -1] = \tfrac{1}{2} e^{-\lambda s}\cosh(\lambda s)$$

The autocorrelation function is then obtained as

$$R_x(s) = (1)(1)(\tfrac{1}{2}) \, e^{-\lambda s} \cosh(\lambda s) + (1)(-1)(\tfrac{1}{2}) \, e^{-\lambda s} \sinh(\lambda s)$$

$$+ (-1)(1)(\tfrac{1}{2}) \, e^{-\lambda s} \sinh(\lambda s) + (-1)(-1)(\tfrac{1}{2}) \, e^{-\lambda s} \cosh(\lambda s)$$

$$= e^{-\lambda s}[\cosh(\lambda s) - \sinh(\lambda s)] = e^{-2\lambda s}$$

or expressed in terms of τ

$$R_x(\tau) = e^{-2\lambda|\tau|} \qquad -\infty < \tau < \infty$$

Thus the random telegraph signal is a wide sense stationary random process. $\square$

Some properties of autocorrelation functions of wide sense stationary random processes will now be given.

Property 1.

$$R_x(0) = E[X^2(t)] = \int_{-\infty}^{\infty} x^2 f_{X(t)}(x) \, dx \qquad (7.2.6)$$

which is the mean-square value.

Property 2.

$$R_x(\tau) = R_x(-\tau) \qquad (7.2.7)$$

or the autocorrelation function is an even function of τ. This can be shown as

$$R_x(\tau) = R_x(t_1, t_1 + \tau) = E[X(t_1)X(t_1 + \tau)] = E[X(t_1 + \tau)X(t_1)]$$

$$= R_x(t_1 + \tau, t_1) = R_x(-\tau)$$

Property 3.

$$|R_x(\tau)| \le R_x(0) \qquad (7.2.8)$$

or the largest value of the autocorrelation function occurs at $\tau = 0$. This can be shown by considering

$$0 \le E\{[X(t_1) \pm X(t_1 + \tau)]^2\} = E[X^2(t_1) \pm 2X(t_1)X(t_1 + \tau) + X^2(t_1 + \tau)]$$

$$= E[X^2(t_1)] \pm 2E[X(t_1)X(t_1 + \tau)] + E[X^2(t_1 + \tau)]$$

$$= R_x(0) \pm 2R_x(\tau) + R_x(0)$$

which yields

$$R_x(0) \ge \mp R_x(\tau)$$

or the desired result

$$|R_x(\tau)| \le R_x(0)$$

Property 4. If $Y(t) = X(t) + y_0$, with y_0 a constant (dc component) and $E[X(t)] = 0$, then

$$R_y(\tau) = R_x(\tau) + y_0^2 \qquad (7.2.9)$$

This can be shown as

$$R_y(\tau) = E[Y(t_1)Y(t_1+\tau)] = E\{[X(t_1)+y_0][X(t_1+\tau)+y_0]\}$$

$$= E[X(t_1)X(t_1+\tau)+y_0X(t_1)+y_0X(t_1+\tau)+y_0^2]$$

$$= E[X(t_1)X(t_1+\tau)]+y_0E[X(t_1)]+y_0E[X(t_1+\tau)]+y_0^2$$

$$= R_x(\tau)+0+0+y_0^2 = R_x(\tau)+y_0^2$$

which is the desired result.

Property 5. If $Y(t) = X(t) + y_0\cos(\omega t + \Theta)$, with y_0 and ω constants, Θ a random variable uniformly distributed from 0 to 2π, and Θ and $X(t)$ statistically independent for all t, then

$$R_y(\tau) = R_x(\tau) + \left(\frac{y_0^2}{2}\right)\cos(\omega\tau) \qquad (7.2.10)$$

or if $Y(t)$ has a periodic component, then $R_y(\tau)$ will also have a periodic component with the same period. This can be shown as

$$R_y(\tau) = E\{[X(t_1)+y_0\cos(\omega t_1+\Theta)][X(t_1+\tau)+y_0\cos(\omega t_1+\omega\tau+\Theta)]\}$$

$$= E[X(t_1)X(t_1+\tau)]+y_0E[X(t_1+\tau)]E[\cos(\omega t_1+\Theta)]$$

$$\quad +y_0E[X(t_1)]E[\cos(\omega t_1+\omega\tau+\Theta)]$$

$$\quad +y_0^2E[\cos(\omega t_1+\Theta)\cos(\omega t_1+\omega\tau+\Theta)]$$

$$= R_x(\tau)+0+0+\frac{y_0^2}{2}E[\cos(2\omega t_1+\omega\tau+2\Theta)+\cos(\omega\tau)]$$

$$= R_x(\tau)+\frac{y_0^2}{2}[0+\cos(\omega\tau)] = R_x(\tau)+\frac{y_0^2}{2}\cos(\omega\tau)$$

which is the desired result.

Property 6. If $X(t)$ is ergodic and has no periodic component,

$$\lim_{|\tau|\to\infty} R_x(\tau) = \{E[X(t)]\}^2 \qquad (7.2.11)$$

or the mean ($\pm$mean) can be obtained from the autocorrelation function as τ goes to infinity. Conceptually $X(t_1)$ and $X(t_1+\tau)$ tend to become statistically independent as τ goes to infinity. Thus,

$$\lim_{|\tau|\to\infty} R_x(\tau) = \lim_{|\tau|\to\infty} E[X(t_1)X(t_1+\tau)]$$

$$= \lim_{|\tau|\to\infty} E[X(t_1)]E[X(t_1+\tau)] = \{E[X(t)]\}^2$$

since the mean is a constant.

It can readily be seen that the autocorrelation function of the random telegraph signal satisfies these properties, i.e., mean square value of 1, even function of τ, maximum at $\tau = 0$, and $E[X(t)] = 0$. Consider the functions of Fig. 7.2.2 as possible autocorrelation functions. Figure 7.2.2a cannot be an autocorrelation function since $g(0)$ is not the maximum value, while Fig. 7.2.2b cannot be an autocorrelation function since $g(\tau)$ is not an even function. Figure 7.2.2c cannot be an autocorrelation function since neither is $g(0)$ the maximum nor $g(\tau)$ an even function.

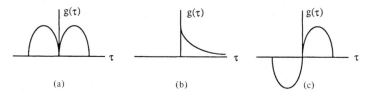

Fig. 7.2.2. Possible autocorrelation functions: (a) rectified sine; (b) exponential; (c) sine.

Example 7.2.9. Consider the autocorrelation function given as

$$R_x(\tau) = 100e^{-10|\tau|} + 50\cos(20\tau) + 25$$

The mean, mean square value, and variance of this random process will be determined by using the properties of the autocorrelation function. The mean square value is obtained as

$$E[X^2(t)] = R_x(0) = 100 + 50 + 25 = 175$$

and using

$$\{E[X(t)]\}^2 = \lim_{|\tau| \to \infty} R_x(\tau)\big|_{\text{with periodic term removed}} = 25$$

the mean is $E[X(t)] = \pm 5$. From this the variance is obtained as

$$\text{Var}[X(t)] = E[X^2(t)] - \{E[X(t)]\}^2 = 175 - 25 = 150 \qquad \square$$

7.3 Spectral Density

As in the deterministic (nonrandom) case, the spectral content of a random process, i.e., the strength of the random process in different frequency bands, is an important consideration. If $X(t)$ is a deterministic signal (voltage or current), the Fourier transform of $X(t)$ transforms this signal from the time domain to the frequency domain with the resultant being an amplitude (voltage or current) distribution of the signal in different frequency bands. Now if $X(t)$ is a random process the Fourier transform of $X(t)$ transforms this into the frequency domain, but since the random process is a function of both time and the underlying random phenomena, the Fourier transform is a random process in terms of frequency (instead of time). This transform may not exist and even if it does a random process does not yield the desired spectral analysis.

A quantity that does yield the desired spectral analysis is the Fourier transform (taken with respect to the variable τ, time difference, of the function) of the autocorrelation function of stationary (at least wide sense stationary) random processes. This Fourier transform is commonly called the power spectral density of $X(t)$ and denoted $S_x(f)$ [it may also be written as $S_x(\omega)$ where $\omega = 2\pi f$]. Thus, $S_x(f)$ is given as

$$S_x(f) = \int_{-\infty}^{\infty} R_x(\tau) \, e^{-j2\pi f\tau} \, d\tau \qquad (7.3.1a)$$

with the inverse Fourier transform given by

$$R_x(\tau) = \int_{-\infty}^{\infty} S_x(f) \, e^{j2\pi f\tau} \, df \qquad (7.3.1b)$$

Evaluating Eq. (7.3.1b) at $\tau = 0$ gives

$$R_x(0) = \int_{-\infty}^{\infty} S_x(f) \, df = E[X^2(t)] \qquad (7.3.2)$$

which justifies the name of power spectral density, since the integral over frequency yields a power (mean square value). The power spectral density then describes the amount of power in the random process in different frequency bands. [More precisely, it describes the amount of power which would be dissipated in a 1-Ω resistor by either a voltage or current random process equal to $X(t)$.] If $X(t)$ is an ergodic random process Eq. (7.3.2) can be written as

$$\int_{-\infty}^{\infty} S_x(f) \, df = \lim_{T \to \infty} \left(\frac{1}{2T}\right) \int_{-T}^{T} X^2(t) \, dt \qquad (7.3.3)$$

which is equivalent to the definition of total average power (which would be dissipated in a 1-Ω resistor by a voltage or current waveform).

For $X(t)$ an ergodic random process an alternative form of the spectral density is

$$S_x(f) = \lim_{T \to \infty} \frac{E[|F_x(f)|^2]}{2T} \qquad (7.3.4)$$

where

$$F_x(f) = \int_{-T}^{T} X(t) \, e^{-j2\pi ft} \, dt \qquad (7.3.5)$$

Example 7.3.1. Determine the power spectral density for the random telegraph signal of Fig. 7.1.3, where the autocorrelation function was determined in Example 7.2.8. The power spectral density is then determined as

$$S_x(f) = \int_{-\infty}^{\infty} e^{-2\lambda|\tau|} e^{-j2\pi f\tau} \, d\tau$$

$$= \int_{-\infty}^{0} e^{(2\lambda - j2\pi f)\tau} \, d\tau + \int_{0}^{\infty} e^{-(2\lambda + j2\pi f)\tau} \, d\tau$$

$$= \frac{1}{2\lambda - j2\pi f} + \frac{1}{2\lambda + j2\pi f} = \frac{4\lambda}{(2\pi f)^2 + 4\lambda^2} \qquad \square$$

Several properties of power spectral densities will now be given.

Property 1.

$$S_x(f) \ge 0 \qquad (7.3.6)$$

That this is true can be observed by assuming that $S_x(f) < 0$ for some frequency band. Then integrating only over this frequency band will yield a negative power, which is impossible, and thus $S_x(f)$ must be nonnegative. This can also be observed from the alternative form of the spectral density, since it is an average of a positive quantity.

Property 2.

$$S_x(-f) = S_x(f) \qquad (7.3.7)$$

or $S_x(f)$ is an even function of frequency. This can be shown by expressing the exponent of Eq. (7.3.1a) as

$$e^{-j2\pi f\tau} = \cos(2\pi f\tau) - j\sin(2\pi f\tau)$$

to yield

$$S_x(f) = \int_{-\infty}^{\infty} R_x(\tau)[\cos(2\pi f\tau) - j\sin(2\pi f\tau)] \, d\tau = \int_{-\infty}^{\infty} R_x(\tau) \cos(2\pi f\tau) \, d\tau$$

since $R_x(\tau)$ is an even function of τ, $\sin(2\pi f\tau)$ is an odd function of τ, the product $R_x(\tau)\sin(2\pi f\tau)$ is an odd function, and the integral of an odd function is 0. Finally, $\cos(2\pi f\tau)$ is an even function of f, which makes $S_x(f)$ an even function of f.

Example 7.3.2. Determine $E[X^2(t)]$ and $R_x(\tau)$ for the random process $X(t)$ with power spectral density $S_x(f) = 1/[(2\pi f)^2 + 0.04]$, $-\infty < f < \infty$. Using Eq. (7.3.2) and $\int [1/(v^2 + c^2)] \, dv = (1/c) \tan^{-1}(v/c)$

$$E[X^2(t)] = \int_{-\infty}^{\infty} \frac{1}{(2\pi f)^2 + 0.04} \, df = \left(\frac{1}{2\pi}\right)^2 \left(\frac{2\pi}{0.2}\right) \tan^{-1}\left(\frac{2\pi f}{0.2}\right) \Bigg|_{f=-\infty}^{f=\infty}$$

$$= 2.5$$

Since the power spectral density $S_x(f)$ is of the same form as the spectral density of Example 7.3.1, the autocorrelation function is of the form

$$R_x(\tau) = a\, e^{-b|\tau|} \qquad -\infty < \tau < \infty$$

The power spectral density, from Eq. (7.3.1a), is expressed as

$$S_x(f) = \int_{-\infty}^{\infty} a\, e^{-b|\tau|}\, e^{-j2\pi f\tau}\, d\tau = \frac{2ab}{(2\pi f)^2 + b^2}$$

Setting this equal to the given $S_x(f)$ yields $a = 2.5$ and $b = 0.2$. Thus,

$$R_x(\tau) = 2.5\, e^{-0.2|\tau|} \qquad -\infty < \tau < \infty$$

and $R_x(0) = 2.5 = E[X^2(t)]$.   □

A noise random process is said to be white noise if its power spectral density is constant for all frequencies, i.e., if

$$S_n(f) = \frac{N_0}{2} \qquad -\infty < f < \infty \tag{7.3.8}$$

where the division by 2 is used when both negative and positive frequencies are considered. Using Eq. (7.3.2), the power in a white noise process can be seen to be infinite, which is impossible in the physical world. But the concept of white noise is important. From quantum mechanics, the power spectral density of thermal noise (noise voltage due to the random motion of electrons in conducting material with resistance R) is given as

$$S_n(f) = \frac{2Rh|f|}{e^{h|f|/kT} - 1} \qquad -\infty < f < \infty \tag{7.3.9}$$

where k (the Boltzmann constant) $= 1.37 \times 10^{-23}$, h (the Planck constant) $= 6.62 \times 10^{-34}$, and T is temperature in kelvins (standard or room temperature $T_0 = 63°F = 290$ K). The maximum value of $S_n(f)$ is $2RkT$ at $f = 0$, which can be obtained by a limiting process. For $|f| = 0.1(kT_0/h) = 6 \times 10^{11}$ Hz, $S_n(f)$ has only dropped to 0.95 of its maximum value, and thus $S_n(f)$ is essentially constant for $|f| < 6 \times 10^{11}$ Hz [for $|f| = 0.01(kT_0/h) = 6 \times 10^{10}$ Hz, $S_n(f)$ equals 0.995 of its maximum value]. Even though thermal noise is not strictly a white noise process, it appears white (constant power spectral density) over most frequencies of interest in engineering ($|f| < 6 \times 10^{11}$ Hz). In engineering applications, then, the power spectral density of thermal noise is given as

$$S_n(f) = 2RkT = 7.946 \times 10^{-21}R \qquad -6 \times 10^{11} < f < 6 \times 10^{11} \tag{7.3.10}$$

The use of a white noise random process is similar to the use of an impulse function in the analysis of linear systems. Just as an impulse function, in reality, has meaning only after it has been passed through a system with a finite bandwidth (integrated), white noise has meaning only after it has been passed through a system with a finite bandwidth. As long as the bandwidth of the noise process is significantly larger than that of the linear system, the noise can be considered to have an infinite bandwidth.

Example 7.3.3.   If the thermal noise voltage in a 1-Ω resistor were measured with a digital voltmeter of bandwidth 100 kHz, this voltage, from Eqs. (7.3.10) and (7.3.2), would be $\sqrt{(7.946 \times 10^{-21})(2 \times 10^5)} = 0.040$ μV (rms), while with a 30-MHz oscilloscope a noise voltage of 0.690 μV would be measured. These are the values that were stated in Section 1.1.   □

The autocorrelation function of a white noise process theoretically can be obtained by taking the inverse Fourier transform of $S_n(f)$ given in Eq. (7.3.8), using Eq. (7.3.1b), as

$$R_n(\tau) = \int_{-\infty}^{\infty} \frac{N_0}{2} e^{j2\pi f\tau} \, df = \frac{N_0}{2} \int_{-\infty}^{\infty} e^{j2\pi f\tau} \, df$$

This integral cannot be evaluated directly, but is equal to an impulse function at $\tau = 0$. Thus,

$$R_n(\tau) = \frac{N_0}{2} \delta(\tau) \qquad (7.3.11)$$

That this is correct can readily be seen by taking the Fourier transform of $R_n(\tau)$ to obtain $S_n(f)$ [putting Eq. (7.3.11) into Eq. (7.3.1a)]. It is not uncommon in Fourier transforms to be easy to obtain the transform (or inverse transform) and be difficult to obtain the inverse transform (or transform). Thus, in many cases the inverse transform is obtained by recognizing the form of the transform (or vice versa). The form of the autocorrelation function for a white noise process indicates that white noise is uncorrelated for $\tau \neq 0$.

Also, from Eqs. (7.3.11) and (7.2.11), the mean of a white noise process $m_n(t) = 0$.

7.4   Linear Systems with Random Inputs

As shown in Section 7.2, the output of a linear system is a Gaussian random process if the input is a Gaussian random process. Thus, the output of a linear system, when the input is a Gaussian random process, can be specified by determining the mean function and the autocorrelation (or covariance) function of the output. For the linear system of Fig. 7.2.1, with impulse response $h(t)$, where the mean function and autocorrelation function of the input random process, $X(t)$, are $m_x(t)$ and $R_x(t_1, t_2)$ respectively, the mean function of the output is obtained as

$$m_y(t) = E[Y(t)] = E\left[\int_{-\infty}^{\infty} X(u)h(t-u)\, du\right] = \int_{-\infty}^{\infty} E[X(u)]h(t-u)\, du$$

or

$$m_y(t) = \int_{-\infty}^{\infty} m_x(u)h(t-u)\, du = \int_{-\infty}^{\infty} m_x(t-u)h(u)\, du \qquad (7.4.1)$$

Likewise, the autocorrelation function of the output is obtained as

$$R_y(t_1, t_2) = E[Y(t_1)Y(t_2)]$$

$$= E\left[\int_{-\infty}^{\infty} X(t_1-u)h(u)\, du \int_{-\infty}^{\infty} X(t_2-v)h(v)\, dv\right]$$

$$= E\left[\int_{-\infty}^{\infty}\int_{-\infty}^{\infty} X(t_1-u)X(t_2-v)h(u)h(v)\, du\, dv\right]$$

$$= \int_{-\infty}^{\infty}\int_{-\infty}^{\infty} E[X(t_1-u)X(t_2-v)]h(u)h(v)\, du\, dv$$

or

$$R_y(t_1, t_2) = \int_{-\infty}^{\infty}\int_{-\infty}^{\infty} R_x(t_1-u, t_2-v)h(u)h(v)\, du\, dv \qquad (7.4.2)$$

The relationships of Eqs. (7.4.1) and (7.4.2) involving the mean function and the autocorrelation function are valid for any random process that is the output of a linear system. They have special meaning, however, in the case of a Gaussian random process, since a knowledge of these functions is sufficient to specify the random process.

For the special case of $X(t)$ being wide sense stationary, $m_x(t) = m_x$ and $R_x(t_1, t_2) = R_x(\tau)$, where $\tau = t_2 - t_1$. In this case, the mean function of $Y(t)$, Eq. (7.4.1), reduces to

$$m_y(t) = \int_{-\infty}^{\infty} m_x h(u)\, du$$

or

$$m_y(t) = m_x \int_{-\infty}^{\infty} h(u)\, du = m_y \qquad (7.4.3)$$

which is a constant. Also, the autocorrelation function of $Y(t)$, Eq. (7.4.2), reduces to

$$R_y(t_1, t_2) = \int_{-\infty}^{\infty} \int_{-\infty}^{\infty} R_x(t_2 - v - (t_1 - u))h(u)h(v) \, du \, dv$$

or

$$R_y(\tau) = \int_{-\infty}^{\infty} \int_{-\infty}^{\infty} R_x(\tau - v + u)h(u)h(v) \, du \, dv$$

(7.4.4)

Thus, $Y(t)$ is wide sense stationary if $X(t)$ is wide sense stationary.

The power spectral density of the output of the linear system can be obtained by rewriting Eq. (7.4.4) as

$$R_y(\tau) = \int_{-\infty}^{\infty} \int_{-\infty}^{\infty} \int_{-\infty}^{\infty} S_x(f) \, e^{j2\pi f(\tau - v + u)} h(u)h(v) \, df \, du \, dv$$

and interchanging the order of integration

$$R_y(\tau) = \int_{-\infty}^{\infty} S_x(f) \left[\int_{-\infty}^{\infty} h(u) \, e^{j2\pi fu} \, du \right]\left[\int_{-\infty}^{\infty} h(v) \, e^{-j2\pi fv} \, dv \right] e^{j2\pi f\tau} \, df$$

Recognizing the integral with respect to v as $H(f)$ and the integral with respect to u as $H^*(f)$ [if $h(t)$ is a real function], this reduces to

$$R_y(\tau) = \int_{-\infty}^{\infty} S_x(f)|H(f)|^2 \, e^{j2\pi f\tau} \, df = \int_{-\infty}^{\infty} S_y(f) \, e^{j2\pi f\tau} \, df$$

Setting the integrands equal, since Fourier transforms are unique, yields

$$S_y(f) = S_x(f)|H(f)|^2$$

(7.4.5)

Example 7.4.1. Consider a white noise process, $X(t)$, as an input to an ideal low-pass filter, whose transfer function is shown in Fig. 7.4.1. With

$$R_x(\tau) = \frac{N_0}{2} \delta(\tau)$$

and

$$S_x(f) = \frac{N_0}{2} \qquad -\infty < f < \infty$$

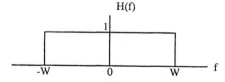

Fig. 7.4.1. Ideal low-pass filter.

the output power spectral density, from Eq. (7.4.5), is obtained as

$$S_y(f) = \frac{N_0}{2} \qquad -W < f < W$$

and the output autocorrelation function, from Eq. (7.3.1b), as

$$R_y(\tau) = \int_{-W}^{W} \frac{N_0}{2} e^{j2\pi f\tau} \, df = W N_0 \left[\frac{\sin(2\pi W\tau)}{2\pi W\tau} \right] \qquad -\infty < \tau < \infty \qquad \square$$

From the output autocorrelation for the ideal low-pass filter it can be seen that this filter has correlated the noise process. The mean square value or power in the output process is given as $R_y(0) = W N_0$, which is finite as expected.

Example 7.4.2.   Consider the RC low-pass filter shown in Fig. 7.4.2. Again, the input is a white noise process with power spectral density $N_0/2$.

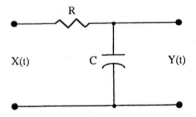

Fig. 7.4.2. RC low-pass filter.

The transfer function of this filter can be obtained, using a voltage divider (ratio of the impedance of the capacitor to the sum of the impedances of the resistor and the capacitor), as

$$H(f) = \frac{1/(j2\pi fC)}{R + 1/(j2\pi fC)} = \frac{1}{1 + j2\pi fRC}$$

or letting $f_c = 1/(2\pi RC)$

$$H(f) = \frac{1}{1 + jf/f_c} \qquad -\infty < f < \infty$$

The impulse response of this filter can be shown to be

$$h(t) = 2\pi f_c e^{-2\pi f_c t} \qquad t \geq 0$$

$$= 0 \qquad \qquad \text{otherwise}$$

$H(f)$ could also have been obtained by taking the Fourier transform of

$h(t)$. The output power spectral density is obtained as

$$S_y(f) = S_x(f)|H(f)|^2 = \frac{N_0/2}{1 + f^2/f_c^2} \qquad -\infty < f < \infty$$

and the autocorrelation function expressed as

$$R_y(\tau) = \int_{-\infty}^{\infty} \frac{N_0/2}{1 + f^2/f_c^2} e^{j2\pi f \tau} \, df$$

which can be recognized as (or using a Fourier transform table, not evaluating the integral)

$$R_y(\tau) = \frac{2\pi f_c N_0}{4} e^{-2\pi f_c |\tau|} \qquad -\infty < \tau < \infty$$

The RC low-pass filter correlates the noise process, and the mean square value of the output process is given as $R_y(0) = 2\pi f_c N_0/4$. $\square$

As a final item consider a random process as the input to two linear systems as shown in Fig. 7.4.3. If the input random process $X(t)$ is Gaussian,

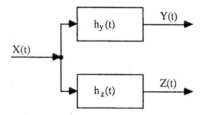

Fig. 7.4.3. Linear systems with common input.

then $Y(t)$ and $Z(t)$ are jointly Gaussian random processes. The cross-correlation of two random processes is defined in a manner similar to the autocorrelation. The cross-correlation of $Y(t)$ and $Z(t)$ is given as

$$R_{yz}(t_1, t_2) = E[Y(t_1)Z(t_2)] \qquad (7.4.6)$$

For the $Y(t)$ and $Z(t)$ given in Fig. 7.4.3 the cross-correlation function is given as

$$R_{yz}(t_1, t_2) = E\left[\int_{-\infty}^{\infty} X(t_1 - u)h_y(u) \, du \int_{-\infty}^{\infty} X(t_2 - v)h_z(v) \, dv \right]$$

which can be expressed in terms of the autocorrelation function of the input as

$$R_{yz}(t_1, t_2) = \int_{-\infty}^{\infty} \int_{-\infty}^{\infty} R_x(t_1 - u, t_2 - v)h_y(u)h_z(v) \, du \, dv \qquad (7.4.7a)$$

If $X(t)$ is wide sense stationary the cross-correlation function is a function only of $t_2 - t_1 = \tau$ as

$$R_{yz}(\tau) = \int_{-\infty}^{\infty} \int_{-\infty}^{\infty} R_x(\tau - v + u) h_y(u) h_z(v) \, du \, dv \qquad (7.4.7b)$$

When the cross-correlation function $R_{yz}(\tau)$ is a function only of τ and $E[Y(t)]$ and $E[Z(t)]$ are constants, $Y(t)$ and $Z(t)$ are defined to be jointly wide sense stationary.

The cross-spectral density (if it exists) is defined as the Fourier transform of the cross-correlation function and written as

$$S_{yz}(f) = \int_{-\infty}^{\infty} R_{yz}(\tau) \, e^{-j2\pi f\tau} \, d\tau \qquad (7.4.8a)$$

Likewise, the cross-correlation function is the inverse Fourier transform of the cross-spectral density and given as

$$R_{yz}(\tau) = \int_{-\infty}^{\infty} S_{yz}(f) \, e^{j2\pi f\tau} \, df \qquad (7.4.8b)$$

The cross-spectral density of $Y(t)$ and $Z(t)$ can be obtained by putting Eq. (7.3.1b) into Eq. (7.4.7b), which yields

$$R_{yz}(\tau) = \int_{-\infty}^{\infty} \int_{-\infty}^{\infty} \left[\int_{-\infty}^{\infty} S_x(f) \, e^{j2\pi f(\tau - v + u)} \, df \right] h_y(u) h_z(v) \, du \, dv$$

and interchanging the order of integration

$$R_{yz}(\tau) = \int_{-\infty}^{\infty} S_x(f) \left[\int_{-\infty}^{\infty} h_y(u) \, e^{j2\pi fu} \, du \right] \left[\int_{-\infty}^{\infty} h_z(v) \, e^{-j2\pi fv} \, dv \right] e^{j2\pi f\tau} \, df$$

Recognizing the integral with respect to v as $H_z(f)$ and the integral with respect to u as $H_y^*(f)$ [if $h_y(t)$ is a real function], this reduces to

$$R_{yz}(\tau) = \int_{-\infty}^{\infty} S_x(f) H_y^*(f) H_z(f) \, e^{j2\pi f\tau} \, df = \int_{-\infty}^{\infty} S_{yz}(f) \, e^{j2\pi f\tau} \, df$$

Setting the integrands equal yields

$$S_{yz}(f) = S_x(f) H_y^*(f) H_z(f) \qquad (7.4.9)$$

If $H_y(f)$ and $H_z(f)$ are nonoverlapping, $R_{yz}(\tau) = 0$ for all τ. In addition, either $H_y(f)$ or $H_z(f)$ must have zero response to a constant (dc) input; i.e., if $H_y(f)$ has zero response to a constant, $Y(t) = 0$ if $X(t) = c$. Since

$$Y(t) = \int_{-\infty}^{\infty} X(t - u) h_y(u) \, du$$

this zero response to a constant implies

$$\int_{-\infty}^{\infty} h_y(u) \, du = 0$$

and using this in Eq. (7.4.3) yields $m_y(t) = 0$. Thus, the covariance between $Y(t)$ and $Z(t)$ is zero, and if $X(t)$ is a Gaussian random process, $Y(t)$ and $Z(t)$ are statistically independent.

The covariance (or cross-covariance) function of the random processes $Y(t)$ and $Z(t)$ is defined, similar to Eq. (7.2.2), as

$$K_{yz}(t_1, t_2) = \text{Cov}[\, Y(t_1)Z(t_2)] = E\{[\, Y(t_1) - E(\, Y(t_1))][Z(t_2) - E(Z(t_2))]\}$$
$$= R_{yz}(t_1, t_2) - m_y(t_1)m_z(t_2) \qquad (7.4.10)$$

Two properties of the cross-correlation function of the jointly wide sense stationary random processes $Y(t)$ and $Z(t)$ are

$$R_{yz}(\tau) = R_{zy}(-\tau) \qquad (7.4.11a)$$

and

$$|R_{yz}(\tau)| \leq \sqrt{R_y(0)R_z(0)} \qquad (7.4.11b)$$

The first property follows from

$$R_{yz}(\tau) = E[\, Y(t_1)Z(t_1 + \tau)] = E[Z(t_1 + \tau)\, Y(t_1)] = R_{zy}(-\tau)$$

and the second property follows from Eq. (4.6.1) with X and Y replaced by $Y(t)$ and $Z(t)$, respectively.

In a manner similar to the definition of the time autocorrelation function given in Eq. (7.2.5), if the random processes $Y(t)$ and $Z(t)$ are ergodic, then the time cross-correlation function of $Y(t)$ and $Z(t)$ is defined as

$$R_{yz}(\tau) = \lim_{T \to \infty} \frac{1}{2T} \int_{-T}^{T} Y(t)Z(t + \tau) \, d\tau \qquad (7.4.12)$$

Thus, when $Y(t)$ and $Z(t)$ are jointly ergodic random processes, the cross-correlation function of $Y(t)$ and $Z(t)$ can be obtained as a time average.

PROBLEMS

7.2.1. For the random process $X(t) = A \cos(\omega_0 t) + B \sin(\omega_0 t)$, where ω_0 is a constant and A and B are uncorrelated zero mean random variables having different density functions but the same variance σ^2, determine whether $X(t)$ is wide sense stationary.

7.2.2. For the random process $X(t) = Y \cos(2\pi t)$ and $f_Y(y) = \frac{1}{2}$, $-1 \leq y \leq 1$, evaluate $E[X(t)]$ and $E[X^2(t)]$ and determine whether $X(t)$ is strict sense stationary, wide sense stationary, or neither.

7.2.3. For the random process $Y(t) = X(t) \cos(2\pi t + \Theta)$, where $X(t)$ is a wide sense stationary random process statistically independent of Θ with $f_\Theta(\theta) = 1/(2\pi)$, $0 \le \theta < 2\pi$, determine whether $Y(t)$ is wide sense stationary.

7.2.4. Determine the covariance matrix of the Gaussian random vector $\mathbf{X}^T = (X(t_1), X(t_2), X(t_3))$ when $t_1 = 1$, $t_2 = 1.5$, and $t_3 = 2.25$, where $X(t)$ is a stationary Gaussian random process with $m_x(t) = 0$ and $R_x(\tau) = \sin(\pi\tau)/(\pi\tau)$.

7.2.5. For a random process $X(t)$ with autocorrelation function $R_x(\tau)$ as shown in Fig. P7.2.5a, determine the autocorrelation function $R_y(\tau)$ for the system shown in Fig. P7.2.5b [$Y(t) = X(t) + X(t-3)$].

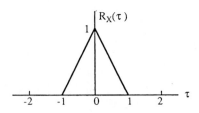

Fig. P7.2.5a.

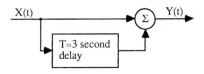

Fig. P7.2.5b.

7.2.6. For a random process $X(t)$ with autocorrelation function $R_x(\tau)$ as shown in Fig. P7.2.5a, determine the autocorrelation function $R_y(\tau)$ for the system with $Y(t) = X(t-2) + X(t-5)$.

7.2.7. Determine $E[X(t)]$, $E[X^2(t)]$, and $\text{Var}[X(t)]$ for $R_x(\tau) = 50\, e^{-10|\tau|} + 25 \cos(5\tau) + 10$.

7.2.8. For $R_x(\tau)$ as shown in Fig. P7.2.8, determine $E[X(t)]$, $E[X^2(t)]$, and $\text{Var}[X(t)]$.

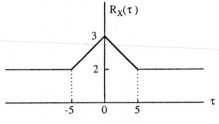

Fig. P7.2.8.

7.2.9. For $R_x(\tau)$ as shown in Fig. P7.2.9, determine $E[X(t)]$, $E[X^2(t)]$, and Var$[X(t)]$.

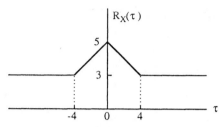

Fig. P7.2.9.

7.2.10. Show that the mean function $m_x(t) = 0$ and the autocorrelation function $R_x(\tau) = (1 - |\tau|/T)$, $-T \le \tau \le T$, for the binary random process $X(t) = A_i$, $iT + v \le t < (i+1)T + v$, $-\infty < i < \infty$, where V is a uniform random variable with $f_V(v) = 1/T$, $0 \le v < T$, $P(A_i = 1) = P(A_i = -1) = 0.5$, and $\{A_i\}$ and V are statistically independent.

7.2.11. For the periodic function $X(t) = \dots, -1, +1, +1, -1, +1, -1, -1, \dots$ where each ±1 is on for 1 sec and $T = 7$ sec, determine the time autocorrelation function $R_x(\tau)$ (obtain for $\tau = 0, 1, 2, 3, 4, 5, 6$).

7.2.12. For the periodic function $X(t) = \dots, -1, +1, +1, +1, -1, +1, \dots$ where each ±1 is on for 1 sec and $T = 6$ sec, determine the time autocorrelation function $R_x(\tau)$ (obtain for $\tau = 0, 1, 2, 3, 4, 5$).

7.3.1. Determine the power spectral density $S_x(f)$ for $R_x(\tau) = 1$, $-2 \le \tau \le 2$.

7.3.2. Determine the power spectral density for the binary random process of Problem 7.2.10 with $T = 1$.

7.3.3. Determine $E[X(t)]$, $E[X^2(t)]$, and $R_x(\tau)$ for the random process $X(t)$ with power spectral density $S_x(f) = 10/[(2\pi f)^2 + 0.16]$, $-\infty < f < \infty$.

7.3.4. For $S_x(f)$ as shown in Fig. P7.3.4, determine $E[X(t)]$, $E[X^2(t)]$, and $R_x(\tau)$.

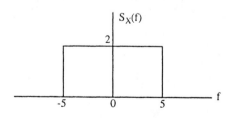

Fig. P7.3.4.

7.3.5. For $S_x(f)$ as shown in Fig. P7.3.5, determine $E[X(t)]$, $E[X^2(t)]$, and $R_x(\tau)$.

7.3.6. Determine the thermal noise voltage in a 1-Ω resistor when it is measured with a 1-MHz oscilloscope and when it is measured with a 5-MHz oscilloscope.

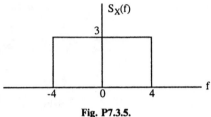

Fig. P7.3.5.

7.3.7. Determine the thermal noise voltage in a 1-Ω resistor when it is measured with (a) a 10-MHz oscilloscope and (b) a 50-MHz oscilloscope.

7.3.8. Can $g(f) = 5 \cos(2\pi f)$ be a power spectral density for the wide sense stationary random process $X(t)$?

7.4.1. Determine the output power spectral density and the output autocorrelation function for a system with impulse response $h(t) = e^{-t}$, $t \geq 0$, whose input is a white noise process $X(t)$ with spectral density $S_x(f) = N_0/2$, $-\infty < f < \infty$.

7.4.2. Determine the output power spectral density and the output autocorrelation function for a system with impulse response $h(t) = 1, 0 \leq t \leq 1$, whose input is a white noise process $X(t)$ with spectra density $S_x(f) = N_0/2$, $-\infty < f < \infty$.

7.4.3. Determine the cross-correlation function of $Z_1(t) = X(t) + Y(t)$ and $Z_2(t) = X(t) - Y(t)$, where $X(t)$ and $Y(t)$ are statistically independent random processes with zero means and autocorrelation functions $R_x(\tau) = e^{-|\tau|}$, $-\infty < \tau < \infty$, and $R_y(\tau) = 2 e^{-|\tau|}$, $-\infty < \tau < \infty$.

7.4.4. For the random processes $X(t) = A \cos(\omega_0 t) + B \sin(\omega_0 t)$ and $Y(t) = B \cos(\omega_0 t) - A \sin(\omega_0 t)$ where ω_0 is a constant and A and B are uncorrelated zero-mean random variables having different density functions but the same variance σ^2, show that $X(t)$ and $Y(t)$ are jointly wide sense stationary.

7.4.5. For the two periodic functions $X(t) = \ldots, -1, +1, +1, -1, +1, -1, -1, \ldots$ and $Y(t) = \ldots, -1, +1, +1, -1, -1, -1, +1, \ldots$ where each ± 1 is on for 1 sec and $T = 7$ sec, determine the time cross-correlation function $R_{xy}(\tau)$ (obtain for $\tau = 0, 1, 2, 3, 4, 5, 6$).

Appendix A
Evaluation of Gaussian Probabilities

A.1 Q Function Evaluation

The Q function, which yields probability statements on the normalized Gaussian random variable, is given from Eq. (2.2.4) as

$$Q(x) = 1 - F_X(x) = \int_x^\infty \frac{1}{\sqrt{2\pi}} e^{-t^2/2} \, dt$$

and the region of integration from Fig. 2.2.3 is shown in Fig. A.1. The Q function is tabulated in Table A.1 for values of the argument from 0.00 to 4.99 in increments of 0.01, where the 10 columns give the second decimal place of the argument. For example, the value of $Q(2.13)$ is found in the row with the value 2.1 under the column 0.03, or $Q(2.13) = 0.01659$. This table lists the values only for positive arguments, but the Q function for negative arguments can be obtained from Eq. (2.28) as

$$Q(-c) = 1 - Q(c)$$

For example, $Q(-0.97) = 1 - Q(0.97) = 1 - 0.16602 = 0.83398$.

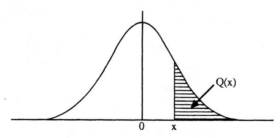

Fig. A.1. Q function for Gaussian probabilities.

269

Table A.1

Gaussian Probabilities

	.00	.01	.02	.03	.04	.05	.06	.07	.08	.09
0.0	.50000	.49601	.49202	.48803	.48405	.48006	.47608	.47210	.46812	.46414
0.1	.46017	.45640	.45224	.44828	.44432	.44038	.43644	.43251	.42858	.42465
0.2	.42074	.41683	.41294	.40905	.40517	.40129	.39743	.39358	.38974	.38591
0.3	.38209	.37828	.37448	.37070	.36693	.36317	.35942	.35569	.35197	.34827
0.4	.34458	.34090	.33724	.33360	.32997	.32636	.32276	.31918	.31561	.31207
0.5	.30854	.30503	.30153	.29806	.29460	.29116	.28774	.28434	.28096	.27760
0.6	.27425	.27093	.26763	.26435	.26109	.25785	.25463	.25143	.24825	.24510
0.7	.24196	.23885	.23576	.23269	.22965	.22663	.22363	.22065	.21770	.21476
0.8	.21186	.20897	.20611	.20327	.20045	.19766	.19489	.19215	.18943	.18673
0.9	.18406	.18141	.17879	.17619	.17361	.17106	.16853	.16602	.16354	.16109
1.0	.15866	.15625	.15386	.15150	.14917	.14686	.14457	.14231	.14007	.13786
1.1	.13567	.13350	.13136	.12924	.12714	.12507	.12302	.12100	.11900	.11702
1.2	.11507	.11314	.11123	.10935	.10749	.10565	.10383	.10204	.10027	.09853
1.3	.09680	.09510	.09342	.09176	.09012	.08851	.08692	.08534	.08379	.08226
1.4	.08076	.07927	.07780	.07636	.07493	.07353	.07215	.07078	.06944	.06811
1.5	.06681	.06552	.06426	.06301	.06178	.06057	.05938	.05821	.05705	.05592
1.6	.05480	.05370	.05262	.05155	.05050	.04947	.04846	.04746	.04648	.04551
1.7	.04457	.04363	.04272	.04182	.04093	.04006	.03920	.03836	.03754	.03673
1.8	.03593	.03515	.03438	.03362	.03288	.03216	.03144	.03074	.03005	.02938
1.9	.02872	.02807	.02743	.02680	.02619	.02559	.02500	.02442	.02385	.02330
2.0	.02275	.02222	.02169	.02118	.02068	.02018	.01970	.01923	.01876	.01831
2.1	.01786	.01743	.01700	.01659	.01618	.01578	.01539	.01500	.01463	.01426
2.2	.01390	.01355	.01321	.01287	.01255	.01222	.01191	.01160	.01130	.01101
2.3	.01072	.01044	.01017	.00990	.00964	.00939	.00914	.00889	.00866	.00842
2.4	.00820	.00798	.00776	.00755	.00734	.00714	.00695	.00676	.00657	.00639
2.5	.00621	.00604	.00587	.00570	.00554	.00539	.00523	.00508	.00494	.00480
2.6	.00466	.00453	.00440	.00427	.00415	.00402	.00391	.00379	.00368	.00357
2.7	.00347	.00336	.00326	.00317	.00307	.00298	.00289	.00280	.00272	.00264
2.8	.00256	.00248	.00240	.00233	.00226	.00219	.00212	.00205	.00199	.00193
2.9	.00187	.00181	.00175	.00169	.00164	.00159	.00154	.00149	.00144	.00139
3.0	1.35E-3	1.31E-3	1.26E-3	1.22E-3	1.18E-3	1.14E-3	1.11E-3	1.07E-3	1.04E-3	1.00E-3
3.1	9.68E-4	9.36E-4	9.04E-4	8.74E-4	8.45E-4	8.16E-4	7.89E-4	7.62E-4	7.36E-4	7.11E-4
3.2	6.87E-4	6.64E-4	6.41E-4	6.19E-4	5.98E-4	5.77E-4	5.57E-4	5.38E-4	5.19E-4	5.01E-4
3.3	4.83E-4	4.67E-4	4.50E-4	4.34E-4	4.19E-4	4.04E-4	3.90E-4	3.76E-4	3.62E-4	3.50E-4
3.4	3.37E-4	3.25E-4	3.13E-4	3.02E-4	2.91E-4	2.80E-4	2.70E-4	2.60E-4	2.51E-4	2.42E-4
3.5	2.33E-4	2.24E-4	2.16E-4	2.08E-4	2.00E-4	1.93E-4	1.85E-4	1.79E-4	1.72E-4	1.65E-4
3.6	1.59E-4	1.53E-4	1.47E-4	1.42E-4	1.36E-4	1.31E-4	1.26E-4	1.21E-4	1.17E-4	1.12E-4
3.7	1.08E-4	1.04E-4	9.96E-5	9.58E-5	9.20E-5	8.84E-5	8.50E-5	8.16E-5	7.84E-5	7.53E-5
3.8	7.24E-5	6.95E-5	6.67E-5	6.41E-5	6.15E-5	5.91E-5	5.67E-5	5.44E-5	5.22E-5	5.01E-5
3.9	4.81E-5	4.62E-5	4.43E-5	4.25E-5	4.08E-5	3.91E-5	3.75E-5	3.60E-5	3.45E-5	3.31E-5
4.0	3.17E-5	3.04E-5	2.91E-5	2.79E-5	2.67E-5	2.56E-5	2.45E-5	2.35E-5	2.25E-5	2.16E-5
4.1	2.07E-5	1.98E-5	1.90E-5	1.81E-5	1.74E-5	1.66E-5	1.59E-5	1.52E-5	1.46E-5	1.40E-5
4.2	1.34E-5	1.28E-5	1.22E-5	1.17E-5	1.12E-5	1.07E-5	1.02E-5	9.78E-6	9.35E-6	8.94E-6
4.3	8.55E-6	8.17E-6	7.81E-6	7.46E-6	7.13E-6	6.81E-6	6.51E-6	6.22E-6	5.94E-6	5.67E-6
4.4	5.42E-6	5.17E-6	4.94E-6	4.72E-6	4.50E-4	4.30E-6	4.10E-6	3.91E-6	3.74E-6	3.56E-6
4.5	3.40E-6	3.24E-6	3.09E-6	2.95E-6	2.82E-6	2.68E-6	2.56E-6	2.44E-6	2.33E-6	2.22E-6
4.6	2.11E-6	2.02E-6	1.92E-6	1.83E-6	1.74E-6	1.66E-6	1.58E-6	1.51E-6	1.44E-6	1.37E-6
4.7	1.30E-6	1.24E-6	1.18E-6	1.12E-6	1.07E-6	1.02E-6	9.69E-7	9.22E-7	8.78E-7	8.35E-7
4.8	7.94E-7	7.56E-7	7.19E-7	6.84E-7	6.50E-7	6.18E-7	5.88E-7	5.59E-7	5.31E-7	5.05E-7
4.9	4.80E-7	4.56E-7	4.33E-7	4.12E-7	3.91E-7	3.72E-7	3.53E-7	3.35E-7	3.18E-7	3.02E-7

An approximation for $Q(x)$, which is easily implemented on a programmable calculator, is given as

$$Q(x) = (b_1 t + b_2 t^2 + b_3 t^3 + b_4 t^4 + b_5 t^5)\, e^{-x^2/2} + e(x) \qquad x \geq 0$$

where the error is bounded as $|e(x)| < 7.5 \times 10^{-8}$, and

$$t = 1/(1 + rx) \qquad r = 0.2316419 \qquad b_1 = 0.127414796$$

$$b_2 = -0.142248368 \qquad b_3 = 0.710706871$$

$$b_4 = -0.726576013 \qquad b_5 = 0.530702714$$

A.2 Inverse Q Function

If the value of $Q(a)$ is given, the value of a can be obtained by linear interpolation in Table A.1. For example, if $Q(a) = 0.02$ the value of a lies between 2.05 and 2.06 [$Q(2.05) = 0.02018$ and $Q(2.06) = 0.01970$], and by linear interpolation between these two points, a is

$$a = 2.05 + \left(\frac{0.02018 - 0.02}{0.02018 - 0.01970} \right)(2.06 - 2.05) = 2.054$$

For values of $Q > 0.5$, Eq. (2.2.8) is used, for example, $Q(b) = 0.75$ to obtain

$$Q(-b) = 1 - Q(b) = 0.25$$

and

$$-b = 0.67 + \left(\frac{0.25143 - 0.25}{0.25143 - 0.24825} \right)(0.68 - 0.67) = 0.674$$

$$b = -0.674$$

A rational approximation for the inverse of $Q(x)$, which is easily implemented on a programmable calculator, is given as

$$x = s - \frac{c_0 + c_1 s + c_2 s^2}{1 + d_1 s + d_2 s^2 + d_3 s^3} + e(Q) \qquad Q \geq 0.5$$

where the error is bounded as $|e(Q)| < 4.5 \times 10^{-4}$, and

$$s = (-2 \ln Q)^{1/2} \qquad c_0 = 2.515517 \qquad c_1 = 0.802853 \qquad c_2 = 0.010328$$

$$d_1 = 1.432788 \qquad d_2 = 0.189269 \qquad d_3 = 0.001308$$

Appendix B
Sum of N Uniform Random Variables

The density function and the distribution function for the sum of N statistically independent random variables uniformly distributed from 0 to 1 is derived. The results are piecewise continuous functions with different expressions over each unity interval. For Z_N the sum of these uniform random variables, a normalized version of the sum, W_N, is defined where the mean of W_N is 0 and the variance of W_N is 1. The density function and distribution function for W_N are also developed. The density function of this normalized sum then facilitates a direct comparison with the normalized Gaussian density function.

Letting Z_N be the sum of N statistically independent uniform random variables as

$$Z_1 = U_1$$
$$Z_N = Z_{N-1} + U_N \qquad N = 2, 3, \ldots$$

where

$$f_{U_i}(u_i) = 1 \qquad 0 < u_i \leq 1 \quad i = 1, 2, \ldots$$
$$= 0 \qquad \text{otherwise}$$

the density function of the sum of N statistically uniform random variables is given as

$$f_{Z_N}(z) = \frac{1}{(N-1)!} \sum_{i=0}^{k} (-1)^i C_i^N (z-i)^{N-1} \qquad k < z \leq k+1$$

$$k = 0, 1, \ldots, N-1 \qquad \text{(B.1)}$$

$$= 0 \qquad\qquad\qquad \text{otherwise}$$

This will be proved by using mathematical induction. Before starting, note from symmetry that

$$f_{Z_N}(z) = f_{Z_N}(N - z) \qquad N = 1, 2, \ldots$$

and the density function of Z_{N+1} is obtained from the density function of Z_N and the density function of U_{N+1} by convolution as

$$f_{Z_{N+1}}(z) = \int_{-\infty}^{\infty} f_{U_{N+1}}(z - x) f_{Z_N}(x) \, dx$$

For a starting value, $N = 1$

$$f_{Z_1}(z) = 1 \qquad 0 < z \le 1$$

and Eq. (B.1) holds. Now assume Eq. (B.1) is true for N and show that it is true for $N + 1$. Three ranges will be considered separately.

First, for $0 < z \le 1$

$$f_{Z_{N+1}}(z) = \int_0^z \frac{1}{(N-1)!} x^{N-1} \, dx = \frac{1}{N!} z^N \tag{B.2a}$$

Now, for $k < z \le k + 1$, $k = 1, 2, \ldots, N - 1$,

$$
\begin{aligned}
f_{Z_{N+1}}(z) &= \frac{1}{(N-1)!} \left[\int_{z-1}^{k} \sum_{i=0}^{k-1} (-1)^i C_i^N (x - i)^{N-1} \, dx \right. \\
&\quad \left. + \int_k^z \sum_{i=0}^{k} (-1)^i C_i^N (x - i)^{N-1} \, dx \right] \\
&= \frac{1}{(N-1)!} \left[\int_{z-1}^{z} \sum_{i=0}^{k-1} (-1)^i C_i^N (x - i)^{N-1} \, dx \right. \\
&\quad \left. + \int_k^z (-1)^i C_i^N (x - i)^{N-1} \, dx \right] \\
&= \frac{1}{N!} \left[\sum_{i=0}^{k-1} (-1)^i C_i^N \{ (z - i)^N - (z - i - 1)^N \} + (-1)^k C_k^N (z - k)^N \right] \\
&= \frac{1}{N!} \left[z^N + \sum_{i=1}^{k} (-1)^k C_k^N (z - k)^N - \sum_{j=1}^{k} (-1)^{j-1} C_{j-1}^N (z - j)^N \right]
\end{aligned}
$$

Using the relationship $C_i^N + C_{i-1}^N = C_i^{N+1}$ yields

$$f_{Z_{N+1}}(z) = \frac{1}{N!} \sum_{i=0}^{k} (-1)^i C_i^{N+1} (z - i)^N \tag{B.2b}$$

Finally, for $N < z \le N+1$

$$f_{Z_{N+1}}(z) = \frac{1}{(N-1)!} \int_{z-1}^{N} \sum_{i=0}^{N-1} (-1)^i C_i^N (x-i)^{N-1} \, dx$$

$$= \frac{1}{(N-1)!} \int_{z-1}^{N} (N-x)^{N-1} \, dx$$

where the last equality comes from the symmetry of $f_{Z_N}(z)$, i.e.,

$$\sum_{i=0}^{N-1} (-1)^i C_i^N (z-i)^{N-1} = (N-z)^{N-1}$$

This is then evaluated as

$$f_{Z_{N+1}}(z) = \frac{1}{N!} (N+1-z)^N = \frac{1}{N!} \sum_{i=0}^{N} (-1)^i C_i^{N+1} (z-i)^N \qquad \text{(B.2c)}$$

where symmetry has again been used in the last equality. Combining Eqs. (B.2a), (B.2b), and (B.2c) yields the desired result of Eq. (B.1).

Using Eq. (B.1), the distribution function for the sum of N statistically independent uniform random variables for $k < z \le k+1$, $k = 0, 1, \ldots, N-1$, is obtained as

$$F_{Z_N}(z) = \sum_{j=0}^{k-1} \int_{j}^{j+1} \frac{1}{(N-1)!} \sum_{i=0}^{j} (-1)^i C_i^N (x-i)^{N-1} \, dx$$

$$+ \int_{k}^{z} \frac{1}{(N-1)!} \sum_{i=0}^{k} (-1)^i C_i^N (x-i)^{N-1} \, dx$$

$$= \frac{1}{N!} \sum_{j=0}^{k-1} \sum_{i=0}^{j} (-1)^i C_i^N [(j+1-i)^N - (j-i)^N]$$

$$+ \frac{1}{N!} \sum_{i=0}^{k} (-1)^i C_i^N (z-i)^N - \frac{1}{N!} \sum_{i=0}^{k} (-1)^i C_i^N (k-i)^N$$

$$= \frac{1}{N!} \sum_{i=0}^{k-1} (-1)^i C_i^N (k-i)^N + \frac{1}{N!} \sum_{j=0}^{k-2} \sum_{i=0}^{j} (-1)^i C_i^N (j+1-i)^N$$

$$- \frac{1}{N!} \sum_{j=1}^{k-1} \sum_{i=0}^{j-1} (-1)^i C_i^N (j-i)^N + \frac{1}{N!} \sum_{i=0}^{k} (-1)^i C_i^N (z-i)^N$$

$$- \frac{1}{N!} \sum_{i=0}^{k-1} (-1)^i C_i^N (k-1)^N$$

$$= \frac{1}{N!} \sum_{m=1}^{k-1} \sum_{i=0}^{m-1} (-1)^i C_i^N (m-i)^N - \frac{1}{N!} \sum_{j=1}^{k-1} \sum_{i=0}^{j-1} (-1)^i C_i^N (j-i)^N$$

$$+ \frac{1}{N!} \sum_{i=0}^{k} (-1)^i C_i^N (z-i)^N$$

which reduces to

$$F_{Z_N}(z) = \frac{1}{N!} \sum_{i=0}^{k} (-1)^i C_i^N (z-i)^N \qquad k < z \le k+1 \quad k = 0, 1, \ldots, N-1$$

$$= 1 \qquad\qquad\qquad z > N \qquad\qquad (B.3)$$

$$= 0 \qquad\qquad\qquad z \le 0$$

The mean of Z_N is obtained as

$$E(Z_N) = \sum_{i=1}^{N} E(U_i) = \sum_{i=1}^{N} \frac{1}{2} = \frac{N}{2}$$

and the variance as

$$\text{Var}(Z_N) = \text{Var}\left(\sum_{i=1}^{N} U_i \right) = \sum_{i=1}^{N} \text{Var}(U_i) = \sum_{i=1}^{N} \frac{1}{12} = \frac{N}{12}$$

For the transformation

$$W_N = \frac{Z_N - N/2}{\sqrt{N/12}} \qquad\qquad (B.4)$$

$E(W_N) = 0$ and $\text{Var}(W_N) = 1$. The density function of W_N is obtained from the density function of Z_N, Eq. (B.1), as

$$f_{W_N}(w) = \frac{\sqrt{N/12}}{(N-1)!} \sum_{i=0}^{k} (-1)^i C_i^N \left[\sqrt{\frac{N}{12}} w + \frac{N}{2} - i \right]^{N-1}$$

$$\frac{k - N/2}{\sqrt{N/12}} < w \le \frac{k - N/2 + 1}{\sqrt{N/12}} \qquad (B.5)$$

$$= 0 \qquad\qquad\qquad \text{otherwise}$$

Likewise, the distribution function of W_N is obtained from the distribution function of Z_N, Eq. (B.3), as

$$F_{W_N}(w) = \frac{1}{N!} \sum_{i=0}^{k} (-1)^i C_i^N \left[\sqrt{\frac{N}{12}} w + \frac{N}{2} - i \right]^{N}$$

$$\frac{k - N/2}{\sqrt{N/12}} < w \le \frac{k - N/2 + 1}{\sqrt{N/12}}$$

$$= 1 \qquad\qquad\qquad w > \frac{k - N/2 + 1}{\sqrt{N/12}} \qquad (B.6)$$

$$= 0 \qquad\qquad\qquad w \le \frac{k - N/2}{\sqrt{N/12}}$$

The density and distribution functions of W_N are listed below for several values of N [only positive values are given since $f_{W_N}(-w) = f_{W_N}(w)$ and

$F_{W_N}(-w) = 1 - F_{W_N}(w)$]. For each N and each range the density function is given first and one minus the distribution function is given next

$N = 1$ $A = B = 0.2887$ $C = 1$

$0 < w \le 1.732$ B

$C(1/2 - Aw)$

$N = 2$ $A = B = 0.4082$ $C = 0.5$

$0 < w \le 2.449$ $B(1 - Aw)$

$C(1 - Aw)^2$

$N = 4$ $A = 0.5774$ $B = 0.09623$ $C = 0.04167$

$1.732 < w \le 3.464$ $B[(2 - Aw)^3]$

$C[(2 - Aw)^4]$

$0 < w \le 1.732$ $B[(2 - Aw)^3 - 4(1 - Aw)^3]$

$C[(2 - Aw)^4 - 4(1 - Aw)^4]$

$N = 8$ $A = 0.8165$ $B = 0.0001620$ $C = 2.480 \times 10^{-5}$

$3.674 < w \le 4.899$ $B[(4 - Aw)^7]$

$C[(4 - Aw)^8]$

$2.449 < w \le 3.647$ $B[(4 - Aw)^7 - 8(3 - Aw)^7]$

$C[(4 - Aw)^8 - 8(3 - Aw)^8]$

$1.225 < w \le 2.449$ $B[(4 - Aw)^7 - 8(3 - Aw)^7 + 28(2 - Aw)^7]$

$C[(4 - Aw)^8 - 8(3 - Aw)^8 + 28(2 - Aw)^8]$

$0 < w \le 1.225$ $B[(4 - Aw)^7 - 8(3 - Aw)^7 + 28(2 - Aw)^7 - 56(1 - Aw)^7]$

$C[(4 - Aw)^8 - 8(3 - Aw)^8 + 28(2 - Aw)^8 - 56(1 - Aw)^8]$

$N = 12$ $A = 1$ $B = 2.505 \times 10^{-8}$ $C = 2.088 \times 10^{-9}$

$5 < w \le 6$ $B[(6 - w)^{11}]$

$C[(6 - w)^{12}]$

$4 < w \le 5$ $B[(6 - w)^{11} - 12(5 - w)^{11}]$

$C[(6 - w)^{12} - 12(5 - w)^{12}]$

$3 < w \le 4$ $B[(6 - w)^{11} - 12(5 - w)^{11} + 66(4 - w)^{11}]$

$C[(6 - w)^{12} - 12(5 - w)^{12} + 66(4 - w)^{12}]$

$2 < w \le 3$ $B[(6 - w)^{11} - 12(5 - w)^{11} + 66(4 - w)^{11} - 220(3 - w)^{11}]$

$C[(6 - w)^{12} - 12(5 - w)^{12} + 66(4 - w)^{12} - 220(3 - w)^{12}]$

$1 < w \le 2$ $B[(6 - w)^{11} - 12(5 - w)^{11} + 66(4 - w)^{11} - 220(3 - w)^{11}$

$+ 495(2 - w)^{11}]$

$C[(6 - w)^{12} - 12(5 - w)^{12} + 66(4 - w)^{12} - 220(3 - w)^{12}$

$+ 495(2 - w)^{12}]$

$0 < w \le 1$ $B[(6 - w)^{11} - 12(5 - w)^{11} + 66(4 - w)^{11} - 220(3 - w)^{11}$

$+ 495(2 - w)^{11} - 792(1 - w)^{11}$

$C[(6 - w)^{12} - 12(5 - w)^{12} + 66(4 - w)^{12} - 220(3 - w)^{12}$

$+ 495(2 - w)^{12} - 792(1 - w)^{12}$

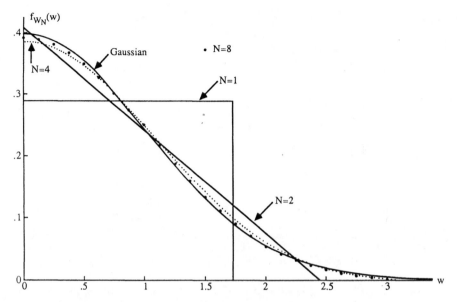

Fig. B.1. Density function for the sum of N uniform random variables.

Figure B.1 gives a comparison of the density function of the normalized Gaussian random variable with the density function of W_N for $N = 1$, 2, 4, 8. From this figure it can be seen that the density functions are very close for N as small as 8. Likewise, for one minus the distribution function (the Q function) with $w = 1$ (1 standard deviation) the error relative to the Gaussian probability for $N = 4$, 8, and 12 is 4.2, 2.0 and 1.3%, respectively, which is quite close. Even for $w = 2$ (2 standard deviations) the error is small; i.e., for $N = 4$, 8, and 12 the error is 6.5, 3.2, and 2.1%, respectively. But for $w = 3$ (3 standard deviations) the error relative to the Gaussian probability for $N = 4$, 8, and 12 is 84.1, 38.8, and 25.4%, respectively, which is quite large. Also, for $w = 4$ (4 standard deviations) the error for $N = 4$, 8, and 12 the error is 100, 93.4, and 73.1%. It can be concluded that the sum of uniform random variables for small N is a good approximation to a Gaussian random variable if the argument of the variable is within 2 standard deviations, but is a poor approximation for values on the tails (large arguments) of the random variable.

Appendix C
Moments of Random Variables

The mean (first moment), the variance (second central moment), and the characteristic function (Fourier transform of the density function or probability function) are given for some frequently encountered random variables. Along with these moments, the range where the probability density function or probability function is nonzero is given and the range of the parameters of the probability density function or probability function is given.

Table C.1 gives these moments for the discrete random variables along with their probability function. Table C.2 gives these moments for the continuous random variables along with their probability density function.

Table C.1

Moments for Discrete Random Variables

Bernoulli

$$P(X = k) = p^k(1-p)^{1-k} \qquad k = 0, 1 \quad 0 < p < 1$$
$$E(X) = p \qquad \text{Var}(X) = p(1-p) \qquad \phi_X(\omega) = p\,e^{j\omega} + 1 - p$$

Binomial

$$P(X = k) = C_k^N p^k(1-p)^{N-k} \qquad k = 0, 1, \ldots, N \quad N = 1, 2, 3, \ldots \quad 0 < p < 1$$
$$E(X) = Np \qquad \text{Var}(X) = Np(1-p) \qquad \phi_X(\omega) = [p\,e^{j\omega} + 1 - p]^N$$

Poisson

$$P(X = k) = \frac{e^{-a}a^k}{k!} \qquad k = 0, 1, 2, \ldots \quad 0 < a < \infty$$
$$E(X) = a \qquad \text{Var}(X) = a \qquad \phi_X(\omega) = \exp[a(\exp(j\omega) - 1)]$$

Geometric

$$P(X = k) = (1-p)^{k-1}p \qquad k = 1, 2, 3, \ldots \quad 0 < p < 1$$
$$E(X) = \frac{1}{p} \qquad \text{Var}(X) = \frac{1-p}{p^2} \qquad \phi_X(\omega) = \frac{p\,e^{j\omega}}{1 - (1-p)\,e^{j\omega}}$$

Table C.2

Moments for Continuous Random Variables

Uniform

$$f_X(x) = \frac{1}{b-a} \qquad -\infty < a < x < b < \infty$$

$$E(X) = \frac{b+a}{2} \qquad \text{Var}(X) = \frac{(b-a)^2}{12} \qquad \phi_X(\omega) = \frac{e^{jb\omega} - e^{ja\omega}}{j(b-a)\omega}$$

Gaussian

$$f_X(x) = \frac{1}{\sqrt{2\pi\sigma^2}} \exp\left[\frac{-(x-\mu)^2}{2\sigma^2}\right] \qquad -\infty < x < \infty \quad -\infty < \mu < \infty \quad 0 < \sigma < \infty$$

$$E(X) = \mu \qquad \text{Var}(X) = \sigma^2 \qquad \phi_X(\omega) = \exp(j\omega\mu - \omega^2\sigma^2/2)$$

Exponential

$$f_X(x) = a\,e^{-ax} \qquad 0 \le x < \infty \quad 0 < a < \infty$$

$$E(X) = \frac{1}{a} \qquad \text{Var}(X) = \frac{1}{a^2} \qquad \phi_X(\omega) = \frac{1}{1 - j\omega/a}$$

Gamma

$$f_X(x) = \left[\frac{a^{b+1}x^b}{\Gamma(b+1)}\right] e^{-ax} \qquad 0 \le x < \infty \quad 0 < a < \infty \quad 0 \le b < \infty$$

$$E(X) = \frac{b+1}{a} \qquad \text{Var}(X) = \frac{b+1}{a^2} \qquad \phi_X(\omega) = \left(1 - \frac{j\omega}{a}\right)^{-b-1}$$

Cauchy

$$f_X(x) = \left(\frac{a}{\pi}\right)\left(\frac{1}{x^2 + a^2}\right) \qquad -\infty < x < \infty \quad 0 < a < \infty$$

$$E(X) \text{ undefined} \qquad \text{Var}(X) = \infty \qquad \phi_X(\omega) = e^{-a|\omega|}$$

Rayleigh

$$f_X(x) = \left(\frac{x}{b}\right) \exp\left(\frac{-x^2}{2b}\right) \qquad 0 \le x < \infty \quad 0 < b < \infty$$

$$E(X) = \sqrt{\pi b/2} \qquad \text{Var}(X) = \frac{(4-\pi)b}{2}$$

Beta

$$f_X(x) = \frac{\Gamma(a+b+2)}{\Gamma(a+1)\Gamma(b+1)} x^a(1-x)^b \qquad 0 \le x \le 1 \quad 0 \le a < \infty \quad 0 \le b < \infty$$

$$E(X) = \frac{a+1}{a+b+2} \qquad \text{Var}(X) = \frac{(a+1)(b+1)}{(a+b+3)(a+b+2)^2}$$

Appendix D
Matrix Notation

An introduction to matrix notation and examples of matrix manipulation are given in this appendix. A matrix is an array of numbers or symbols and its utility is the ease of representing many scalar quantities in shorthand notation. Matrices will be represented by boldface letters. The general matrix $\mathbf{A}$ is given as

$$\mathbf{A} = \begin{bmatrix} a_{11} & a_{12} & \cdots & a_{1m} \\ a_{21} & a_{22} & \cdots & a_{2m} \\ \vdots & \vdots & & \vdots \\ a_{n1} & a_{n2} & \cdots & a_{nm} \end{bmatrix} = \{a_{ij}\}$$

where there are n rows and m columns and $\mathbf{A}$ is referred to as an $n \times m$ matrix. The element in the ith row and jth column is a_{ij} and the set representation means the set of all elements a_{ij}. If $n = m$, $\mathbf{A}$ is said to be a square matrix. The transpose of the matrix $\mathbf{A}$, $\mathbf{A}^T$, is the matrix obtained by interchanging the rows and columns of $\mathbf{A}$ and is written

$$\mathbf{A}^T = \{a_{ji}\}$$

and the element in the ith row and the jth column is a_{ji}. If $\mathbf{A}$ is $n \times m$, $\mathbf{A}^T$ is $m \times n$.

Example D.1. For

$$\mathbf{A} = \begin{bmatrix} 1 & 4 \\ 2 & 5 \\ 3 & 6 \end{bmatrix}$$

a 3×2 matrix, the transpose is

$$\mathbf{A}^T = \begin{bmatrix} 1 & 2 & 3 \\ 4 & 5 & 6 \end{bmatrix}$$

a 2×3 matrix. $\square$

A row vector is a matrix with a single row and a column vector is a matrix with a single column. The vectors considered here will normally be column vectors, which makes the transpose a row vector. For $\mathbf{x}$ an $n \times 1$ column vector, the transpose

$$\mathbf{x}^T = \{x_i\} = [x_1, x_2, \dots, x_n]$$

is a $1 \times n$ row vector. Two matrices are equal

$$\mathbf{A} = \mathbf{B} = \{b_{ij}\} = \{a_{ij}\}$$

if $a_{ij} = b_{ij}$ for all i and j, which implies that $\mathbf{A}$ and $\mathbf{B}$ must be the same size. The matrix $\mathbf{A}$ is symmetric if

$$\mathbf{A} = \mathbf{A}^T = \{a_{ji}\} = \{a_{ij}\}$$

or $a_{ij} = a_{ji}$ for all i and j. To be symmetric $\mathbf{A}$ must be a square or $n \times n$ matrix.

For matrix addition to be defined, the matrices of the sum must be of the same size. If $\mathbf{A}$ and $\mathbf{B}$ are both $n \times m$ matrices the matrix addition is defined as

$$\mathbf{C} = \mathbf{A} + \mathbf{B} = \{a_{ij} + b_{ij}\} = \{c_{ij}\}$$

where the sum matrix is also $n \times m$. Thus, an element in $\mathbf{C}$ is the sum of the corresponding elements in $\mathbf{A}$ and $\mathbf{B}$. It can easily be shown that matrix addition is both associative and commutative.

Example D.2. If $\mathbf{A}$ and $\mathbf{B}$ are given as

$$\mathbf{A} = \begin{bmatrix} 1 & 4 \\ 2 & 5 \\ 3 & 6 \end{bmatrix} \qquad \mathbf{B} = \begin{bmatrix} 2 & -1 \\ 7 & -3 \\ 8 & 1 \end{bmatrix}$$

then the sum of $\mathbf{A}$ and $\mathbf{B}$ is

$$\mathbf{C} = \begin{bmatrix} 3 & 3 \\ 9 & 2 \\ 11 & 7 \end{bmatrix} \qquad \square$$

The product of a scalar d and an $n \times m$ matrix $\mathbf{A}$ is defined as

$$\mathbf{B} = d\mathbf{A} = \{da_{ij}\} = \{b_{ij}\}$$

where **B** is $n \times m$ and each element in the product is the scalar times each corresponding element in **A**.

Example D.3. For **A** given in Example D.2, the product of $d = 3$ and **A** is

$$\mathbf{B} = 3\begin{bmatrix} 1 & 4 \\ 2 & 5 \\ 3 & 6 \end{bmatrix} = \begin{bmatrix} 3 & 12 \\ 6 & 15 \\ 9 & 18 \end{bmatrix} \quad \Box$$

The multiplication of the two matrices **A** $n \times m$ and **B** $m \times p$ is defined as

$$\mathbf{C} = \mathbf{AB} = \left\{ \sum_{k=1}^{m} a_{ik}b_{kj} \right\} = \{c_{ij}\}$$

where **C** is an $n \times p$ matrix. The ijth element of the product matrix is obtained as a summation of the elements in the ith row of **A** (the matrix on the left in the product) times the elements in the jth column of **B** (the matrix on the right). For these terms to match up, the number of elements in the ith row of **A** must equal the number of elements in the jth column of **B**; i.e., the number of columns of **A** must equal the number of rows of **B** for the multiplication to be defined. Matrix multiplication may not be commutative,

$$\mathbf{AB} \neq \mathbf{BA}$$

since for **A** $n \times m$ and **B** $m \times p$, the product **BA** ($p \neq n$) is not defined. Even if the product **BA** was defined (**A** is $n \times m$ and **B** is $m \times n$), matrix multiplication is in general not commutative.

Example D.4. For **A** 2×3 and **B** 3×2 given as

$$\mathbf{A} = \begin{bmatrix} 1 & 2 & 3 \\ 4 & 5 & 6 \end{bmatrix} \quad \mathbf{B} = \begin{bmatrix} -2 & -3 \\ -1 & 1 \\ 2 & 3 \end{bmatrix}$$

the product **AB** is evaluated as

$$\mathbf{C} = \begin{bmatrix} 1 & 2 & 3 \\ 4 & 5 & 6 \end{bmatrix}\begin{bmatrix} -2 & -3 \\ -1 & 1 \\ 2 & 3 \end{bmatrix} = \begin{bmatrix} 1(-2)+2(-1)+3(2) & 1(-3)+2(1)+3(3) \\ 4(-2)+5(-1)+6(2) & 4(-3)+5(1)+6(3) \end{bmatrix}$$

which is obtained as the sum of the product of elements in the ith row times corresponding elements in the jth column. This product reduces to

$$\mathbf{C} = \begin{bmatrix} 2 & 8 \\ -1 & 11 \end{bmatrix} \quad \Box$$

For $\mathbf{A}$ $n \times m$, $\mathbf{B}$ $m \times p$, and $\mathbf{C}$ $p \times q$

$$(\mathbf{AB})\mathbf{C} = \left\{ \sum_{k=1}^{m} a_{ik}b_{kj} \right\}\{c_{ij}\} = \left\{ \sum_{r=1}^{p} \left[\left(\sum_{k=1}^{m} a_{ik}b_{kr} \right) c_{rj} \right] \right\} = \left\{ \sum_{k=1}^{m} a_{ik} \sum_{r=1}^{p} b_{kr}c_{rj} \right\}$$

$$= \{a_{ij}\} \left\{ \sum_{r=1}^{p} b_{ir}c_{rj} \right\} = \mathbf{A}(\mathbf{BC})$$

and matrix multiplication is associative. The result of the product is an $n \times q$ matrix.

The transpose of the product of matrices is the product of the transposes of the matrices in reverse order, i.e.,

$$(\mathbf{AB})^{\mathrm{T}} = \left\{ \sum_{k=1}^{m} a_{ik}b_{kj} \right\}^{T} = \left\{ \sum_{k=1}^{m} a_{jk}b_{ki} \right\} = \left\{ \sum_{k=1}^{m} b_{ki}a_{jk} \right\} = \mathbf{B}^{\mathrm{T}}\mathbf{A}^{\mathrm{T}}$$

If $\mathbf{A}$ is $n \times m$ and $\mathbf{B}$ is $m \times p$, $\mathbf{AB}$ is $n \times p$ and $(\mathbf{AB})^{\mathrm{T}}$ is $p \times n$. Likewise, $\mathbf{B}^{\mathrm{T}}$ is $p \times m$, $\mathbf{A}^{\mathrm{T}}$ is $m \times n$, and $\mathbf{B}^{\mathrm{T}}\mathbf{A}^{\mathrm{T}}$ is $p \times n$.

A bilinear form is given as

$$\mathbf{x}^{\mathrm{T}}\mathbf{Ay} = \left\{ \sum_{k=1}^{n} x_k a_{kj} \right\}\{y_i\} = \left\{ \sum_{k=1}^{n} \sum_{r=1}^{n} x_k a_{kr} y_r \right\} = \sum_{k=1}^{n} \sum_{r=1}^{n} x_k a_{kr} y_r$$

where $\mathbf{x}^{\mathrm{T}}$ is $1 \times n$, $\mathbf{A}$ is $n \times n$, and $\mathbf{y}$ is $n \times 1$, which makes the bilinear form a scalar. When $\mathbf{y} = \mathbf{x}$, this form is called a quadratic form or $\mathbf{x}^{\mathrm{T}}\mathbf{Ax}$ is a quadratic form (a scalar). A special case of the quadratic form is

$$\mathbf{x}^{\mathrm{T}}\mathbf{x} = \sum_{k=1}^{n} x_k^2$$

which is the magnitude of the vector squared.

If $\mathbf{A}$ is an $n \times n$ (square) matrix and if for a matrix $\mathbf{B}$ ($n \times n$),

$$\mathbf{BA} = \mathbf{AB} = \mathbf{I}$$

where $\mathbf{I}$ is the identity matrix, $\mathbf{B}$ is said to be the inverse of $\mathbf{A}$ ($\mathbf{B} = \mathbf{A}^{-1}$). $\mathbf{B}$ and $\mathbf{I}$ are $n \times n$ matrices and $\mathbf{I}$ has 1's on the main diagonal and 0's everywhere else.

In order to evaluate the inverse of a matrix a few terms will first be defined. Letting M_{ij} be the minor of the element a_{ij}, M_{ij} is equal to the determinant formed by deleting the ith row and the jth column of $\mathbf{A}$. Also, letting A_{ij} be the cofactor of the element a_{ij},

$$A_{ij} = (-1)^{i+j} M_{ij}$$

The determinant of $\mathbf{A}$ is given in terms of the cofactors as

$$|\mathbf{A}| = \sum_{j=1}^{n} a_{ij}A_{ij} = \sum_{i=1}^{n} a_{ij}A_{ij}$$

which states that the determinant can be obtained by summing the product of elements of any row times their corresponding cofactors or by summing the product of elements of any column times their corresponding cofactors. If **B** equals **A** with the jth column replaced by the ith column (columns i and j are the same in **B**), the determinant of **B** is 0 and

$$|\mathbf{B}| = 0 = \sum_{k=1}^{n} a_{ki} A_{kj} \qquad i \neq j$$

The determinant is also 0 if the jth row is replaced by the ith row (rows i and j are the same). Combining these statements with $|\mathbf{A}|$ yields

$$\sum_{k=1}^{n} a_{ki} A_{kj} = \sum_{k=1}^{n} a_{ik} A_{jk} = \delta_{ij} |\mathbf{A}|$$

where $\delta_{ij} = 1$, $i = j$, and $\delta_{ij} = 0$, $i \neq j$. Now **Cof A** $= \{A_{ij}\}$, **Cof A**$^{\mathrm{T}} = \{A_{ji}\}$, and

$$\mathbf{A} \ \mathbf{Cof} \ \mathbf{A}^{\mathrm{T}} = \left\{ \sum_{k=1}^{n} a_{ik} A_{jk} \right\} = \{|\mathbf{A}|\delta_{ij}\} = |\mathbf{A}|\mathbf{I}$$

If $|\mathbf{A}| \neq 0$

$$\mathbf{A}^{-1} = \mathbf{Cof} \ \mathbf{A}^{\mathrm{T}}/|\mathbf{A}|$$

Also, $(\mathbf{AB})^{-1} = \mathbf{B}^{-1}\mathbf{A}^{-1}$ and $(\mathbf{A}^{-1})^{\mathrm{T}} = (\mathbf{A}^{\mathrm{T}})^{-1}$.

Example D.5.   Consider the matrix

$$\mathbf{A} = \begin{bmatrix} 1 & 2 & 3 \\ -1 & 4 & -2 \\ -3 & 6 & 5 \end{bmatrix}$$

The cofactors are calculated as

$$A_{11} = \begin{vmatrix} 4 & -2 \\ 6 & 5 \end{vmatrix} = 32 \qquad A_{12} = -\begin{vmatrix} -1 & -2 \\ -3 & 5 \end{vmatrix} = 11 \qquad A_{13} = \begin{vmatrix} -1 & 4 \\ -3 & 6 \end{vmatrix} = 6$$

$$A_{21} = -\begin{vmatrix} 2 & 3 \\ 6 & 5 \end{vmatrix} = 8 \qquad A_{22} = \begin{vmatrix} 1 & 3 \\ -3 & 5 \end{vmatrix} = 14 \qquad A_{23} = -\begin{vmatrix} 1 & 2 \\ -3 & 6 \end{vmatrix} = -12$$

$$A_{31} = \begin{vmatrix} 2 & 3 \\ 4 & -2 \end{vmatrix} = -16 \qquad A_{32} = -\begin{vmatrix} 1 & 3 \\ -1 & -2 \end{vmatrix} = -1 \qquad A_{33} = \begin{vmatrix} 1 & 2 \\ -1 & 4 \end{vmatrix} = 6$$

which yields

$$\mathbf{Cof} \ \mathbf{A} = \begin{bmatrix} 32 & 11 & 6 \\ 8 & 14 & -12 \\ -16 & -1 & 6 \end{bmatrix}$$

Now

$$|\mathbf{A}| = a_{11}A_{11} + a_{12}A_{12} + a_{13}A_{13} = 1(32) + 2(11) + 3(6) = 72$$

and finally the inverse is

$$\mathbf{A}^{-1} = \frac{1}{72}\begin{bmatrix} 32 & 8 & -16 \\ 11 & 14 & -1 \\ 6 & -12 & 6 \end{bmatrix} \qquad \square$$

An alternative procedure for finding a matrix inverse is the Gauss–Jordan method. This method consists of solving the matrix equation $\mathbf{AB} = \mathbf{I}$ for $\mathbf{B}$, which is $\mathbf{A}^{-1}$. By performing row operations the augmented matrix $[\mathbf{A}:\mathbf{I}]$ is manipulated to the form $[\mathbf{I}:\mathbf{B}]$, which yields the inverse directly.

Example D.6. For $\mathbf{A}$ of Example D.5 the augmented matrix is given as

$$\begin{bmatrix} 1 & 2 & 3 : 1 & 0 & 0 \\ -1 & 4 & -2 : 0 & 1 & 0 \\ -3 & 6 & 5 : 0 & 0 & 1 \end{bmatrix} \rightarrow \begin{bmatrix} 1 & 2 & 3 : 1 & 0 & 0 \\ 0 & 6 & 1 : 1 & 1 & 0 \\ 0 & 12 & 14 : 3 & 0 & 1 \end{bmatrix}$$

where in the first step the element in row 1 column 1 is normalized to 1 to obtain a new row 1. Next a new row 2 is obtained, such that the element in column 1 is 0, as old row 2 minus (-1) times new row 1, and a new row 3 is obtained, such that the element in column 1 is 0, as old row 3 minus (-3) times new row 1.

In the second step the element in row 2 column 2 is normalized to obtain a new row 2. Then a new row 1 is obtained, such that the element in column 2 is 0, as old row 1 minus (2) times new row 2, and a new row 3 is obtained, such that the element in column 2 is 0, as old row 3 minus (12) times new row 2. The second and third steps are given as

$$\rightarrow \begin{bmatrix} 1 & 0 & \frac{8}{3} : \frac{2}{3} & -\frac{1}{3} & 0 \\ 0 & 1 & \frac{1}{6} : \frac{1}{6} & \frac{1}{6} & 0 \\ 0 & 0 & 12 : 1 & -2 & 1 \end{bmatrix} \rightarrow \begin{bmatrix} 1 & 0 & 0 : \frac{4}{9} & \frac{1}{9} & -\frac{2}{9} \\ 0 & 1 & 0 : \frac{11}{72} & \frac{7}{36} & -\frac{1}{72} \\ 0 & 0 & 1 : \frac{1}{12} & -\frac{1}{6} & \frac{1}{12} \end{bmatrix}$$

As shown for the third step the element in row 3 column 3 is normalized to obtain a new row 3. Then a new row 1 is obtained, such that the element in column 3 is 0, as old row 1 minus $(\frac{8}{3})$ times new row 3, and a new row 2 is obtained, such that the element in column 3 is 0, as old row 2 minus $(\frac{1}{6})$ times new row 3.

Thus $\mathbf{A}^{-1}$ is obtained as

$$\mathbf{A}^{-1} = \begin{bmatrix} \frac{4}{9} & \frac{1}{9} & -\frac{2}{9} \\ \frac{11}{72} & \frac{7}{36} & -\frac{1}{72} \\ \frac{1}{12} & -\frac{1}{6} & \frac{1}{12} \end{bmatrix}$$

which is the same result as in Example D.5.   □

The rank r of an $n \times m$ matrix $\mathbf{A}$ is the size of the largest square submatrix of $\mathbf{A}$ whose determinant is nonzero. A symmetric $n \times n$ matrix $\mathbf{A}$ is positive definite if the quadratic form $\mathbf{x}^T \mathbf{A} \mathbf{x} > 0$ for each nonzero $\mathbf{x}$ and is positive semidefinite if the quadratic form $\mathbf{x}^T \mathbf{A} \mathbf{x} \geq 0$ for each nonzero $\mathbf{x}$ and $\mathbf{x}^T \mathbf{A} \mathbf{x} = 0$ for at least one nonzero $\mathbf{x}$. The rank of $\mathbf{A}$ is equal to n if $\mathbf{A}$ is positive definite, and the rank of $\mathbf{A}$ is less than n if $\mathbf{A}$ is positive semidefinite. Also, $a_{ii} > 0$ for all $i = 1, 2, \ldots, n$ if $\mathbf{A}$ is positive definite, and $a_{ii} \geq 0$ for all $i = 1, 2, \ldots, n$ if $\mathbf{A}$ is positive semidefinite.

A matrix $\mathbf{A}$ is positive definite if and only if the leading principal minors are greater than zero, i.e.,

$$a_{11} > 0, \qquad \begin{vmatrix} a_{11} & a_{12} \\ a_{21} & a_{22} \end{vmatrix} > 0, \ldots, |\mathbf{A}| > 0$$

Likewise, a matrix $\mathbf{A}$ is positive semidefinite if and only if the leading principal minors are greater than or equal to zero.

In Section 4.4 the quadratic form of the exponent of the N-dimensional Gaussian density function must be positive semidefinite and $\mathbf{\Sigma}_x^{-1}$ or $\mathbf{\Sigma}_x$ (an $n \times n$) is a positive semidefinite matrix. That this is so can be seen by observing that for any subset of the random variables the determinant of the covariance matrix of the subset must be greater than or equal to zero. The subsets can be picked such that all of the leading principal minors are greater than or equal to zero, which makes $\mathbf{\Sigma}_x$ positive semidefinite. If $\mathbf{\Sigma}_x$ is positive definite (rank n), then there is no impulse function in the density function (if rank $< n$ there would be an impulse function in the density function). For the transformation $\mathbf{Y} = \mathbf{A}\mathbf{X} + \mathbf{B}$ where $\mathbf{\Sigma}_y = \mathbf{A}\mathbf{\Sigma}_x\mathbf{A}^T$, $\mathbf{\Sigma}_y$ is at least a positive semidefinite matrix since it is a covariance matrix. If $\mathbf{A}$ is $m \times n$ $\mathbf{\Sigma}_y$ is $m \times m$ and if $m > n$ the rank of $\mathbf{A}$ is at most n and the rank of $\mathbf{\Sigma}_y$ at most n or $\mathbf{\Sigma}_y$ cannot be positive definite (there must be an impulse in the density function of $\mathbf{Y}$).

An $n \times n$ matrix $\mathbf{A}$ is positive definite if and only if there exists an $n \times n$ matrix $\mathbf{B}$ of rank n such that $\mathbf{B}^T\mathbf{B} = \mathbf{A}$. Likewise, an $n \times n$ matrix $\mathbf{A}$ is positive semidefinite if and only if there exists an $n \times n$ matrix $\mathbf{B}$ of rank less than n such that $\mathbf{B}^T\mathbf{B} = \mathbf{A}$. This property is used in Section 5.6 to obtain a transformation from statistically independent random variables to random variables with a desired covariance matrix.

Example D.7. Consider the Gaussian random vector $\mathbf{Y}^T = (Y_1, Y_2, Y_3)$ with $\boldsymbol{\mu}_y^T = (0, 0, 0)$ and

$$\boldsymbol{\Sigma}_y = \begin{bmatrix} 16 & 12 & 20 \\ 12 & 13 & 11 \\ 20 & 11 & 29 \end{bmatrix}$$

Since

$$16 > 0, \quad \begin{vmatrix} 16 & 12 \\ 12 & 13 \end{vmatrix} = 64 > 0, \quad \text{and} \quad \begin{vmatrix} 16 & 12 & 20 \\ 12 & 13 & 11 \\ 20 & 11 & 29 \end{vmatrix} = 0$$

the rank of $\boldsymbol{\Sigma}_y$ is 2. Thus $f_Y(\mathbf{y})$ contains an impulse function. The impulse function can be determined using Eq. (5.6.2) to obtain $\mathbf{T}$ ($\mathbf{Y} = \mathbf{TX}$ with $\boldsymbol{\Sigma}_x = \mathbf{I}$) as

$$\mathbf{T} = \begin{bmatrix} 4 & 0 \\ 3 & 2 \\ 5 & -2 \end{bmatrix}$$

where $t_{33} = 0$ (and the third column is omitted). Then using Eq. (5.6.4) $\mathbf{A}$ ($\mathbf{X} = \mathbf{AY}$) is obtained as

$$\mathbf{A} = \begin{bmatrix} 0.25 & 0 \\ -0.375 & 0.5 \end{bmatrix}$$

where the last row of $\mathbf{A}$ is omitted since $t_{33} = 0$. Finally,

$$\mathbf{Y} = \mathbf{TAY} = \begin{bmatrix} 1 & 0 \\ 0 & 1 \\ 2 & -1 \end{bmatrix} \mathbf{Y}$$

which yields the dependency $Y_3 = 2Y_1 - Y_2$. Letting $\mathbf{Y}'^T = (Y_1, Y_2)$ the conditional density of Y_3 given $\mathbf{Y}'$ is the impulse (obtained from $Y_3 = 2Y_1 - Y_2$) given as

$$f_{Y_3|\mathbf{Y}'}(y_3|\mathbf{y}') = \delta(y_3 - 2y_1 + y_2)$$

Now

$$\boldsymbol{\Sigma}_{y'} = \begin{bmatrix} 16 & 12 \\ 12 & 13 \end{bmatrix}$$

and

$$\boldsymbol{\Sigma}_{y'}^{-1} = \frac{1}{64} \begin{bmatrix} 13 & -12 \\ -12 & 16 \end{bmatrix}$$

which gives

$$f_{\mathbf{Y}'}(\mathbf{y}') = \frac{1}{16\pi} \exp[-(13y_1^2 - 24y_1y_2 + 16y_2^2)/128]$$

$$-\infty < y_1 < \infty, \quad -\infty < y_2 < \infty$$

The density function of **Y** is then obtained as

$$f_{\mathbf{Y}}(\mathbf{y}) = f_{\mathbf{Y}'}(\mathbf{y}')f_{Y_3|\mathbf{Y}'}(y_3|\mathbf{y}')$$

or

$$f_{\mathbf{Y}}(\mathbf{y}) = \frac{1}{16\pi} \exp[-(13y_1^2 - 24y_1y_2 + 16y_2^2)/128] \, \delta(y_3 - 2y_1 + y_2) \qquad \square$$

Appendix E
Mathematical Quantities

E.1 Trigonometric Identities

$e^{jx} = \cos x + j \sin x$

$\cos x = \dfrac{e^{jx} + e^{-jx}}{2}$

$\sin x = \dfrac{e^{jx} - e^{-jx}}{2j}$

$\cos(x \pm y) = \cos x \cos y \mp \sin x \sin y$

$\cos\left(x \pm \dfrac{\pi}{2}\right) = \mp \sin x$

$\sin(x \pm y) = \sin x \cos y \pm \cos x \sin y$

$\sin\left(x \pm \dfrac{\pi}{2}\right) = \pm \cos x$

$\cos x \cos y = \frac{1}{2}[\cos(x+y) + \cos(x-y)]$

$\sin x \sin y = \frac{1}{2}[\cos(x-y) - \cos(x+y)]$

$\sin x \cos y = \frac{1}{2}[\sin(x+y) + \sin(x-y)]$

$\cos x + \cos y = 2 \cos[\frac{1}{2}(x+y)] \cos[\frac{1}{2}(x-y)]$

$\cos x - \cos y = -2 \sin[\frac{1}{2}(x+y)] \sin[\frac{1}{2}(x-y)]$

$\sin x \pm \sin y = 2 \sin \frac{1}{2}(x \pm y)\cos \frac{1}{2}(x \mp y)$

$\cos 2x = \cos^2 x - \sin^2 x$

$\sin 2x = 2 \sin x \cos x$

$\cos^2 x = \frac{1}{2}(1 + \cos 2x)$

$\sin^2 x = \frac{1}{2}(1 - \cos 2x)$

$A \cos x - B \sin x = R \cos(x + \theta)$

where $R = \sqrt{A^2 + B^2}$ and $\theta = \tan^{-1}\left(\dfrac{B}{A}\right)$

E.2 Indefinite Integrals

$\displaystyle \int u \, dv = uv - \int v \, du$

$\displaystyle \int (a + bx)^n \, dx = \dfrac{(a+bx)^{n+1}}{b(n+1)}, \; n \neq -1$

$\displaystyle \int \dfrac{dx}{a + bx} = \dfrac{1}{b} \ln|a + bx|$

$\displaystyle \int e^{ax} \, dx = \dfrac{1}{a} e^{ax}$

$\displaystyle \int x e^{ax} \, dx = \dfrac{e^{ax}}{a^2}(ax - 1)$

$\displaystyle \int x^2 e^{ax} \, dx = \dfrac{e^{ax}}{a^3}(a^2 x^2 - 2ax + 2)$

$$\int \cos ax \, dx = \frac{1}{a} \sin ax$$

$$\int x \cos ax \, dx = \frac{1}{a^2} (ax \sin ax + \cos ax)$$

$$\int x^2 \cos ax \, dx = \frac{1}{a^3} (a^2 x^2 \sin ax + 2ax \cos ax - 2 \sin ax)$$

$$\int \sin ax \, dx = -\frac{1}{a} \cos ax$$

$$\int x \sin ax \, dx = \frac{1}{a^2} (-ax \cos ax + \sin ax)$$

$$\int x^2 \sin ax \, dx = \frac{1}{a^3} (-a^2 x^2 \cos ax + 2ax \sin ax + 2 \cos ax)$$

$$\int e^{ax} \cos bx \, dx = \frac{e^{ax}}{a^2 + b^2} (a \cos bx + b \sin bx)$$

$$\int e^{ax} \sin bx \, dx = \frac{e^{ax}}{a^2 + b^2} (a \sin bx - b \cos bx)$$

$$\int \frac{dx}{a^2 + b^2 x^2} = \frac{1}{ba} \tan^{-1} \left(\frac{bx}{a} \right)$$

$$\int \frac{dx}{\sqrt{a^2 - b^2 x^2}} = \frac{1}{b} \sin^{-1} \left(\frac{bx}{a} \right)$$

E.3 Definite Integrals

$$\int_0^\infty x^m e^{-ax} \, dx = \frac{m!}{a^{m+1}} = \frac{\Gamma(m+1)}{a^{m+1}}$$

$$\text{where } \Gamma(b) = \int_0^\infty y^{b-1} e^{-y} \, dy,$$

$$\Gamma(b+1) = b\Gamma(b), \ \Gamma\left(\frac{1}{2}\right) = \sqrt{\pi}$$

$$\int_{-\infty}^\infty e^{-a^2 x^2 + bx} \, dx = \frac{\sqrt{\pi}}{a} e^{b^2/(4a^2)}, \ a > 0$$

$$\int_0^\infty x^m e^{-a^2 x^2} \, dx = \frac{\Gamma[(m+1)/2]}{2a^{m+1}}$$

$$\int_0^\infty e^{-a^2 x^2} \cos bx \, dx = \frac{\sqrt{\pi} \, e^{-b^2/(4a^2)}}{2a}, \ a > 0$$

$$\int_0^1 x^{a-1} (1-x)^{b-1} \, dx = \frac{\Gamma(a)\Gamma(b)}{\Gamma(a+b)}, \ a > 0, b > 0$$

$$\int_0^\infty \frac{\sin x}{x} \, dx = \frac{\pi}{2}$$

$$\int_0^\infty \left(\frac{\sin x}{x} \right)^2 \, dx = \frac{\pi}{2}$$

E.4 Series

$$\sum_{i=1}^N i = \frac{N(N+1)}{2}$$

$$\sum_{i=1}^N i^2 = \frac{N(N+1)(2N+1)}{6}$$

$$\sum_{i=0}^N x^i = \frac{x^{N+1} - 1}{x - 1}$$

$$\sum_{i=0}^N C_i^N x^i y^{N-i} = (x+y)^N,$$

$$\text{where } C_i^N = \frac{N!}{i!(N-i)!}$$

$$\sum_{i=1}^\infty a^i = \frac{a}{1-a}, \ 0 \le a < 1$$

$$\sum_{i=1}^\infty i a^i = \frac{a}{(1-a)^2}, \ 0 \le a < 1$$

E.5 Fourier Transforms

Description	$f(t)$	$F(\omega)$
Definition	$f(t) = \dfrac{1}{2\pi} \displaystyle\int_{-\infty}^{\infty} F(\omega)\, e^{j\omega t}\, d\omega$	$F(\omega) = \displaystyle\int_{-\infty}^{\infty} f(t)\, e^{-j\omega t}\, dt$
Shifting (time)	$f(t - t_0)$	$e^{-j\omega t_0} F(\omega)$
Shifting (frequency)	$e^{j\omega_0 t} f(t)$	$F(\omega - \omega_0)$
Duality	$F(t)$	$2\pi f(-\omega)$
Scaling	$f(at)$	$\dfrac{1}{|a|} F\left(\dfrac{\omega}{a}\right)$
Differentiation (time)	$\dfrac{d^n f(t)}{dt^n}$	$(j\omega)^n F(\omega)$
Differentiation (frequency)	$(-jt)^n f(t)$	$\dfrac{d^n F(\omega)}{d\omega^n}$
Integration (time)	$\displaystyle\int_{-\infty}^{t} f(u)\, du$	$\dfrac{1}{j\omega} F(\omega) + \pi F(0)\delta(\omega)$
Integration (frequency)	$-\dfrac{j}{t} f(t) + \pi f(0)\delta(t)$	$\displaystyle\int_{-\infty}^{\omega} F(u)\, du$
Conjugation (time)	$f^*(t)$	$F^*(-\omega)$
Conjugation (frequency)	$f^*(-t)$	$F^*(\omega)$
Convolution (time)	$\displaystyle\int_{-\infty}^{\infty} f_1(\tau) f_2(t - \tau)\, d\tau$	$F_1(\omega) F_2(\omega)$
Convolution (frequency)	$f_1(t) f_2(t)$	$\dfrac{1}{2\pi} \displaystyle\int_{-\infty}^{\infty} F_1(u) F_2(\omega - u)\, du$
Parseval's theorem	$\displaystyle\int_{-\infty}^{\infty} f_1(t) f_2^*(t)\, dt = \dfrac{1}{2\pi} \int_{-\infty}^{\infty} F_1(\omega) F_2^*(\omega)\, d\omega$	
Impulse	$\delta(t)$	1
Step	$u(t)$	$\dfrac{1}{j\omega} + \pi\delta(\omega)$
Constant	K	$2\pi K\delta(\omega)$
Exponential	$e^{-at} u(t)$	$\dfrac{1}{a + j\omega}$
Exponential (times t)	$t\, e^{-at} u(t)$	$\dfrac{1}{(a + j\omega)^2}$
Exponential (two-sided)	$e^{-a|t|}$	$\dfrac{2a}{a^2 + \omega^2}$
Cosine	$\cos(\omega_0 t)$	$\pi[\delta(\omega - \omega_0) + \delta(\omega + \omega_0)]$

Description	$f(t)$	$F(\omega)$
Sine	$\sin(\omega_0 t)$	$-j\pi[\delta(\omega - \omega_0) - \delta(\omega + \omega_0)]$
Cosine (positive time)	$\cos(\omega_0 t)u(t)$	$\dfrac{\pi}{2}[\delta(\omega - \omega_0) + \delta(\omega + \omega_0)]$ $+\dfrac{j\omega}{\omega_0^2 - \omega^2}$
Sine (positive time)	$\sin(\omega_0 t)u(t)$	$-j\dfrac{\pi}{2}[\delta(\omega - \omega_0) - \delta(\omega + \omega_0)]$ $+\dfrac{\omega_0}{\omega_0^2 - \omega^2}$
Rectangular pulse	$1, \ -\dfrac{T}{2} \le t \le \dfrac{T}{2}$	$T\dfrac{\sin(\omega T/2)}{\omega T/2}$
Triangular pulse	$1 - \dfrac{2}{T}|t|, \ -\dfrac{T}{2} \le t \le \dfrac{T}{2}$	$\dfrac{T}{2}\left[\dfrac{\sin(\omega T/4)}{\omega T/4}\right]^2$
Gaussian pulse	$e^{-a^2 t^2}$	$\dfrac{\sqrt{\pi}}{a}e^{-\omega^2/4a^2}$

Bibliography

Abramowitz, M., and I. A. Stegun. *Handbook of Mathematical Functions*. New York: Dover, 1964.

Bratley, P., B. L. Fox, and L. E. Schrage. *A Guide to Simulation*. New York: Springer-Verlag, 1983.

Brown, R. G. *Introduction to Random Signal Analysis and Kalman Filtering*. New York: Wiley, 1983.

Carlson, A. B. *Communication Systems: An Introduction to Signals and Noise in Electrical Communication*, 3d ed. New York: McGraw-Hill, 1986.

Cooper, G. R., and C. D. McGillem. *Probabilistic Methods of Signal and System Analysis*, 2nd ed. New York: Holt, Rinehart, and Winston, 1986.

Davenport, W. B., Jr. *Probability and Random Processes: An Introduction for Applied Scientists and Engineers*. New York: McGraw-Hill, 1970.

Gray, R. M., and L. D. Davisson. *Random Processes: A Mathematical Approach for Engineers*. Englewood Cliffs, New Jersey: Prentice-Hall, 1986.

Graybill, F. A. *Theory and Application of the Linear Model*. North Scituate, Massachusetts: Duxbury, 1976.

Helstrom, C. W. *Probability and Stochastic Processes for Engineers*. New York: Macmillan, 1984.

Hogg, R. V., and A. T. Craig. *Introduction to Mathematical Statistics*, 2nd ed. New York: Macmillan, 1965.

Larsen, R. J., and M. L. Marx. *An Introduction to Probability and Its Applications*. Englewood Cliffs, New Jersey: Prentice-Hall, 1985.

Maisel, H. and G. Gnugnoli. *Simulation of Discrete Stochastic Systems*. Chicago, Illinois: Science Research Associates, 1972.

Melsa, J. L., and A. P. Sage. *An Introduction to Probability and Stochastic Processes*. Englewood Cliffs, New Jersey: Prentice-Hall, 1973.

O'Flynn, M. *Probabilities, Random Variables, and Random Processes*. New York: Harper and Row, 1982.

Papoulis, A. *Probability, Random Variables, and Stochastic Processes*, 2nd ed. New York: McGraw-Hill, 1984.

Parzen, E. *Stochastic Processes*. San Francisco, California: Holden-Day, 1962.

Peebles, P. Z., Jr. *Probability, Random Variables, and Random Signal Principles*. New York: McGraw-Hill, 1980.

Peebles, P. Z. *Communication System Principles.* Reading, Massachusetts: Addison-Wesley, 1976.

Schaeffer, R. L., and J. T. McClave. *Probability and Statistics for Engineers,* 2nd ed. Boston: Duxbury, 1986.

Stark, H., and J. W. Woods. *Probability, Random Processes, and Estimation Theory for Engineers.* Englewood Cliffs, New Jersey: Prentice-Hall, 1986.

Thomas, J. B. *Introduction to Probability.* New York: Springer-Verlag, 1986.

Thomas, J. B. *An Introduction to Statistical Communication Theory.* New York: Wiley, 1969.

Trivedi, K. S. *Probability and Statistics with Reliability, Queuing, and Computer Science Applications.* Englewood Cliffs, New Jersey: Prentice-Hall, 1982.

Van Trees, H. L. *Detection, Estimation, and Modulation Theory,* Part I. New York: Wiley, 1968.

Walpole, R. E., and R. H. Myers. *Probability and Statistics for Engineers and Scientists,* 3rd ed. New York: Macmillan, 1985.

Wong, E. *Introduction to Random Processes.* New York: Springer-Verlag, 1983.

Wozencraft, J. M., and Jacobs, I. M. *Principles of Communication Engineering.* New York: Wiley, 1965.

Ziemer, R. E., and W. H. Tranter. *Principles of Communications.* Boston, Massachusetts: Houghton Mifflin, 1976.

ANSWERS TO SELECTED PROBLEMS

Chapter 1

1.2.1. $\{2, 3, 4, 5, 6, 7, 8, 9, 10, 11, 12\}$

1.2.3. $\{WA, WB, WC, RA, RB, RC\}$

1.2.5. $A \cap (B \cup C) = A \cap C$

1.2.7. $(A \cup B) \cap C = B \cup (A \cap C)$

1.2.9. $C \subset A \cup B$

1.2.11. $(A \cap C) \cup B = \{3, 4, 5, 6, 7, 8\}$, $(A \cup C)^c \cap B = \{6, 8\}$

1.3.1. $\mathscr{A} = \{S, \varnothing, \{1\}, \{1, 3, 4\}, \{2, 3, 4\}, \{2\}, \{1, 2\}, \{3, 4\}\}$

1.3.3. $\mathscr{A} = \{S, \varnothing, \{1, 3, 5\}, \{2, 3, 4, 5, 6\}, \{2, 4, 6\}, \{1\}, \{1, 2, 4, 6\}, \{3, 5\}\}$

1.3.5. $\{P\} = \{1, 0, \frac{3}{5}, \frac{3}{5}, \frac{2}{5}, \frac{2}{5}, \frac{4}{5}, \frac{1}{5}\}$

1.3.7. $P(A \cup B) \le P(B \cup C)$

1.3.9. $P[A \cap (B \cup C)] \le P(A \cap B) + P(A \cap C)$

1.3.11. $P(\text{At least one H in 3 tosses}) = .875$

1.4.1. $P(1_1 \cup 1_2) = 0.438$, $P(1_1 \cup 1_2 \cup 1_3) = 0.578$, $P(\text{no 1's in 3 tosses}) = 0.422$

1.4.3. $P(\text{at least two match}) = 0.444$

1.4.5. $P(w) = 0.493$

1.4.7. $P(C \mid W) = 0.25$, C and W are statistically independent, $P(G) = 0.4$

1.4.9. Given B_0 decide A_0, Given B_1 decide A_0, Given B_2 decide A_1, $P(e) = 0.31$

1.4.11. $m_0 \rightarrow A_0$ and $m_1 \rightarrow A_1$ $P(e) = 0.22$, $m_0 \rightarrow A_1$ and $m_1 \rightarrow A_0$, $P(e) = 0.18$ (the minimum $P(e)$)

1.4.13. $P(\text{comm}) = 0.54$

1.4.15. $P(\text{comm}) = 0.618$

1.4.19. Series $P_1 = 0.965$, parallel $P_1 = 0.536$

1.4.21. $P_1 = 0.652$

1.4.23. Best assignment $C \rightarrow 3$, $A \rightarrow 1$, $B \rightarrow 2$ (or $A \rightarrow 2$, $B \rightarrow 1$), $P(\text{comm}) = 0.846$

1.4.25. $P(A \mid B) = 0.571$

1.4.27. $P(B) = 0.75$

1.4.29. $P(A^c \mid B) \le P(A^c)$

Chapter 2

2.1.1. $P(X \le 3) = 0.875$, $P(X > 4) = 0.0625$, $F_X(j) = 1 - (0.5)^j$, $j = 1, 2, \ldots$

2.1.3. $P(1 < X \le 2) = 0.233$, $P(X > 3) = 0.0498$

2.1.5. $a = 1$, $b = -1$

2.1.7. $f_X(x) = e^{-x} u(x)$

2.1.9. $p = 0.5$

2.1.11. $f_X(x) = e^{-2x} u(x) + \frac{1}{6} \delta(x) + \frac{1}{3} \delta(x - 1)$

2.1.13. $0 < x < 1$, $f_X(x) = x/2$, $x = 1$, $f_X(x) = \frac{1}{4} \delta(x - 1)$; $1 < x \le 3$, $f_X(x) = \frac{1}{4}$

2.1.15. $a = 0.133$, $P(-0.5 < X \le 0.5) = 0.533$

2.1.17. $P[(X - 3)^2 > 4] = F_X(1) + 1 - F_X(5)$

2.2.1. $P(1 < X \le 10) = 1 - Q(0.25) - Q(2) = 0.5759$

2.2.3. $\mu = 7$, $\sigma^2 = 9$

2.2.5. $a = 5$

2.2.7. $A_c = \mu + 1.282\sigma$, $B_c = \mu + 0.524\sigma$, $C_c = \mu - 0.524\sigma$, $D_c = \mu - 1.282\sigma$

2.3.1. $F_X(x) = \frac{1}{2} e^x$, $-\infty < x < 0$; $F_X(x) = 1 - \frac{1}{2} e^{-x}$, $0 \le x < \infty$

2.3.3. $P(0 \text{ bit errors in block}) = 0.478$, $P(1 \text{ bit error in block}) = 0.372$, $P(\text{block error}) = 0.150$

2.3.5. $a = 1.609$, $P(0, 1, \text{or } 2 \text{ photons}) = 0.781$

2.4.1. $f_{XY}(x, y) = 2e^{-x} e^{-2y}$, $x \ge 0$, $y \ge 0$, $P(1 \le X \le 3, 1 \le y \le 2) = 0.0372$

2.4.3. $f_x(x) = 2x$, $0 \le x \le 1$; $f_Y(y) = 0.75(y^2 + 1)$, $0 \le y \le 1$; $F_X(x) = x^2$, $0 \le x \le 1$; $F_Y(y) = 0.25(y^3 + 3y)$, $0 \le y \le 1$; X and Y are statistically independent

2.4.5. $P(X + Y > 1) = 0.9583$

2.4.7. $P(X < 2Y + 1) = 0.9028$

2.4.9. $P(190 \le R_0 \le 210) = 0.5$, $P(190 \le R_1 + R_2 \le 210) = 0.75$

2.4.11. $P(285 \le R_0 \le 315) = 0.5$, $P(285 \le R_1 + R_2 \le 315) = 0.719$

2.4.13. $P(\text{failure} < 30) = 0.268$

2.4.15. $T = 14.82$ months

2.5.1. $f_X(x) = \dfrac{1}{\sqrt{2\pi(5)}} \exp\left(-\dfrac{x^2}{2(5)}\right),$

$f_{Y|X}(y|z) = \dfrac{1}{\sqrt{2(0.2)}} \exp\left(-\dfrac{(y - 0.6x)^2}{2(0.2)}\right)$

2.5.3. $f_X(x) = \dfrac{1}{\sqrt{2\pi(10)}} \exp\left(-\dfrac{x^2}{2(10)}\right),$

$f_{Y|X}(y|x) = \dfrac{1}{\sqrt{2\pi(6.4)}}$

$\times \exp\left(-\dfrac{(y - 0.4x)^2}{2(6.4)}\right)$

2.5.5. $F_Y(1 | X \le 1) = 0.3161$

Chapter 3

3.1.1. $f_Y(y) = 2y$, $0 < y \le 1$

3.1.3. $f_Y(y) = 2e^{-2y}$, $0 \le y < \infty$

3.1.5. $x = \ln(2u)$, $0 \le u < 0.5$; $x = -\ln[2(1 - u)]$, $0.5 \le u \le 1$

3.1.7. $x = \sqrt{3u}$ $0 \le u < \frac{1}{3}$; $x = (3u + 1)/2$, $\frac{1}{3} \le u \le 1$

3.1.9. $x = u/(1 - u)$, $0 \le u \le 1$

3.1.11. $f_{Z_L}(z) = 5 \times 10^{-3}$, $900 \le z \le 1100$

3.2.1. $f_{Y_1 Y_2}(y_1, y_2) = y_2 e^{-y_2}$, $0 \le y_1 \le 1$, $0 \le y_2 < \infty$

3.2.3. $f_{Y_1 Y_2}(y_1, y_2) = e^{-y_1 - y_2}$, $0 \le y_1 < \infty$, $0 \le y_2 < \infty$

3.3.1. $f_Y(y) = \dfrac{1}{2\sqrt{2\pi y}} e^{-(\sqrt{y} - 2)^2/2}[1 + e^{-4\sqrt{y}}]$, $0 \le y < \infty$

3.4.1. $z < 0$, $f_Z(z) = 0$; $0 \le z < 1$, $f_Z(z) = 1 - e^{-z}$; $z \ge 1$, $f_Z(z) = e^{-(z-1)} - e^{-z}$

3.4.3. $z < 1$, $f_Z(z) = 0.5(e^{z-1} - e^{z-2})$; $1 \le z < 2$, $f_Z(z) = 1 - 0.5(e^{z-2} + e^{-(z-1)})$; $z \ge 2$, $f_Z(z) = 0.5(e^{-(z-2)} - e^{-(z-1)})$

3.4.5. $z < 0$, $f_Z(z) = 0$, $z \ge 0$; $f_Z(z) = 0.5z^2 e^{-z}$

3.4.7. $f_Z(z) = \displaystyle\int_{-\infty}^{\infty} f_X(x) f_Y(x - z)\, dx$

3.4.9. $P(Z = k) = C_k^6 (0.3)^k (0.7)^{6-k}$, $k = 0$, 1, 2, 3, 4, 5, 6

3.4.11. $P(Z = 3) = 0.195$

3.4.13. $P(285 \le Z \le 315) = 0.859$

3.5.1. $f_Y(y) = 3y^2$, $0 \le y \le 1$, $P(Y \ge 0.75) = 0.578$

3.5.3. $f_Z(z) = 0.06e^{-0.06z}$, $z \ge 0$, $P(Z \le 30) = 0.835$

Chapter 4

4.1.1. $E(X) = \dfrac{n+1}{a}$, $E(X^2) = \dfrac{(n+2)(n+1)}{a^2}$, $\text{Var}(X) = \dfrac{n+1}{a^2}$

4.1.3. $E(X) = a$, $E(X^2) = a^2 + a$, $\text{Var}(X) = a$

4.1.5. No

4.1.7. $a = \pm 4$, $b = 9$

4.1.9. $c = E(X)$

4.1.11. $E(R) = 100$, $E(G) = 0.01003$

4.1.13. $E(L) = 1$ mH, $E(Z_L) = 10\ \Omega$

4.1.15. $E(C) = 0.1\ \mu\text{F}$, $E(Z_C) = 200.67\ \Omega$

4.2.1. $\phi_X(\omega) = \dfrac{e^{j\omega b} - e^{j\omega a}}{j\omega(b - a)}$

4.2.3. $\phi_X(\omega) = \dfrac{e^{ja\omega}}{1 + b^2 \omega^2}$

4.2.5. $\phi_X(\omega) = (pe^{j\omega} + 1 - p)^N$

4.2.7. $E(X) = (n+1)b$, $E(X^2) = (n+1)(n+2)b^2$, $\text{Var}(X) = (n+1)b^2$

4.2.9. $E(X) = b$, $E(X^2) = 2b^2$, $\text{Var}(X) = b^2$

4.2.11. $E(X) = Np,$
$E(X^2) = N(N-1)p^2 + Np,$
$\text{Var}(X) = Np(1-p)$

4.2.13. $E(X) = \dfrac{b+a}{2}, \ E(X^2) = \dfrac{b^2 + ab + a^2}{3},$
$\text{Var}(X) = \dfrac{(b-a)^2}{12}$

4.3.1. $\text{Var}(Y) = 53$

4.3.3. $E[(X+Y)^i] = \dfrac{(b+a)^{i+2} - b^{i+2} - a^{i+2}}{ab(i+1)(i+2)}$

4.3.5. $\text{Cov}(X, Y) = 0, \ \rho = 0,$ X and Y are uncorrelated

4.3.7. $\text{Cov}(X, Y) = a\,\text{Var}(X), \ \rho = 1, \ a > 0;$
$\rho = -1, \ a < 0; \ \rho = 0, \ a = 0$

4.3.9. $a = 0.5, \ b = \pm 0.866$

4.3.11. $a = -6, \ b = 3; \ a = 6, \ b = -3$

4.3.13. $P(Y = k) = \dfrac{e^{-a} a^k}{k!},$
$k = 0, 1, 2, \ldots, \ a = a_1 + a_2 + a_3$

4.3.15. $P(Y = 7) = 0.138$

4.4.1. $\boldsymbol{\mu}_y = \begin{bmatrix} 0 \\ 17 \end{bmatrix}, \boldsymbol{\Sigma}_y = \begin{bmatrix} 93 & -3 \\ -3 & 37 \end{bmatrix};$
$\boldsymbol{\mu}_z = \begin{bmatrix} 3 \\ 1 \end{bmatrix}, \boldsymbol{\Sigma}_z = \begin{bmatrix} 3 & 2 \\ 2 & 4 \end{bmatrix}$

4.4.3. $f_{X_1 X_2}(x_1, x_2) =$
$\dfrac{1}{2\pi} \exp\left(-\dfrac{2x_1^2 - 6x_1 x_2 + 5x_2^2}{2} \right)$

4.4.5. $\boldsymbol{\mu}_x = \begin{bmatrix} 0 \\ 0 \end{bmatrix}, \boldsymbol{\Sigma}_x = \begin{bmatrix} 7 & 4 \\ 4 & 3 \end{bmatrix}$

4.4.7. $P(X > Y) = Q(\sqrt{2}) = 0.07868$

4.4.9. $P(X > Y) = Q(2) = 0.02275$

4.5.1. $N = 10$

4.5.3. $P(e) = 0.000266, \ P_H(e) = 0.001374$

4.6.1. $P\left[\left| \dfrac{1}{N} \sum_{i=1}^{N} X_i - p \right| \geq \varepsilon \right] \leq 0.050$
Chebyshev inequality, $\leq 8.48 \times 10^{-5}$
Chernoff bound

4.6.3. $P\left[\left| \dfrac{1}{N} \sum_{i=1}^{N} X_i - p \right| \geq \varepsilon \right] \leq 0.075$
Chebyshev inequality, ≤ 0.0024863
Chernoff bound

4.7.1. $P\left[\left| \dfrac{1}{N} \sum_{i=1}^{N} X_i - p \right| \geq \varepsilon \right] \cong 7.75 \times 10^{-6}$

4.7.3. $P\left[\left| \dfrac{1}{N} \sum_{i=1}^{N} X_i - p \right| \geq \varepsilon \right] \cong 2.61 \times 10^{-4}$

Chapter 5

5.1.1. $x_i = 0, 1, 2, 3, 4, 5, \ i = 0, 1, \ldots, 5,$
$\hat{f}_i(x) = 0.632, 0.233, 0.085, 0.032,$
$0.011, \ i = 1, 2, \ldots, 5$

5.1.3. $x_i = 0, 0.6, 1.2, 1.8, 2.4, 3.0, 3.6, 4.2,$
$i = 0, 1, \ldots, 7$
$\hat{f}_i(x) = 0.752, 0.413, 0.226, 0.124,$
$0.068, 0.037, 0.021, \ i = 1, 2, \ldots, 7$

5.2.1. IX = IX * 277,
IF(IX.LT.0)IX = (IX + 32767) + 1,
U = IX * .30518 × 10^{-4}

5.2.3. IM = IX/118,
IX = 277*(IX − IM*118) − IM * 81,
IF(IX.LT.0)IX = IX + 32767,
U = IX * 0.30519 × 10^{-4}

5.3.1. $x_i = -2.4, -1.221, -0.764, -0.430,$
$-0.139, 0.139, 0.430, 0.764, 1.221,$
$2.4, \ i = 0, 1, \ldots, 9$
$\hat{f}_i(x) = 0.085, 0.201, 0.349, 0.401,$
$0.420, 0.430, 0.299, 0.328, 0.071, \ i =$
$1, 2, \ldots, 9$

5.3.3. $x_i = -2.4, -0.842, -0.253, 0.253,$
$0.842, 2.4, \ i = 0, 1, \ldots, 5$
$\hat{f}_i(x) = 0.112, 0.325, 0.511, 0.297,$
$0.128, \ i = 1, 2, \ldots, 5$

5.3.5. $x_i = -2.4, -1.44, -0.48, 0.48, 1.44,$
$2.4, \ i = 0, 1, \ldots, 5. \ \hat{f}_i(x) = 0.078,$
$0.208, 0.417, 0.286, 0.052, \ i =$
$1, 2, \ldots, 5$

5.4.1. $T = 3.450, \ P[C_{120}(9) \geq T] = 0.903$

5.4.3. $T = 2.833, \ P[C_{120}(5) \geq T] = 0.586$

5.4.5. $T = 2.721, \ P[C_{120}(5) \geq T] = 0.605$

5.5.1. Confidence = 0.731

5.5.3. $N = 149600$

5.5.5. $\hat{p} = 0.0333, \ \hat{p} = 0.0333$

5.5.7. $\hat{p} = 2.14 \times 10^{-3}$

5.6.1. $Y_1 = 3X_1, \ Y_2 = -2X_1 + X_2,$
$Y_3 = -X_1 + 2X_2 + X_3$

5.6.3. $Y_1 = 4X_1 + 8, \ Y_2 = 2X_1 + 3X_2 + 7,$
$Y_3 = 5X_1 + 2X_2 + X_3 + 6$

5.6.5. $X_1 = Y_1, \ X_2 = -2Y_1 + \frac{1}{2}Y_2,$
$X_3 = 3Y_1 - Y_2 + \frac{1}{3}Y_3$

Chapter 6

6.2.1. $\hat{\theta} = \dfrac{1}{N} \sum\limits_{i=1}^{N} X_i$, $\hat{\theta}$ is unbiased,

Cramer–Rao bound $= \dfrac{\theta^2}{N}$,

$\hat{\theta}$ is efficient

6.2.3. $\hat{b} = \left(\dfrac{1}{N} \sum\limits_{i=1}^{N} X_i \right)^2$, $E(\hat{b}) = \dfrac{N+1}{N} b$,

$\hat{b}$ biased

6.2.5. $\hat{a} = \left(\dfrac{1}{2N} \sum\limits_{i=1}^{N} X_i \right)^2$, $E(\hat{a}) = \dfrac{2N+1}{2N} a$,

$\hat{a}$ biased

6.2.7. $\hat{\theta} = \dfrac{1}{2N} \sum\limits_{i=1}^{N} X_i^2$, $\hat{\theta}$ is unbiased,

Cramer–Rao bound $= \dfrac{\theta^2}{N}$, $\hat{\theta}$ is

efficient

6.2.9. $\text{Var}(\hat{\theta}) = \dfrac{2\theta^2}{N}$, Carmer–Rao bound $=$

$\dfrac{2\theta^2}{N}$, $\hat{\theta}$ is efficient

6.2.11. $\hat{p} = N \Big/ \sum\limits_{i=1}^{N} X_i$, $E(\hat{p}) \neq p$, $\hat{p}$ is biased

6.2.13. $\hat{M} = \sum\limits_{i=1}^{N} Y_i^2 \Big/ N\sigma_x^2$, $\hat{M}$ is unbiased,

Cramer–Rao bound $= 2M^2/N$, $\hat{M}$ is

efficient

6.2.15. Cramer–Rao bound $=$

$2(N-1)^2 \sigma^4 / N^3$

6.3.1. $\hat{\theta}_N = \hat{\theta}_{N-1} + \dfrac{1}{N} \left(\dfrac{X_N}{2} - \hat{\theta}_{N-1} \right)$

6.3.3. $\hat{W}_N = \hat{W}_{N-1} + \dfrac{1}{N-1}$

$\times \left[\dfrac{N}{N-1} (X_N - \hat{\mu}_N)^2 - \hat{W}_{N-1} \right]$,

$n = 2, 3, \ldots, \hat{W}_0 = \hat{W}_1 = 0$

6.3.5. $\hat{\mu}_N = 0.236, -0.550, -0.608, -0.370,$
$-0.435, -0.351, -0.279, -0.344,$
$-0.401, -0.511$
$\hat{V}_N = 0, 0.619, 0.419, 0.485, 0.406,$
$0.374, 0.352, 0.337, 0.326, 0.403$

6.3.7. $N = 799$

6.4.1. $\hat{\theta} = (N+1) \Big/ \left(1 + \sum\limits_{i=1}^{N} X_i \right)$

6.4.3. $\hat{\theta} = \left(a + \sum\limits_{i=1}^{N} X_i \right) \Big/ (mN + a + b)$

Chapter 7

7.2.1. $E[X(t)] = 0$, $E[X(t_1)X(t_2)] =$
$R_x(\tau) = \sigma^2 \cos(\omega_0 \tau) -\infty < \tau < \infty$;
$X(t)$ is wide sense stationary

7.2.3. $E[Y(t)] = 0$, $E[Y(t_1)Y(t_2)] =$
$R_y(\tau) = 0.5 R_x(\tau) \cos(2\pi\tau)$, $-\infty <$
$\tau < \infty$; $Y(t)$ is wide sense stationary

7.2.5. $R_y(\tau) = 2R_x(\tau) + R_x(\tau + 3)$
$+ R_x(\tau - 3)$

7.2.7. $E[X(t)] = \pm 3.162$, $E[X^2(t)] = 85$,
$\text{Var}[X(t)] = 75$

7.2.9. $E[X(t)] = \pm 1.732$, $E[X^2(t)] = 5$,
$\text{Var}[X(t)] = 2$

7.2.11. $R_x(\tau) = 7, -1, -1, -1, -1, -1, -1,$
$\tau = 0, 1, 2, 3, 4, 5, 6$

7.3.1. $S_x(f) = 4 \dfrac{\sin(4\pi f)}{4\pi f}$, $-\infty < f < \infty$

7.3.3. $E[X(t)] = 0$, $E[X^2(t)] = 12.5$,
$R_x(\tau) = 12.5 e^{-0.4|\tau|}$, $-\infty < \tau < \infty$

7.3.5. $E[X(t)] = 0$, $E[X^2(t)] = 24$, $R_x(\tau) =$
$24 \dfrac{\sin(8\pi\tau)}{8\pi\tau}$, $-\infty < \tau < \infty$

7.3.7. $V = 0.399$ μv (10 MHz), $V = 0.891$ μv
(50 MHz)

7.4.1. $S_y(f) = \dfrac{N_0}{2} \dfrac{1}{1 + (2\pi f)^2}$, $-\infty < f < \infty$;
$R_y(\tau) = \dfrac{N_0}{4} e^{-|\tau|}$, $-\infty < \tau < \infty$

7.4.3. $R_{z_1 z_2}(t_1, t_2) = R_{z_1 z_2}(\tau) = -e^{-|\tau|}$, $-\infty <$
$\tau < \infty$

7.4.5. $R_{xy}(\tau) = 3, -1, -1, -5, 3, 3, -1$, $\tau = 0,$
$1, 2, 3, 4, 5, 6$

Index